CALIFORNIA:
THE GEOGRAPHY
OF DIVERSITY

CALIFORNIA:
THE GEOGRAPHY OF DIVERSITY

Crane S. Miller

Richard S. Hyslop

California State Polytechnic University, Pomona

MAYFIELD PUBLISHING COMPANY

Library of Congress Catalog Card Number: 82-073744
International Standard Book Number: 0-87484-441-X

Manufactured in the United States of America
Mayfield Publishing Company
285 Hamilton Avenue, Palo Alto, California 94301

Manuscript editor: Victoria Nelson
Managing editor: Pat Herbst
Designer: Nancy Sears
Cover designer: Albert Burkhardt
Cover photographer: David Muench © 1983
Production manager: Cathy Willkie
Photo researcher: Deborah Cogan
Compositor: Imperial Litho/Graphics
Printer and binder: Bookcrafters

CONTENTS

MAPS AND DRAWINGS

PREFACE

California geography is a fascinating discipline, but students often fail to realize this because of the textbooks they have to read. In putting together this book, our goal was neither to write "just another" volume on the topic nor even to produce the newest text on California. Rather, our aim was to provide a solid base of up-to-date information in language that is enjoyable to read. Our desire was to convey a sense of the drama, beauty, and diversity of the Golden State, as well as our own enthusiasm for the subject.

California: The Geography of Diversity is not encyclopedic in coverage. Our approach is topical, rather than regional, with emphasis on the most vital, significant, and fascinating aspects of California's physical and cultural landscape. Diversity *is* the hallmark of the state. The variety and sweep of California—evident in climate, landforms, and cultural phenomena—is truly astonishing. Our text mirrors this broad sweep. Coverage includes traditional material, of interest to geographers, on weather, landform provinces, ecological regions, and settlement patterns. However, we also present material of a less traditional nature, on historical geography, cultural oddities, and regional personalities. We have blended the physical with the cultural, the scientific with the literary, to provide a balanced, comprehensive, and (we believe) compelling account of the geography of California.

Of course, we owe much to many individuals who have encouraged and supported us in the development of this book. Various people at Mayfield Publishing Company have been patient, helpful, and generous. Our original editor, Alden Paine, is to be credited with providing the encouragement (and sometimes the needle) to get us moving when we bogged down. Even in retirement, he has remained interested and helpful. Likewise, the other Mayfield people have been very supportive.

We have been fortunate to have an excellent group of reviewers, whose suggestions, comments, and critiques went far toward helping us create a sound and substantial finished product. Our acknowledgment and thanks thus go to James D. Blick, San Diego State University; Susan W. Book, Cosumnes River College; Robert W. Christopherson, American River College; Howard F. Gregor, University of California, Davis; Donald G. Holtgrieve, California State University, Hayward; Ronald F. Lockman, University of Southern California; Richard F. Logan, University of California, Los Angeles; Gertrude M. Reith, California State University, Fullerton; and Christopher L. Salter, University of California, Los Angeles.

We have had invaluable assistance from a variety of other people. Our cartographer, Dick Crooker, deserves special praise and recognition for his patience and outstanding performance. The quality of the cartographic work speaks volumes for Dick's ability and devotion. Otis Starkey, Professor Emeritus of Geography at the University of Indiana, has given generously of his time and expertise in the thankless task of indexing and from the beginning he provided psychic support. Dennis Johnson of the University of Alberta also worked long and hard to prepare the index, for which effort we are grateful. A number of our students provided assistance on cartographic projects: Marc Blodgett, Jeff Dunn, Karen Geissler, Norene Heath, Robert Huson, Whitney Miller, David Vechik, and Brett Wilson. Our typing chores were lightened considerably by Barbara Miller (manuscript), Elizabeth Cox (captions), Regina O'Connell (bibliography), and Norene Heath (index). Finally, we thank our students for motivating us to write this book and for sparking the enthusiasm that pervades our view of California—the geography of diversity!

C.S.M.
R.S.H.

CALIFORNIA:
THE GEOGRAPHY
OF DIVERSITY

LOTUS LAND
REVISITED

Contemporary California appears to be at a crossroads in both its development and its reputation. In the 1980s, the Golden State still lays claim to geographic superlatives among the 50 states, but the dynamics of California's geography have moderated noticeably in recent years. Noted for its mildness, California's lotus land climate has no duplicate elsewhere in the nation, but smog and drought increasingly temper its appeal. California's spectacular coastal headlands, lofty mountains, and deep valleys (see Figs. 1.1 and 1.2) are surpassed in dimension only by those of Alaska. But this diverse terrain is made less inviting by the very geological events that created it, natural cataclysms still echoed in such deadly, destructive modern episodes as the San Fernando earthquake of February 9, 1971. California's 24 million residents render it the most populous state, but environmental and economic problems threaten this dominance. California continues among the ranking states in mining, forest products, manufacturing, retail trade, and finance; at the same time, however, chronically high unemployment rates in certain industries, a changing energy base, keen competition from other states for federal contracts, and various environmental constraints tend to erode these standings. Trendsetting in architecture, education, entertainment, fashions, and recreation endures as a tradition in California, but it is one that is now shared by a growing number of states.

Many intangibles, as well as identifiable natural and human events, account for the slowdown of the 1970s and 1980s following the phenomenal growth of the 1950s and 1960s. Explanations range from statements such as "California can't stay in a rapid growth mode forever," to "Less defense spending in the state means fewer out-of-state aerospace workers will be looking for jobs here," to "Increased environmental awareness is bound to put a damper on development of any sort." Whatever the reasons, California presently appears to be well into an extended period of relatively slow population growth but nonetheless moderate economic gain. Whether this period is viewed as a breather before the next big boom or, less optimistically, as a forerunner of hard times, it is an opportunity for Californians to reflect on the pitfalls of the last boom, the better to avoid them in the future.

If there is, in fact, reliable cause for optimism about California's future growth, then the state's geographical diversity lies at the heart of this hope. Unparalleled diversity and wealth of natural and human resources have made California what it is today and are the promise for tomorrow. At a glance, Figure 1.3 offers a sample of that diversity.

TRAVELOGUE TALES AND ROMANTIC MUSINGS

There has always been a certain mystique about California. The name itself evokes thoughts of golden sunshine, golden opportunities, and the good life. This is hardly a purely contemporary phenomenon; much of the written history of the area abounds with these images. Whether in references to the fabulous Seven Cities of Gold, the glowing reports of the Forty-Niners, or the Hollywood images that have flashed on the screens of the nation in more recent times, California is seldom portrayed as anything less than magical.

How did such a glowing identity emerge? It is astonishing how consistent this enthusiastic boosterism has been throughout the written history of the region. Before Europeans ever set foot in California, a tourist tale equal to any travelogue promotion had been concocted on the Iberian Peninsula. During the sixteenth century, romance writers in Spain indulged in many fanciful and exotic literary creations. (Cervantes's tale of Don Quixote was a classic parody of these imaginative stories.) One such popular tale, by Ordóñez de Montalvo, spoke of an idyllic kingdom on an island near the Indies called "California." This mythical (or not-so-mythical) paradise came complete with many of the characteristics we now readily associate with the Golden State: balmy climate, beautiful women, easy wealth, and eternal happiness. The tale was a travel agent's dream, a classic early advertisement for a mythical land that really existed—and one that would try to live up to these early fantasies three or four centuries later.

Figure 1.1 Entering the Golden Gate, California's Pacific gateway. The view is eastward with Marin Peninsula to the north (left), connected to San Francisco Peninsula in the foreground by Golden Gate Bridge. This photo was taken from near the Pacific side of the Presidio, a 1,500-acre U.S. Army reservation. As the Spanish military had intended when it established a garrison here in 1776, the site commands a sweeping view of the ocean, coastline, and San Francisco Bay. (Roger M. Rhiner)

Figure 1.2 Returning to California from Oregon via Interstate 5, California's main transportation link with the Pacific Northwest. The valleylike lowland separates 14,162-ft Mount Shasta (extreme left) and the Southern Cascades Range to the east from the Klamath Mountains to the west (right). (Crane Miller)

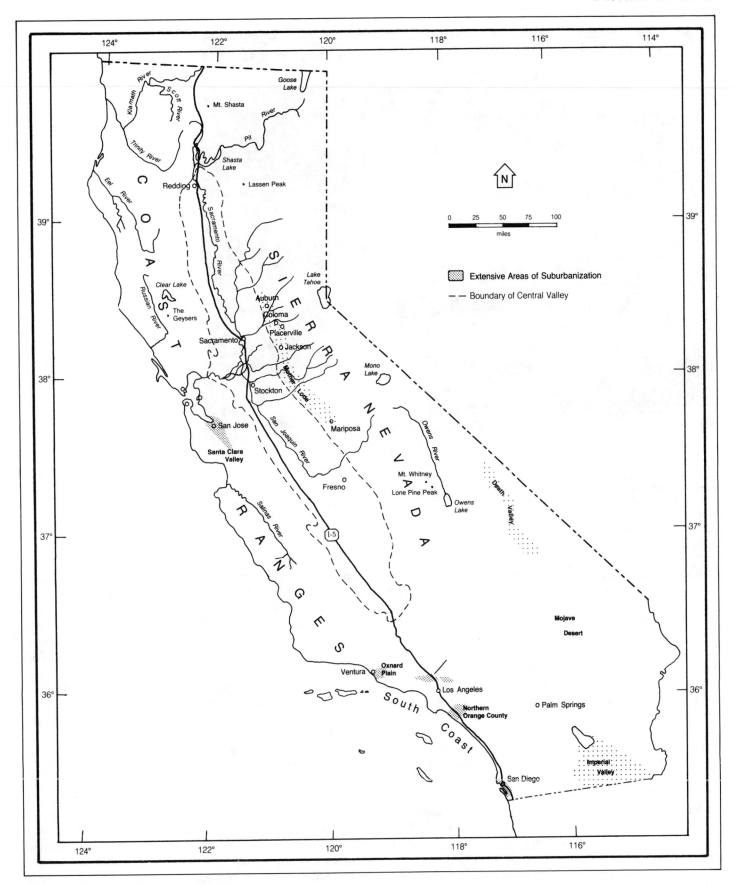

Figure 1.3 A glimpse of California's diversity. Many of the Golden State's environmental and cultural contrasts are highlighted in this reference map. (Richard Crooker)

Figure 1.4 San Luis Rey Mission, in the Peninsular Ranges north of San Diego, was established in 1798 by the Franciscan Order of the Roman Catholic Church as the seventeenth in their 21-mission system in coastal Alta California. The missions proved to be the effective vanguard of Spanish settlement in the farflung frontier province, the *presidios* (military garrisons) and *pueblos* (civilian towns) playing less significant roles than originally anticipated. (Union Pacific Railroad)

California Through the Eyes of the Spanish

Among the first eyewitness accounts of California were those provided by the Spanish. Indeed, some of the earliest written historical remembrances of the land are found in the diaries and reports of these early Spanish explorers and missionaries, and, for the most part, they reinforce rather than contradict the Spanish literary myth. Working their way northward from Mexico beginning in the mid-sixteenth century, the explorer-missionaries made some initial superficial observations about California, particularly its coastal regions, where they discovered "beautiful valleys and groves" as well as other flat and rough country. As for the native inhabitants, many of the various explorers described them in glowing terms as mostly peaceful, gentle, and attractive people. Other comments on the climate, water, and fertility of the soil were frequent and effusive. In fact, these explorers and missionaries described a California familiar to most of present-day America: a beautiful sun-drenched land with friendly natives lolling about, usually grateful recipients of culture from the rest of the world. The expected and familiar result of such enthusiastic reports was to encourage the establishment of missions and permanent settlements by Hispanic (Spanish and Mexican) colonists in this remarkable land—initiating what was to become a common theme throughout the history of the state. This is not to say that there were no detractors of the area. Indeed, one crusty Spaniard, Gaspar de Portolá, speculated on whether it would

have been better to let the Russians have the country. In all fairness, it may be that Portolá's disposition was somewhat soured by several weeks of dieting on mules that he had been forced to kill along his route to feed his expedition. His journey of exploration from Baja (now Mexico) into Alta California (now the U.S. state) in 1769 was fraught with perils. Moreover, Portolá's dim view of Baja California probably carried over into Alta California; his expedition occurred at the tail end of a long period of exploration, after the Spanish had finally decided to settle Alta California.

Over the course of approximately 230 years, beginning in 1542 with Juan Rodríguez Cabrillo, a respected sailor and navigator, sea and land expeditions were sent out from Mexico on a sporadic basis to explore and report back. It was not until the 1770s that the Spanish made any significant efforts to colonize Alta California on a wide scale. Perhaps this delay may partly be explained by the fact that 2,000 miles separated this area from the Spanish population centers in Mexico—certainly not a casual stroll around the plaza! Once Spain perceived a threat to its territory by other powers, however, it began its three-part (pueblo-presidio-mission) colonization of Alta California, and by the close of the eighteenth century it had established the area as Spanish Alta California. The attitudes and commentaries of the various mission fathers, settlers, and officials during the subsequent period reflected the desires of the Spanish government to encourage and expand the scope of settlement

(Fig. 1.4). The people who most benefited from the largesse of the government—the Californian rancheros, soldiers, and priests—were most often those who wrote extolling the virtues of the land. Through their eyes, pastoral Spanish California became transformed into a romantic "Spanish Arcadia," an image that has had amazing staying power.

The Spanish settlers of California took little active note of the revolt against Spain taking place in Mexico. When they learned that an independent government had been formed in Mexico, however, they soon adopted the new political loyalty. This Spanish period lasted until the early 1820s, when it was succeeded by the Mexican period—a brief quarter of a century remarkable for three significant changes. The first change was the secularization of the missions, with resulting economic and social dislocations that fell especially heavily upon the indigenous inhabitants of California, whom the Spaniards dubbed "Indians." The second was the rise of the cattle rancho (Fig. 1.5), replacing the mission as the focus of settlement. The third was the increase of foreign influence and importance in California, particularly of American interests. The Americans who trickled into California during this brief period sang the praises of the locale and certainly eased the way for acceptance of American rule in 1848. Although the Treaty of Guadalupe Hidalgo made California a part of United States territory in 1848, it was the discovery of gold the same year that made statehood a reality in 1850.

Early American Images
Although the Spanish were the first serious white colonizers and "tourists" of California, they were not alone in their efforts. Others, including the Russians and the British as well as the Americans, were active in their tentative incursions into the area.

Following the American Revolution, the British Admiralty indulged in some exploration, mapping, and surveying of the California coast (Fig. 1.6). In a somewhat stuffy vein, the British commentator-explorers frequently described the manner of life they observed as being too lazy, too relaxed, and too nonproductive. For example, British naval officer George Vancouver remarked on the Spanish Californians' "habitual indolence and want of industry" and concluded that true civilization would probably be a long time in coming.

The British observations were generally reinforced by various Yankee writers who frequented the ports of California for purposes of trade. Primarily focusing upon the Spanish and Californian officials with whom they dealt, the American seamen often found little to admire. The Californians were frequently described as pompous or cowardly, greedy or lazy, disorganized or frivolous, or all of these things. Indeed, many Americans seemed to share the opinion of U.S. Naval Lieutenant Charles Wilkes: "Although the Californians are comparatively few in number, yet they have a distinctive character. Descended from the old Spaniards, they are unfortunately found to have all their vices, without a proper share of their virtues."

However negative their comments may have been about the inhabitants, the descriptions of the climate, land, and physical features of the area were hardly discouraging. One of the first American writers, Captain William Shaler, in probably one of the least effusive descriptions described the land and climate as "dry and temperate, and remarkably healthy," while another, Alfred Robinson, perhaps more typically spoke of the "fairy spots . . . met with so often in California."

The initial American coastal contacts with California were soon followed by a series of reports, comments, letters, and enthusiastic tall tales from explorers who crossed the continent seeking the golden clime and op-

Figure 1.5 Cattle on a thousand hills, a pastoral scene reminiscent of Alta California during the rancho era when Mexico governed the province. Although Mexico opened up the interior of California with the free granting of large tracts of land in the Great Central Valley, the new Californios by and large preferred settlement in the hills and valleys fronting the coast, as seen here near Santa María. Milder climate and closer access to ocean ports, from which their cattle hides and tallow could be shipped, were among the deciding factors. The rancho quickly rose to replace the mission as the focus of settlement in Alta California during the Mexican Era. (Crane Miller)

Figure 1.6 Stinson Beach, on the Pacific side of Marin Peninsula. The English explorer and privateer Sir Francis Drake is known to have beached his vessel, the *Golden Hinde,* for repairs somewhere in the vicinity in June of 1579. The exact location is either nearer Point Reyes, about two dozen miles to the north, or on the interior or San Pablo Bay side of Marin Peninsula. During his 36-day stay, Drake got along well with local Miwok Indians and decided to claim the region for England, naming it Nova (New) Albion. Nothing ever became of the proposed English settlement, other than its stirring anew Spain's claim to all of California. (Crane Miller)

portunities that beckoned from the land of the dons. Beginning with mountain man Jedediah Smith, Americans gradually began to reach California by the overland route. After their arduous trek across mountain, plain, and desert, California did indeed appear a paradise to many of these travelers. As these men began to settle and establish themselves in the area, they started a round of enthusiastic and positive letters and comments on the wonders of California. Seeking to encourage more Yankees to settle in the area and thus increase the American influence, these promoters described a fertile, verdant area ripe for settlement—that is, until 1848, when such promotion was no longer necessary. The cry of "gold" became the overnight stimulus to the growth of California, beginning an odyssey of fortune seeking that has continued in various forms up to the present.

Literary Visions

Although truth is often stranger than fiction, the "factual" reports of California frequently ranged dangerously close to outright fantasy. Likewise, the fiction writers who used the region as a backdrop in their works may have been no more imaginative or creative than the authors of "true accounts." In any event, the images of California that emerged from the pens of some of America's most popular literary figures did not vary greatly from their previous (and contemporary) "truthful" colleagues. Continuing in the now-established positive and colorful vein, these literary visions usually perpetuated the myth of the Golden State—certainly not discouraging new immigration and interest in the region. Although the number of writers who undertook to describe California is too great to permit exhaustive treatment here, a stellar few bear mentioning.

Richard Henry Dana is noted not for his promotion of California but rather for his crusade for the rights of sailors. When his classic work *Two Years Before the Mast* was published in 1840, however, it did act as a major influence in attracting American settlers to California. His vivid descriptions painted word pictures of handsome people, attractive land, pleasing climate, and boundless opportunities for aggressive Americans in this sleepy economy.

Another well-known figure, Washington Irving, wrote of "the plains of New California, a fertile region extending along the coast, with magnificent forests, verdant savannas and prairies that look like stately parks." The great regional authors of the mid-1800s also found eager audiences for their tales of the Far West. Bret Harte, Artemus Ward, and Mark Twain spun romantic tales of the gold rush towns, colorful characters, high Sierra country, and unusual occurrences of the California scene. Twain's story "The Celebrated Jumping Frog of Calaveras County" was only one of many amusing fictions whose pages provided enticing whiffs of the golden land. Even Walt Whitman created a tribute to one aspect of California in "Song of the Redwood Tree"; and although Rebecca of Sunnybrook Farm never visited California, her creator, Kate Douglas Wiggins, sang the praises of the state and particularly of Santa Barbara, which she called her "Paradise on Earth." Even more widely read were the romantic crusades of Helen Hunt Jackson, who in *Ramona* and other works about the old Spanish period shed further light upon the development and historical roots of the state.

As means of transportation and communication improved, writings by and about Californians became even more popular with the American reading public. Of major importance to the naturalistic school of American fiction were several California authors now considered important writers in their own right. Frank Norris effectively utilized the diversity of the California landscape as a dramatic backdrop for his epic novels such as *McTeague* (with scenes ranging from glittering San Francisco to a dramatic climax in Death Valley) and *The Octopus* (which dealt with the wheat production of the San Joaquin Valley and the farmers' battle with railroad interests). Likewise, Jack London derived inspiration and mood from his birthplace in the Bay Area. His descriptions of fog in the Golden Gate, the slums and dives of San Francisco, Sausalito (Fig. 1.7), and Oakland, and the characters he had known there, were particularly vivid and evocative. Indeed, he began one of his best-known works, *The Sea Wolf*, with a tremendously mood-creating depiction of the clammy, blanketing fog of San Francisco Bay—a description instantly recognizable to anyone who has experienced that phenomenon. Other well-known writers, such as Upton Sinclair (*Oil!*) portrayed the scattered and sometimes tawdry development of the state, and Sinclair Lewis had his run at exposing San Francisco to the public eye. Many other popular and respected authors, poets, and journalists also paid tribute to the Golden State in their works, either directly or through the settings used in their creations.

In all, California provided a rich source of material for the literary endeavors of the nation. This attention effectively drew attention to the state, further enhanced its mystery, attraction, and legend, and nurtured the desire in multitudes of people to see firsthand the areas that had been so vividly described. Thus, both directly and indirectly, the literary visions of three more centuries further expanded the almost hypnotic appeal first created in Ordóñez de Montalvo's sixteenth-century tale of a mythical California.

Figure 1.7 Sausalito yacht harbor, on the bay side of the southern tip of Marin Peninsula. Today's affluent, fashionable waterfront community originated out of Rancho Saucelito ("willow grove"), whose first settler was William Richardson in 1838. (Crane Miller)

Figure 1.8 The famed Rose Bowl in Pasadena. Every New Year's Day, more than 100,000 football fans watch the "Best from the West" battle the "Best from the Midwest," often for the national college football championship. Earlier that same day, more than a million people line nearby Colorado Boulevard to watch the Rose Parade. Since flower-decorated floats are entered by nations and agencies from all around the world and the event is beamed by communications satellite to many countries outside the United States, the Tournament of Roses is truly international in scope. (Pasadena Tournament of Roses)

A Taste of Today

The fascination felt by the American populace for the state of California has not substantially subsided even to this day. There is still an aura of otherworldliness to the region. While temperatures bottom out in the East and Midwest, millions of Americans enviously watch the sun shine on scantily clad drum majorettes at the Rose Parade and Rose Bowl game (Fig. 1.8) televised every January 1. In the face of subfreezing weather outside their windows, many people cannot help but view the balmy surroundings pictured on their television sets as a taste of paradise.

Modern writers have continued to reflect this interest in their writings, wherein California's unique position (climatically, geographically, and historically) plays a key role. Certainly the works of John Steinbeck must top the list in influence, style, and importance; his great *Grapes of Wrath* described a California able to produce winter crops that were impossible to grow in many other parts of the country (at a time when no one could afford to buy them). In this and other works, Steinbeck exposed the very soul of much of the state, particularly the rich farm areas such as the Salinas Valley, and in the process became a modern California classic himself.

Nor is Steinbeck alone. William Saroyan's Fresno comes alive in his words; Joseph Wambaugh's Los Angeles gains in notoriety through his widely read police stories; Eugene Burdick has exposed politics, California style, to millions of readers. Thus, through these and other current writers, the myth-making process continues. Television and movies, magazines, and newspapers constantly spread the virtues and mystique of the golden land, in the process keeping intact the august tradition of travelogue tales and romantic musings about California.

DIVERSITY IN PERSPECTIVE

Few regions on earth can lay legitimate claim to the degree of geographical diversity that is California's. Where else in a single area of less than 160,000 sq mi are found glaciated mountains, verdant river valleys, countless seascapes, snowless winters, redwood rainforests, dry deserts, deep lakes, plenty of petroleum, bountiful agriculture, and 24 million people with national and ethnic origins representing all of humanity? We could go on and on with such superlatives, some of them seemingly paradoxical, and thus render the question even less answerable, but the inescapable conclusion is that California is in fact *uniquely* diverse.

Environmental Diversity

One need not look outside California for either a quick change of scenery or a more permanent move to a better physical environment. There is diversity enough in California's physical geography to satisfy just about anyone's environmental needs (except for the person seeking the humid tropics). For the Angeleno who suddenly feels the urge to commune with nature rather than commuting the Santa Monica Freeway, the majestic isolation of 14,000-ft mountains in the Sierra Nevada (Fig. 1.9) is only a few hours away by car (and foot). For the Mojave Desert dweller who needs more relief from summer's dry heat than an air conditioner can provide, Lake Tahoe's cool alpine setting (Fig. 1.10) provides the needed environmental diversion and is only a half day's drive. For the San Joaquin Valley farmer overdue for a vacation by the seashore, there is more than 1,000 miles of it along the Pacific just over the Coast Ranges to the west. For the San Franciscan yearning for fogless skies, a trip to balmy Palm Springs is likely to provide them. Thus does California alone in the nation offer such environmental contrasts. Perhaps this self-contained versatility explains why Californians are sometimes said to be defensively parochial. "After all," they say, "why travel out of the state when it's all right here?"

Besides furnishing Californians with seemingly boundless recreational opportunities, the state's environmental diversity is also the basis for an abundance of natural resources. The geography of California's natural resources is uneven but predictable, when the

Figure 1.9 Ansel Adams Rock and Lone Pine Peak in the southeastern Sierra. Like John Steinbeck, Ansel Adams was born in 1902 in California (San Francisco), but Adams has captured the California landscape with camera rather than pen. An internationally renowned photographer, Adams has published some 30 books of his photos, including *My Camera in the National Parks* (1950), *Images, 1923–1974* (1974), and *Born Free and Equal* (1944). The latter work concerned "loyal Japanese-Americans at Manzanar," a World War II relocation camp for Nisei (American-born U.S. citizens) and other Japanese, which was located about 10 miles north of where this photo was taken in the Alabama Hills of southern Owens Valley. (Crane Miller)

state's 158,693 square mile area (third largest in the United States) and the variety of geologic, climatic, and biotic processes that formed it are taken into consideration. Gold is created in the Sierras and is subsequently weathered, eroded, and carried down by countless streams to *placer* (laid down by water) deposits in the foothills; petroleum and natural gas are found in the sedimentary formations of the Coast Ranges and offshore on the continental shelf; borates and potash accumulate in the basins of interior drainage that dominate the arid eastern deserts; high-grade iron ore is formed in the mountains of those deserts; water, the most vital mineral of all, is stored in the snows and lakes of the Cascades, Klamaths, and Sierras (Fig. 1.11), whose towering peaks originally forced the moisture from winter storms; soil formed from deep alluvial deposits in the San Joaquin, Sacramento, Salinas, Imperial, and numerous lesser valleys is the very foundation of California's agricultural supremacy; timber comes from the coastal redwood rainforest, the Douglas fir stands of the northwest, and the yellow pine belt of the western Sierra Nevada (Fig. 1.12). Augmenting this enviable resource base, California has an ocean and freshwater fishery rivaled in few other states, and a developed geothermal energy resource, at the Geysers and in the Imperial Valley, that no other state except Hawaii possesses.

Figure 1.10 Lake Tahoe in the northeastern Sierra. Its name derived from the Washo Indian word for water or lake and presently shared by California and Nevada, Lake Tahoe measures 22 miles long by 12 miles wide and lies 6,229 ft above sea level. The lake is about 2,000 ft deep, which helps maintain its outstanding clarity in spite of the impacts of intense urban development along and upslope from its shoreline. (California Office of Tourism)

Figure 1.11 Eastern Sierras, Alabama Hills, and Los Angeles Aqueduct. Aqueducts like this form an extensive fresh water redistribution system in California, carrying the vital mineral from mountain watersheds, where it is usually abundant, to coastal metropolises, where it would otherwise be in short supply. (Crane Miller)

Exploitation of these varied natural resources fluctuates with supply and demand, official perception of environmental impact, technological capability, governmental constraints, natural phenomena, and other concerns both evident and not so evident. For instance, though it was once the national leader in gold production, today California is unranked even though its reserves are still plentiful. One of several deterrents to a revival of gold mining is that most of the existing ores are of insufficiently high grade to be profitably mined. Petroleum production, in which California ranks with the Gulf states and Alaska, provides another case in point: Local demand far outstrips local supply. Furthermore, there will be increased import of petroleum as local reserves of natural gas near total depletion. But however California ranks in individual resource categories, the state remains unchallenged in resource versatility. And if any other constraint besides actual depletion is placed on this resource potential, it is likely to be the limits of human ingenuity.

Cultural Diversity

Debatable though the point may be, the thesis that environmental diversity determines cultural diversity bears strong witness in California. Moreover, environmental variety has fostered a distinctive heritage for California through its successive cultures. California Indians were not only the most populous aboriginal group for an area California's size in pre-Columbian North America, but their ecological and linguistic diversity compared with that of the entire continent. The aboriginals' habitat adaptation and survival ranged from fishing for salmon and steelhead trout in the prolific streams of the northwest, to gathering oak acorns as a staple food source in the Great Central Valley, to practicing simple flood plain agriculture along the lower Colorado River. Their linguistic diversity—six language families composed of dozens of languages and dialects— could be likened to that of Europe.

The Hispanic cultures that superseded them contributed relatively few immigrants to California but noticeably modified the cultural landscape with the development of a 600-mile, 21-station coastal mission system (Fig. 1.4) and numerous ranchos (Fig. 1.5) whose land areas were often larger than those of small states. This condition of sparse population abruptly ended with the Gold Rush, when hordes of Yankees invaded the Mother Lode (Fig. 1.13), some only to leave the new state (admitted to the Union September 9, 1850) once the placers played out, but many to stay on and pursue more reliable livelihoods than picking and panning offered.

Perhaps more important than generating California's first genuine population boom, the Gold Rush marked the initial unlocking of a vast treasure of natural resources. Wells were drilled for water and oil, and irrigation agriculture (Fig. 1.14) and petroleum mining boomed. Logging of seemingly inexhaustible stands of virgin redwood and Douglas fir began in earnest. Whalers, sealers, and fishers tapped the bounty of the Pacific. The railroads came, linking California to an Eastern market eager for its products. The news of the state's perpetual spring also disseminated eastward, starting a "Health Rush" that continues to this day. The infant motion picture and aircraft industries, perceiving an essential natural resource in California's mild climate

Figure 1.12 Sierran forest, Sugar Pine State Park. The yellow pine belt, lying on the 400-mile western face of the Sierra at elevations from 4,500 to 8,000 ft above sea level, constitutes one of western America's great softwood timber reserves. These coniferous forests and those of northwestern California enable the state to be one of the nation's leading producers of construction lumber and other wood products. (California Department of Parks and Recreation)

Figure 1.13 Sutter's Mill at Coloma, some 40 miles upstream from Sacramento on the American River. While deepening the tailrace of his partner's mill on January 24, 1848, James Marshall discovered gold. A gold rush involving some 100,000 miners swelled California's population almost overnight, a feat of immigration desired but never achieved by the Spanish and Mexican regimes. California and other Mexican territories were granted to the United States under terms of the Treaty of Guadalupe Hidalgo, which concluded the war with Mexico and was signed February 2, 1848. (California Department of Parks and Recreation)

Figure 1.14 Sonoma Vineyards under drip irrigation. In 1824, the Franciscan fathers established the last of their 21 missions and introduced viticulture to the Sonoma and Napa Valleys in the northern Coast Ranges. The valleys have since become the premier wine-producing region of California and the nation. (Crane Miller)

(for landing planes and shooting movies could both best be done on sunny days), gravitated to the state and subsequently expanded. Industry in general continued to grow and diversify in California, lending credence to a notion that has persisted since the Gold Rush: "California is the land of economic opportunity."

Environmental amenity thus attracted millions of migrants to the Golden State from the four corners of the earth. The new Californians came from Africa, Asia, Europe, and Oceania, as well as the Americas. Thus the ethnic diversity of today's 24 million Californians is obvious, if not always clearly definable. The 65 percent majority, variously referred to as white or Anglo or something else, is itself a veritable ethnic jumble of Western and Eastern European origins to which such labels hardly have universal application. Groups among the 35 percent ethnic "minority," however, are more distinctly defined: Of all Californians, nearly 18 percent are Mexican-Americans or Chicanos; approximately 7 percent are blacks; another 7 percent are about equally spread among Chinese, Filipinos, Japanese, Portuguese, and Puerto Ricans; and slightly less than 1 percent are native American Indians. These minorities as a whole may become the majority well before 1990. Whether or not California soon becomes the nation's first Third World state, the existing degree of ethnic variety constitutes the essence of an already unparalleled cultural diversity.

Population Trends

If mild climate is singled out as the chief physical attraction of California, the most apparent cultural response to it—spectacular population growth—has been the major *human* event in the state. The influx of people since statehood has variously flowed and trickled, proving that climate, a none too reliable constant in itself,

is only one of several factors governing population trends.

Consider for a moment the decennial (by decade) changes shown in Table 1.1. From 1920 to 1930, for instance, California's proportional growth rate was nearly 66 percent, the second highest of any single decade since statehood. Yet in the following decade the rate fell to less than 22 percent, the lowest decennial rate until the 1970s. Socioeconomic conditions affecting the entire nation were at play here: The Great Depression of the 1930s came close on the heels of the economic prosperity of the Roaring Twenties. Americans standing in breadlines and selling apples were simply less mobile and less likely to have children than when they had "a chicken in every pot and two cars in every garage."

Table 1.1
Population Change, 1850–1980

Census Year	Population	Percent Change
1850	165,000	
1860	379,994	+ 130.3
1870	560,247	+ 32.1
1880	864,694	+ 54.3
1890	1,213,398	+ 40.3
1900	1,485,053	+ 22.4
1910	2,377,549	+ 60.1
1920	3,426,861	+ 44.1
1930	5,677,251	+ 65.7
1940	6,907,387	+ 21.7
1950	10,586,223	+ 53.5
1960	15,717,204	+ 48.5
1970	19,971,069	+ 27.1
1980	23,545,061	+ 17.9

Source: U.S. Department of Commerce, Bureau of the Census, *1980 Census of Population and Housing* (Preliminary Reports), and reports for previous decades.

Two other decades worthy of examination are the 1950s and 1960s, during which combined time a near doubling of population took place: from more than 10.5 million to almost 20 million. This greatest of numerical increases over any other two decades can be attributed to a number of factors, not the least of which was the rise of the aerospace and electronics industries to national prominence in California. Growth in these industries was rapid during World War II and was sustained well into and beyond the postwar period by such varied events as the Korean War, the Cold War, Sputnik, the Jet Age, and the Vietnam War. So what, as we turn to the final decade, accounts for the growth slowdown of the 1970s? One explanation concerns the aforementioned industries: Although in the 1950s and 1960s they provided many jobs for newcomers to California, in the seventies they began laying off workers as firms in Texas and other Sun Belt states outcompeted California companies for contracts.

Two regional population variables, *migration* (net immigration or in-migration, and net emigration or out-migration) and *natural change* (the difference between births and deaths, or *natural increase* or *decrease*) underlie these and other reasons given for population trends in California. It would appear from Figure 1.15 that in-migration since statehood has contributed more to population growth than natural increase. Since the late sixties, however, the pattern has reversed, resulting in the number of native-born Californians equaling those from out-of-state by the end of the 1970s. Numerically speaking, net average annual immigration to California has fallen dramatically in recent years: from more than 300,000 during the 1950s and 1960s to less than 100,000 during the 1970s. Moreover, even though natural increase is now contributing more to California's population growth than immigration, the present *fertility rate* of 2.1 live births per woman is very near the hypothetical "zero population growth" (ZPG) mark.

Household formation, or literally the number of people making up the average household, may provide a more reliable predictor of population trends than fertility rates or migration patterns, mainly because those Cal-

ifornians who will form future households can be counted now. Average household size is unmistakably declining in California: For example, a California Department of Finance (DOF) estimate for 1970–1975 for Los Angeles, Orange, and San Diego counties indicated the average number of persons per household dropped from 2.89 in 1970 to 2.72 in 1975 and to a projected 2.63 by 1980. Nationwide, the slide is not as steep, a phenomenon that is attributable to, among other factors, a lower divorce rate nationally (about one third of all U.S. marriages end in divorce) than in some large urban counties in California. For example, one of every two Los Angeles marriages turns sour or, in household formation parlance, "a broken home forms two households." Other life-style changes that have curtailed household size and in which Californians tend often to exceed national norms include couples postponing marriage and childbearing or simply doing neither, more women going into careers rather than staying home, and couples simply having fewer children. Regarding the last phenomenon, it is noteworthy that Americans are now statistically down to less than one child per household. (In all good jest, one wonders what rearing nine tenths of a child must be like.)

Age and sex distributions also influence household formation and overall population trends. California is clearly past its frontier days when men greatly outnumbered women. A population pyramid would now show the number of males and females as being roughly equal, but with a slightly higher proportion of males than females in the lower age brackets and a lower proportion of males than females in the senior citizen years. The relatively high proportion of people in the lower age brackets portends well for those who hope ZPG is not upon California. In the next five to fifteen years, this group will swell the ranks of those in the most productive childrearing years of 20 to 35, which should sustain and perhaps accelerate natural increase. The proportion of people in the over-60 brackets of the pyramid will also increase, as will life expectancy. These trends indicate that *vital rates* (birth and death) have stabilized at a relatively low level, placing California in a nearly steady state stage in its *demographic transition* away from rapid population growth.

Despite sluggish population growth of late, the population itself has remained mobile within California, a phenomenon that is reflected at the county level. Some urban counties—Los Angeles and San Francisco, for example—lost population in the first half of the 1970s, whereas neighboring counties grew phenomenally in the same five-year period as they received the spillover from more built-up, higher-density counties. Orange County, on the other hand, has been numerically the first or second fastest-growing county for two decades, taking in a significant portion of its new residents from adjacent Los Angeles County. Explanations for the emigration from Los Angeles to Orange include "white flight to the suburbs," more land available at lower prices, and less smog. But with time the validity of these rationales diminishes, as growth in Orange County is accompanied by upward socioeconomic mobility and thus greater geographic mobility among minorities, equalization of land and housing prices between the two counties, and more

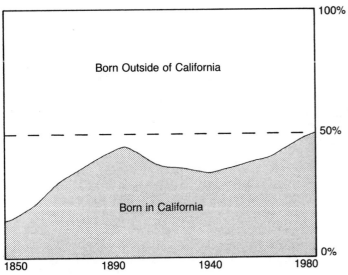

Source: U.S. Bureau of the Census and California Department of Finance.

Figure 1.15 Origin of population, 1850–1980. (Richard Crooker)

cars and industry creating more air pollution. A similar set of circumstances has already affected Ventura County, Los Angeles's other coastal neighbor, especially since the early 1960s, by which time the San Fernando Valley was essentially developed and many of its residents began looking northwestward for less congested living. Also, the partiality of Californians for seashore residence is significant in explaining why Orange and Ventura counties have grown more rapidly than Los Angeles County's landlocked neighbors.

These urban to suburban shifts are not unusual in California—or anywhere else in the nation, for that matter. A new migration trend, however, from suburban to "recreational rural," may be surfacing that is more than merely seasonal or transitory in nature. Note in Figure 1.16 and Table 1.2, for example, the growth of

Placer and El Dorado counties, which share Lake Tahoe with the state of Nevada; Mono County, which includes the Mammoth Mountain ski resorts; and Shasta County, which takes in all of the Shasta Lake National Recreation Area and part of Lassen Volcanic National Park. Year-round retirement, recreational, and tourist industry opportunities abound in these counties, and as this economic base grows, so does the probability of greater numbers of immigrants. Some resort areas in the counties could become the cities of the future, and probably already are. Lake Tahoe, for instance, already has a peak winter population of 128,000, an increasing proportion of which is composed of permanent residents. Adverse environmental impact or drought could slow down the development of these resort areas, but their alpine environments will no doubt remain among the most at-

Figure 1.16 Population: rank by rate of increase, 1970–1980. (Norene Heath)

Table 1.2

California Counties: Population Change, 1970–1980

Rank by Rate of Increase	County	1970 Population	Rank by 1970 Population	1980 Population	Rank by 1980 Population	Percent Increase	Rank by Numerical Increase
1	Alpine	484	58	1,093	58	125.8	56
2	Mono	4,016	56	8,589	56	113.9	49
3	Nevada	26,346	40	51,751	38	96.4	27
4	El Dorado	43,833	35	85,709	33	94.4	20
5	Lake	19,548	42	36,507	42	86.8	33
6	Mariposa	6,015	55	11,055	54	83.8	46
7	Amador	11,821	50	19,261	48	62.9	40
8	Trinity	7,615	53	11,849	53	55.6	50
9	Tuolumne	22,169	41	33,921	43	53.0	35
10	Madera	41,519	37	63,078	36	51.9	29
11	Placer	77,632	30	117,293	27	51.1	22
12	Santa Cruz	123,790	23	186,873	23	51.0	13
13	Calaveras	13,585	48	20,442	47	50.5	42
14	Plumas	11,707	51	17,365	51	48.3	45
15	Shasta	77,640	29	114,986	28	47.8	23
16	San Luis Obispo	105,690	24	154,745	24	46.4	18
17	Riverside	456,916	11	660,430	9	44.4	5
18	Sonoma	204,885	19	292,275	17	42.6	11
19	Ventura	378,497	13	533,615	12	41.0	7
20	Butte	101,969	26	143,655	25	40.4	21
21	San Diego	1,357,854	3	1,859,623	3	37.0	1
22	San Benito	18,226	43	24,910	44	36.7	43
23	Stanislaus	194,506	20	265,671	19	36.6	14
24	Orange	1,421,233	2	1,925,840	2	35.5	2
25	Solano	171,989	22	230,228	21	33.9	15
26	Tehama	29,517	39	38,876	41	31.7	37
27	Mendocino	51,101	33	66,751	35	30.6	34
28	Sierra	2,365	57	3,069	57	29.8	55
29	Tulare	188,322	21	244,546	20	29.9	16
30	Lassen	16,796	45	21,674	45	29.0	48
31	San Bernardino	682,233	7	877,636	6	28.6	6
32	Merced	104,629	25	134,252	26	28.3	25
33	Del Norte	14,580	47	18,210	49	24.9	52
34	Sutter	41,935	36	52,336	37	24.6	36
35	Yolo	91,788	28	113,305	29	23.4	30
36	Imperial	74,492	31	91,874	32	23.1	32
37	Sacramento	634,373	8	780,391	7	23.0	8
38	Napa	79,140	28	97,361	31	23.0	31
39	Fresno	413,329	12	507,005	13	22.7	10
40	Glenn	17,521	44	21,333	46	21.8	51
41	Kern	330,234	14	401,540	14	21.6	12
42	Santa Clara	1,065,313	5	1,290,487	4	21.1	4
43	Siskiyou	33,225	38	39,715	40	19.5	44
44	San Joaquin	291,073	15	347,312	15	19.3	17
45	Contra Costa	556,116	10	650,748	10	17.0	9
46	Monterey	247,450	17	289,301	18	16.9	19
47	Modoc	7,469	54	8,618	55	15.4	54
48	Inyo	15,571	46	17,871	50	14.8	53
49	Santa Barbara	264,324	16	297,722	16	12.6	24
50	Yuba	44,736	34	49,671	39	11.0	47
51	Kings	66,717	32	73,819	34	10.6	41
52	Humboldt	99,692	27	108,486	30	8.8	38
53	Los Angeles	7,041,980	1	7,445,721	1	5.7	3
54	San Mateo	557,361	9	582,814	11	4.6	28
55	Marin	208,652	18	218,085	22	4.1	39
56	Alameda	1,071,446	4	1,101,070	5	2.8	26
57	Colusa	12,430	49	12,738	52	2.5	57
58	San Francisco	715,674	6	674,150	8	-5.8	58

Source: U.S. Department of Commerce, Bureau of the Census, *1980 Census of Population and Housing* (Preliminary Reports).

tractive to Californians, whether for a vacation or a permanent move.

The trends discussed so far notwithstanding, California's population is predominantly urban and its landscape is predominantly rural. This paradox is evident in Figure 1.17, where the state's *urbanized areas* in 1970 held 81 percent of the population but only some 2 percent of the land area. Thirty-four of California's 58 counties have no urbanized areas at all and in most of the 24 that do, such as San Bernardino, urbanized areas occupy a minutely small percentage of total land area. When *urban places* of 2,500 or more inhabitants (also a U.S. Bureau of the Census designation for "urban") are calculated together with populations of urbanized areas in Califor-

nia, the 1980 Census then shows more than 90 percent of the population as being urban. By any definition, California is unquestionably one of the most urban states in the Union; but at the same time, most of its 158,693 square miles are virtually empty (Fig. 1.17) and seem likely to remain so.

California's relative emptiness seems all the more perplexing when its sprawling pattern of suburban development is considered. Low-density tracts of single-family detached homes, regional shopping centers, and industrial parks have spread out from every large city, consuming millions of acres of scarce prime agricultural land in what has become an irreversible process. Seas of rooftops intermingled with other suburban land uses

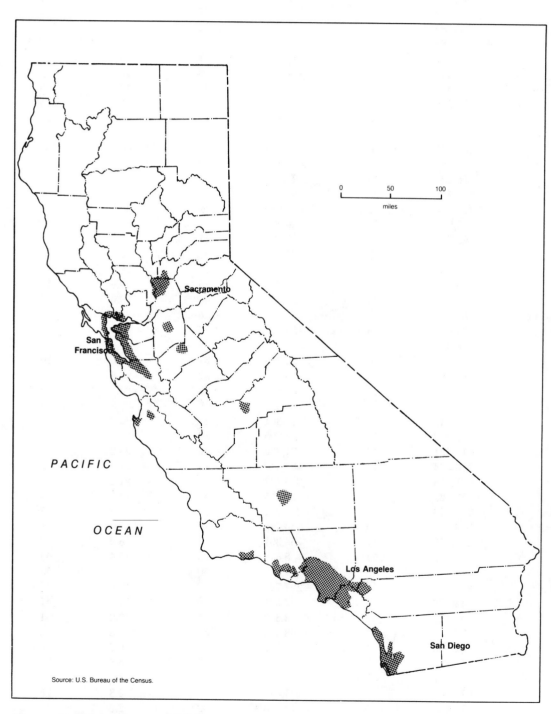

Source: U.S. Bureau of the Census.

Figure 1.17 Urbanized areas of California. An urbanized area includes at least one city of 50,000 or more residents or twin cities with contiguous boundaries and with a combined population of 50,000, the smaller of the two cities having a population of at least 15,000. (Marc Blodgett)

Figure 1.18 Eastern Oxnard Plain and Camarillo from the air. Irreplaceable prime farmland is being urbanized at alarming rates in Ventura and other rapidly growing coastal counties. Most Californians still prefer to reside in land-consuming, single-family detached houses despite high purchase prices and exorbitant interest rates. (Crane Miller)

and nonuses (usually vacant land priced out of agriculture by rising property taxes) have long since replaced prune orchards in the Santa Clara Valley, orange groves in the San Gabriel Valley, row crops in parts of the Oxnard Plain (Fig. 1.18), and other valuable crop areas in the path of urban sprawl. However, farmland property "tax break" legislation, restoration of existing neighborhoods, a mounting trend towards higher density in new residential development, and increased development of hillside home sites have somewhat decelerated the rate of land conversion in recent years. If these emerging development patterns continue to gain favor, suburbia, where most Californians reside, may soon begin to appear a more compactly settled landscape than it has been since the postwar population boom began. Rising opposition to further development of freeways, mostly from the suburbanites who must travel them regularly, reinforces the trend to more compact urban development. Above all, a contiguous developing suburbia is less likely to prejudice as much prime valley farmland as one that leapfrogs in a hit-and-miss fashion over the landscape.

ISOLATION OR UNIQUENESS

Isolation is a frequently mentioned theme in studies of California. Since as far back as the time of Ordóñez de Montalvo's mythical island, the region has attracted continued references to its relative isolation from the rest of the country (and at times the world).

In 1579, the famous English adventurer Sir Francis Drake's explorations and subsequent efforts at cartography, as well as those of other European geographers, resulted in the widespread conviction that California was indeed an island—and so it was depicted in the maps of the early period. Not until the explorations of Father Eusebio Francisco Kino over a hundred years later was California recognized to be a part of the North American mainland.

Although the Spanish discovered that they could reach the area by a land route, this did not substantially affect the concept of California's isolation. Removed from the settled areas of Mexico, the area was difficult to get to either by sea or land owing respectively to adverse coastal headwinds and currents and forbidding, barren desert wastes located between the central Spanish empire and this remote outpost. Thus, once settlers arrived in California, they were not much inclined to engage in active travel back and forth to Mexico. This very real cutting off contributed to their sense of isolation.

The Mexican period saw little change in the patterns of settlement in the area first established by the Spanish. Not until the discovery of gold was there a concerted effort to reach the region by outsiders. Yet even with the lure of gold to draw them on, travelers from the States had to contend with the arid expanse of the Great Basin (Fig. 1.19) between the Rocky Mountain and the Sierra Nevada, the imposing barrier of the Sierra itself, the barren desert wastes of the Mojave or the semiarid regions of the Central Valley. The alternative was a long, costly, and time-consuming ocean voyage around Cape Horn or an ocean-land-ocean route ultimately ending in San Francisco. In either case, the trip to California constituted a significant separation in terms of time and distance. Without the impetus of gold, the journey took

Figure 1.19 Owens Valley and the rest of the Great Basin region of eastern California are well isolated from urban California both in distance and by significant landform barriers. But sparseness of population and abundance of open space can also be attributed to the aridity and seasonal temperature extremes characteristic of regions in the lee of high mountain ranges. In the case of the Owens Valley, the export of its surface and ground waters by the City of Los Angeles has all but precluded growth. (Crane Miller)

on even greater overtones of sacrifice, and until the completion of the transcontinental railroad the isolation of the California settlers was very real and very marked.

The initiation first of overland mail, the telegraph, and the railroad and eventually of radio, television, airplanes, and autos did reduce the physical isolation of the West Coast, but often not the psychological isolation. The fact remains that California still is somewhat distant from the centers of Eastern and Midwestern population. Even today, time and distance are factors of importance to most visitors to the state. Likewise, most Californians must give serious thought to a vacation trip back East, especially when there is everything they could desire, from beach to mountain, desert to river recreation, readily available within the state itself.

Thus, as some authorities have noted, California in many ways continues to be "an island upon the land," especially that portion of it west of the San Andreas rift or fault zone. Actually, this elongate sliver of coastal California is apparently moving about 2 inches per year northwestward with respect to the rest of the continent, a migration that could conceivably place it offshore from the British Columbia mainland and the Alaska panhandle about 50 million years from now. Californians, now and for generations to come, won't actually see this inevitable breaking-up of their land, but they will feel it every time an earthquake rumbles through their unstable landscape.

2

THE UNSTABLE LANDSCAPE

California forms part of the *Pacific rim (or ring) of fire*, an ominous collection of active volcanoes and earthquake faults that more or less encircles the entire Pacific Basin. Like it or not, membership in this unsettling outer circle is unavoidable if one resides almost anywhere on the Pacific side of Asia, Japan, the Philippines, Melanesia, New Zealand, South America, Central America, or North America. This places "Pacific World" residents in the unenviable position of living on the most unstable terrain on earth. For Californians, there are such recent reminders of this uneasy instability as the 1906 San Francisco earthquake, and the quakes that shook the Mammoth Mountain area between 1980 and 1982. Apparently, though, the hazards of living where the earth regularly shakes are far outweighed by the environmental amenities the state has to offer. To conclude otherwise is to ask why California is the most populous state and still growing. Earthquakes and earthquake disaster films may remind Californians of their perpetual peril, but these lessons are soon forgotten and detract little from the state's lotus land reputation.

A CASE STUDY
THE SAN FERNANDO EARTHQUAKE

It was barely 6 o'clock that morning of February 9, 1971, when an ominous rumbling abruptly awakened many Southern Californians. Within seconds, walls and floors in their homes began vibrating and glass could be heard shattering as mirrors shook loose from walls and dishes rattled from shelves and crashed to the floor. As though by instinct, parents rushed to children's rooms, pulled them from their beds, and then scurried to the nearest doorway or crawled under the piano or dining room table to wait out the first shock of the San Fernando earthquake.

Although the initial shaking was of short duration, it was sufficiently severe for residents almost anywhere in Los Angeles, Orange, and Ventura counties to assume that the quake was centered near their home. Yet the radio soon told Southern Californians that the *epicenter*

(surface point of origin) of the earthquake was located just north of Sylmar in the extreme northern portion of the San Fernando Valley, or about 25 miles north of downtown Los Angeles.

Compared to other major California quakes (as shown in Fig. 2.1), the *magnitude* of the San Fernando earthquake at 6.6 on the logarithmic *Richter scale*[1] is considered only moderately high. The 8.3 ratings assigned the 1872 Lone Pine (Owens Valley) and 1906 San Francisco quakes are much higher, representing seismograph readings many times that of the San Fernando quake. The amount of actual energy released by an earthquake when measured by Richter magnitude is even more impressive, for with every whole number increase on the scale there is a thirty-twofold increase in energy.

Nonetheless, 6.6 was sufficiently strong to topple hospital buildings at two sites in Sylmar, severely damage the Pacific Intertie converter station at Sylmar, collapse parts of the Golden State Freeway (Fig. 2.2), crack the earthfill Van Norman Dam (causing the evacuation of flood-threatened valley communities lasting until the reservoir was drained), and damage scores of homes, many severely enough to cause their condemnation. Had the initial tremor lasted longer and/or come later during the morning rush hour, the damage to property and loss of life would have been considerably greater. As it was, the human toll was 64 lives and the cost exceeded half a billion dollars.

Most of the loss occurred in the northern San Fernando Valley near the epicenter of the quake, which was located in a zone of minor faults a little farther north in the San Gabriel Mountains but still some 15 miles south of the San Andreas fault.[2] Obviously, the damage potential of a quake diminishes as distance from the epicenter

[1]Where each whole number represents a tenfold or exponential change; for example, 8.0 would be 10^4 or 10,000 times as great as 4.0.

[2]Faults are fractures in rock where movement of one side with respect to the other side occurs. Such movement can be up or down (*vertical* or *normal faulting*), horizontal (*lateral faulting*), or diagonal (*overthrusting*) in direction and is often caused by the release of elastic strain that has built up along the fault line.

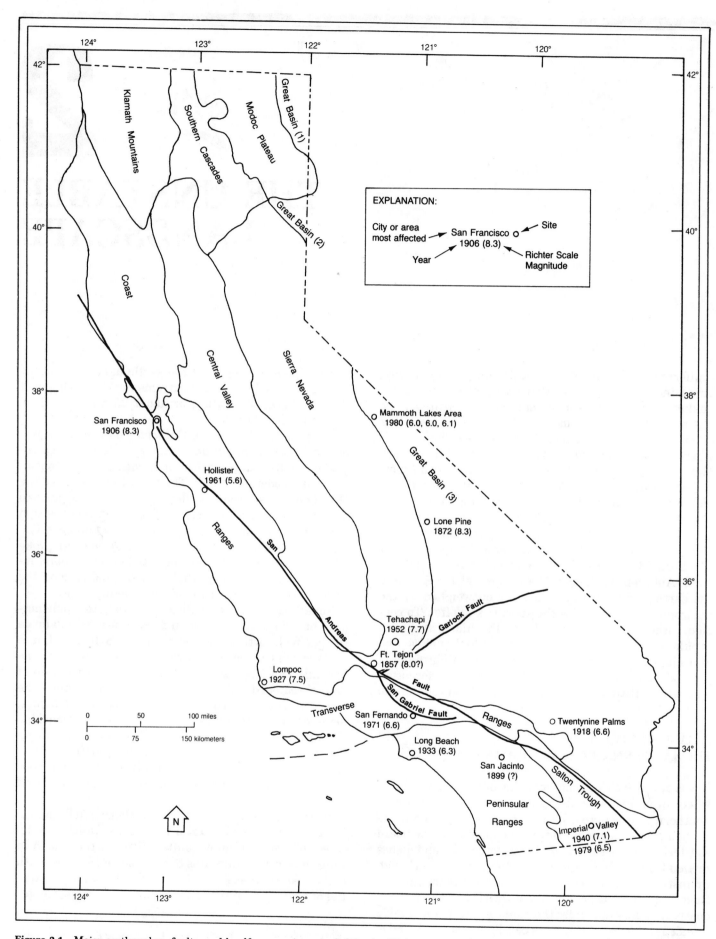

Figure 2.1   Major earthquakes, faults, and landform provinces in California. (Richard Crooker)

Figure 2.2 Collapse of overpass connecting Foothill Boulevard and Golden State Freeway, caused by the February 9, 1971, San Fernando earthquake. (U.S. Geological Survey)

or point of surface rupture (if different) increases and as density of urban development decreases. Sylmar, a residential community composed predominantly of single-family, detached homes of no more than two stories, lies in the northern suburban fringe of the valley away from major apartment, commercial, and industrial developments. If the density of urban development intensifies in Sylmar, as it inevitably seems to do in most California suburbs, then there will simply be more people and more structures of greater height subject to potential devastation in the event of another 6.6 earthquake.

It should be noted here that Richter magnitudes are not used to estimate damage, for a 6.6 quake in a barren, unpopulated region may do nothing more than frighten some wildlife. How much this higher risk is counterbalanced by more stringent structural safety codes, *seismic safety elements* in general plans (for example, prohibiting development on or near active faults), and other precautionary regulations is unknown. After all, even supposedly earthquake-resistant buildings can collapse in a 6.6 earthquake, as did the Olive View Hospital

in Sylmar in 1971,[3] and inactive faults can suddenly release long built-up strain. Worse yet, the San Andreas fault, which was not the direct source of the 1971 earthquake but which is still too close for comfort, is apparently capable of producing an 8.0 + earthquake![4]

FAULTS, FOLKLORE, AND FACT

A good deal of folklore surrounds the subject of earthquakes, especially their predictability or lack of it and

[3]According to the California Division of Mines and Geology, "San Fernando, California, Earthquake of 9 February 1971," *Bulletin* 196 (1975), p. 341, not all of the many buildings in the County of Los Angeles' Olive View Hospital complex were seriously damaged. However, excessive damage did occur to the newly completed (1970) "earthquake-resistive Medical Treatment and Care Building" and three lives were lost therein. Although the magnitude (M) of the San Fernando earthquake was tentatively given at 6.6, the "Foreword" in the *Bulletin* notes an M of 6.5 and later (p. 260) a reassignment of M 6.4.

[4]The San Andreas is best (or worst?) thought of as a fault zone or system—that is, the San Andreas fault itself plus auxiliary faults such as the one from which the San Fernando earthquake originated.

what to do if one happens. So-called "earthquake weather" is said by some self-styled prognosticators to be a warning that a quake is imminent. But there is no real consensus on what constitutes earthquake weather. Some say it's when the air is stagnant and muggy. Others contend that earthquake probability increases following a rainstorm. It so happens that on February 9, 1971, a mildly windy Santa Ana condition prevailed in the San Fernando Valley. Admittedly, that merely helped to complete the long list of different types of weather that precede or accompany earthquakes. In short, earthquake weather can be *any* kind of weather.

Perhaps more believable are certain forms of aberrant behavior among animals. For example, domesticated animals have been observed to become unusually fidgety immediately before an earthquake. Among wild animals there is the sudden, ominous silence of neighborhood birds, sometimes preceding a tremor by several minutes. Because separating fact from folklore is difficult in determining links between animal behavior and earthquake prediction, more scientific investigation may be warranted.

In looking beyond the earth itself for ways of predicting earthquakes, some scientists hypothesize that the alignment of the planets in our solar system in 1982 might have triggered major quakes in California. The last such alignment occurred in 1803, when historical recordkeeping of seismic events was limited to a few widely separated Spanish settlements along the coast, and none of these reported major quakes. Noteworthy, though, was the recording of ground shaking and damage to some missions and presidios three years earlier in 1800, evidently due to major tremors. Perhaps it is the other way around and the approaching alignment of the planets signals major earthquakes, the day of final alignment being well past the peak period of danger.

Seismic and related events from 1979 to 1982 that may have been symptoms of the planets coming into alignment include: the 6.5 Imperial Valley earthquake; a spate of 6.0 jolts around Mammoth Lakes; the Mount St. Helens eruptions in Washington state; movement in the Hayward fault zone east of Oakland; a 5.1 quake epicentered offshore from Los Angeles on that city's two hundredth birthday, September 4, 1981; and a series of quakes near Eureka. The Eureka area episodes seem extraordinarily significant in that they started on November 8, 1980, with a 7.0 jolt, the most powerful earthquake to be recorded in northwestern California in half a century. Fortunately, property damage (to highways and buildings) and injuries (to five people) were minimal and no lives were lost.

Understanding the mechanics of earthquakes themselves rather than other supposedly related environmental phenomena seems most likely to provide the key to predicting when they are going to happen. Seismologists have known for some time that the sudden rupture and displacement of rock along a fault line due to the release of accumulated strain has triggered many a local earthquake. In the case of the San Fernando quake, the subsurface focus of initial energy release, or *hypocenter*, was located 8 miles deep and more than 7 miles north of the point where ground shaking was most severe in Sylmar. This indicated that the fault motion was brought to the surface along a fault inclined at an angle that broke the surface in Sylmar. Such a fault is called an *overthrust*.

Quite often, several days or even weeks before an earthquake, the ground surface on one side of a fault line will increasingly tilt and even change the direction of its tilt, then revert to its original position following an earthquake. This change is measurable with a *tiltmeter* and thus may be a reliable indicator of an impending earthquake. If the rate of ground movement accelerates rapidly, as it sometimes does before an earthquake, an *accelerometer* can monitor the change.

Other techniques that may bring us to an earlier realization of accurate earthquake prediction include monitoring fluctuations in the earth's magnetic field, studying the periodicity of the moon's gravitational influence on seismic events originating on earth, measuring fault movements with lasers, and utilizing the visual-historical record provided through aerial photography and other forms of *remote sensing*. Especially promising are chronological series of stereopairs of vertical airphotos from which changing surface fault patterns can be monitored three-dimensionally.

Gradual movement along a fault, or *fault creep*, appears to be more predictable than an earthquake but does not necessarily presage an earthquake. Rather, a creep episode involving a mere fraction of an inch of movement may last several days and is nonviolent, although creep episodes cumulatively spanning several years are capable of slowly but surely causing costly damage in built-up areas. It is significant that "the first successful prediction of ground motion on the San Andreas fault"[5] was of fault creep in the late 1960s. Predicting creep episodes is one matter and earthquakes quite another, however. We still appear to be years away from predicting the latter with precision as to time, location, and severity. Furthermore, earthquake aftershocks and creep, once thought to be related, now appear to be independent processes for relieving stresses along an existing fault surface.

Another body of earthquake superstition has grown up around what to do if one happens. Suggestions for self-preservation if a severe earthquake strikes one's own community range from the practical to the outrageous. Where a person is when the ground first starts shaking is of paramount concern. If one is in an open area, such as a city park, he or she may be well advised to stay there; the ground is not likely to open up and swallow anybody. Besides, when people start scurrying to the nearest building, there is a good chance they will be hit by bricks, glass, or other falling debris on the way. On the other hand, people inside a building shouldn't rush outside and expose themselves to all those airborne hazards. Getting in a doorway or under a desk, piano, or some other strong piece of furniture is advised unless an orderly evacuation can be accomplished or is recommended.

An increasing proportion of buildings meeting stringent earthquake-resistant standards are coming into existence in California, so the chances that a person will

[5]California Division of Mines and Geology, *Mineral Information Service* 22, 4 (April 1969): 68.

be living or working in such a structure if and when the "big one" comes are improving. Steel frame and reinforced concrete structures, even high-rise buildings, are likely to fare well in a major earthquake, as will older and newer wood frame low-rise houses that are securely attached to their foundations. Brick buildings and others with masonry facades can be hazardous, especially to people immediately outside the walls.

Of course, there is no guarantee that any of these steps is right or will save a person from injury or something worse. This disclaimer is not meant to imply that one should not take shelter in a safe place. But in a city or a suburb, where is the safest place when an 8.0+ earthquake hits? Probably the best thing to do is maintain a sense of humor—plan on moving to Oklahoma and learning how to cope with tornadoes. Above all, it is important to remain calm and think through the consequences of any contemplated action. Human panic merely creates another set of hazards.

Preparations made before an earthquake, even inadvertently, may be of indispensible survival value after the quake has occurred. A classic example is found among those Sylmar residents who before the 1971 earthquake had maintained camping gear. Those equipped with camp stoves and fuel, first aid kits, flashlights, water-purifying tablets, tools, canned food, portable radios, and other artifacts of outdoor living were prepared to ride out any extended disruption of utility services to their homes.

Fortunately, the earthquake struck Sylmar early enough in the morning for most residents to still be at home where such survival paraphernalia was close at hand. It would seem advisable that such equipment be similarly provided at one's place of business. For we still are not capable of predicting exactly when or where the next big earthquake will occur on this unstable landscape we call California.

In closing our discussion of "faults, folklore, and fact," it seems fitting, albeit sobering, to ponder some highlights of California's Division of Mines and Geology 1982 report entitled an "Earthquake Planning Scenario for a Magnitude 8.3 Earthquake on the San Andreas Fault in Southern California."[6] Estimates of the death and destruction in Los Angeles, Orange, Riverside, San Bernardino, and Ventura counties in the event of such an earthquake are staggering. Highways, railroads, pipelines, power lines, and aqueducts crossing the San Andreas into the 5-county region would be damaged if not destroyed, resulting in severe curtailment of the flow of imported goods, food, oil, gas, electrical energy, and water that urban Southern California has become so dependent upon. It might take months for some of these lifelines to be reopened. Within the region itself, from 3,000 to 14,000 people would be killed, between 12,000

[6]California Division of Mines and Geology, "Earthquake Planning Scenario for a Magnitude 8.3 Earthquake on the San Andreas Fault in Southern California," *Special Publication* 60, (1982). Studies indicate at least eight major earthquakes have taken place along the southern San Andreas (from Cajon Pass northwestward approximately 200 miles) in the past 1,200 years, the interval between quakes averaging about 140 years and the most recent being the Fort Tejon earthquake of 1857 (see Figure 2.1). Now that we are nearing the end of the most recent 140-year period, the next big quake epicentered on the southern San Andreas appears closer at hand than most of us would like to admit.

and 55,000 would require hospitalization, and property damage would amount to nearly $20 billion. Hardest hit would be heavily populated areas in alluvium-filled valleys (particularly San Bernardino, San Gabriel, San Fernando, and Simi Valleys), river basins and floodplains (notably of the Santa Ana, Santa Clara, and Santa Clarita rivers), and sandy and clayey coastal lowlands (especially the Oxnard Plain, Marina Del Rey, and from Long Beach southeastward to Newport Beach and inland to Anaheim and Tustin). The dismemberment of structures as the ground beneath them fails would likely be most rampant in the above-mentioned areas where water tables were relatively high and *liquefaction* was occurring, the ground itself taking on the properties of a liquid as a result of earthquake shaking. Structures anchored to solid bedrock and thus subject to lower levels of vibration, on the other hand, might survive intact even if located closer to the earthquake epicenter. Unfortunately, most urban Southern Californians do not live, work, commute, or play over bedrock and thus appear to be in harm's way were this potentially greatest of all natural disasters ever to strike.

CALIFORNIA ADRIFT

The narrow part of California west of the San Andreas fault zone shown in Figure 2.1 is drifting laterally northwestward with respect to the rest of North America. This movement started at least 30 million years ago, when an oceanic rise (Fig. 2.3) in the Pacific Basin literally "hit" the continent, and has continued ever since at an average annual rate of about 2 inches. At that rate and going back in time to 30 million years B.P. (Before Present), the central Coast Ranges of California were located more than 700 miles to the south along the west coast of what is now Mexico. By another 30 million years from now, the Coast Ranges will have moved from their present position northwestward some 700 miles, putting San Francisco abreast of Seattle, Washington.

These movements are dramatic in the context of geologic time but move along at a comparative snail's pace in a human lifetime. In other words, San Diegans, Angelenos, San Franciscans, and other coastal Californians reading these pages are not likely to find themselves suddenly being flung into the Pacific Ocean by some cataclysmic earthquake emanating from the San Andreas system. Yet each 2.0 magnitude earthquake, the smallest normally felt by humans, will at least remind them that they are inching northwestward and that California is merely a small part of a grander, worldwide design still referred to popularly as *continental drift*. Continental drift, sea floor spreading, and seismic and volcanic activity all fall within the unifying concept of *plate tectonics*, which we will explore in the next section. We shall also examine what may be an aberration of plate tectonics, Southern California's mysterious Palmdale Bulge.

Plate Tectonics
Most major forms of earth movement, including earthquakes as well as the motions of continents and ocean

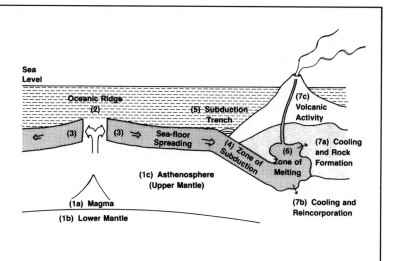

Explanation of Tectonic Forces Responsible for the Creation of California:

- *Magma* (1a) rises from lower mantle (1b) through less rigid *Asthenosphere* or upper mantle (1c).
- Magma rises to surface to form *oceanic ridge* (2) composed of volcanoes and fault block mountains.
- *Sea-floor spreading* (3). Newer rock created by cooling lavas forces older rock to "slide" across less rigid Asthenosphere and away from the oceanic ridge.
- *Subduction* (4). Lighter plate made of lavas is forced under adjacent plate.
- Marine sediments are deposited by undersea currents in *subduction trench* (5).
- Rock forced under continental plate melts (6) due to crustal pressure from above and higher temperatures of Asthenosphere.
- Melted rock either: (7a) cools to form granitic rock, (7b) returns to mantle as magma, or (7c) rises to surface as lavas.

Figure 2.3 Idealized plate tectonics diagram. (Richard Crooker)

basins, ultimately emanate from the relative movements of huge sections of the earth's solid rock or *lithosphere* crust, referred to as *lithospheric plates.* Stresses acting on the rock strata in these 15- to 100-kilometer (km) thick plates cause them to deform into the major features of *structural relief* or *landforms* of the earth's surface, such as mountain and valley systems. The building of these structural features and their internal causes are collectively referred to as *tectonics.* Figure 2.3 depicts this internal energy *convecting* upwards through a partially molten, 75- to 175-km deep *asthenosphere* to the overlying lithosphere, bringing about plate tectonics at the earth's surface.

The ultimate source of this *geothermal heat* energy is believed to be elements undergoing *radioactive decay* deep within the *core* of the earth. The heat energy (estimated by some at 4,200° C) is transmitted from the core, which has a radius of about 3,500 km, through approximately 2,700 km of *mantle* before reaching the athenosphere (at about 1,200° C or near the melting point of rock). As shown in Figure 2.4, mantle-derived *magma* (molten rock) then rises up through a rift in the relatively thin oceanic plate, causing the plate to spread apart (*sea floor spreading*) in opposite directions. In the process, the magma cools and *lithifies* (becomes solid rock), forming an oceanic rise or ridge of *igneous* rock (rock formed by fire or literally by being "ignited").

In the case of California, the eastward-moving Pacific Plate probably collided with the North American Plate about 250 million B.P. and then proceeded to plunge under it, creating a trench that filled with sediments carried down by streams eroding the continental surface. The Pacific Plate and trench sediments then descended (*subducted*) deeper under the continental plate, eventually reaching the athenosphere and melting. From the melting zone shown in Figure 2.4, magma intruded upward into the continental plate to form a giant *batholith* (deep rock mass) that became the granitic backbone of the Sierra Nevada and other mountain ranges composed of igneous and capping *metamorphic* rocks (rocks changed by heat and pressure from the original *sedimentary* rocks).

By about 30 million B.P., the east Pacific rise (Figure 2.4) intersected with the continent and the collision course of the two plates gave way to a sliding of one past the other that continues to this day. The San Andreas fault zone marks the interface of this shearing. Thus it is the Pacific Plate, which includes that small part of California west of the San Andreas, that appears to be "rotating" counterclockwise or northwestward, as seen in Figure 2.5. This horizontal motion along the San Andreas is referred to as *right-lateral faulting,* for as one looks out across the fault from either side, the opposite side appears to be moving to the right (Fig. 2.6). This effect can be seen in the form of *stream channel offset* to the right along the San Andreas fault.

The northwestward movement of the Pacific Plate portion of California may not be uniform throughout. Rather, it appears to be fragmented. Evidently, where the northwestward-moving Peninsular Ranges meet the batholithic roots of the Sierra Nevada, the San Andreas fault zone and the Transverse Ranges are forced to bend to the west or left. As evidenced by several feet of vertical displacement occurring during the San Fernando earthquake and other recent seismic events in the region, the east-west trending Transverse Ranges appear to be rising. The "growing up" of this young mountain range just north of the Los Angeles Basin is probably attributable to its location in a zone of compression between the Peninsular Ranges to the south and the Coast Ranges to the north.

Meanwhile, on the North American Plate the Mojave Desert is being shoved eastward by lateral movement in that general direction along the Garlock and San Andreas faults. As Figure 2.7 shows, the Mojave is in a sense being squeezed eastward between the two fault zones. Which leads us to our next topic, the Palmdale Bulge.

Palmdale: To Bulge or Not to Bulge?

Along the bend in the San Andreas there may be a 32,000 sq mi "bulge" in the earth's surface. If the bulge exists, its uplift started in 1959 and reached a maximum of 18 inches (45 cm) about halfway between Palmdale and Blythe (Fig. 2.7) by 1974. Since then, the bulge ap-

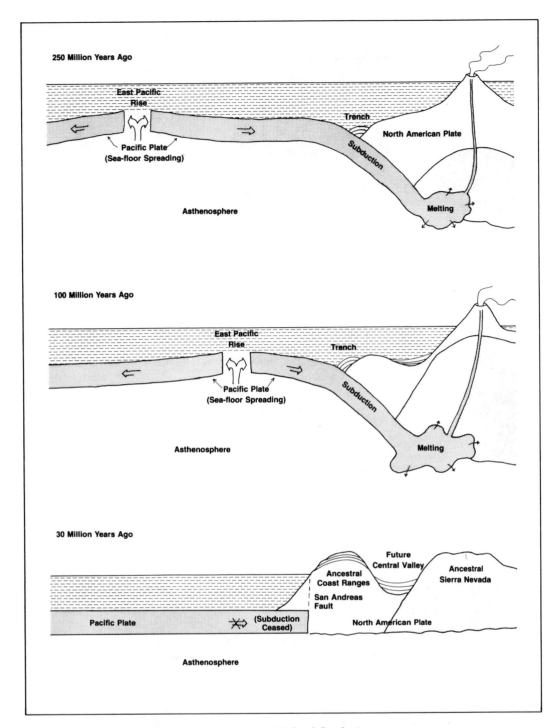

Figure 2.4 Early geologic evolution of California. (Richard Crooker)

parently has downdropped several inches in different spots, one notably near Palmdale.

The significance of these elevation changes, even after a 1978 field study of the bulge funded by the U.S. Geological Survey, is still not totally understood. They could possibly indicate the gradual release of strain along the San Andreas and thus appear to lessen the likelihood of a single major earthquake. On the other hand, their undulating, wavelike ups and downs underline their resemblance to sea waves, which crest and break: A cresting land wave that breaks could be a potentially devastating earthquake. A third possibility is that the bulge may totally subside. Lastly, the bulge's relationship to California's only major left-lateral fault, the Garlock, is unknown.

Ambivalence about the Palmdale Bulge has steadily mounted, perhaps culminating in doubt that it even exists, as expressed recently by three UCLA earth scientists: "The inference of widespread aseismic uplift in southern California is not justified." Their conclusion stems partly from studies indicating the strong possibility of surveying errors in discovering the bulge, namely through inadequate rod calibration and refraction.[7] Corrected data now point to no episodic uplift in Southern California in recent years, or in other words,

[7]David D. Jackson, Wook B. Lee, Chi-Ching Liu, "Aseismic Uplift in Southern California: An Alternative Interpretation," *Science* 210 (October 31, 1980): 534–536. In surveying, *refraction,* or curvature along a line of sight, is caused by variations in atmospheric conditions, such as temperature, air pressure, and relative humidity.

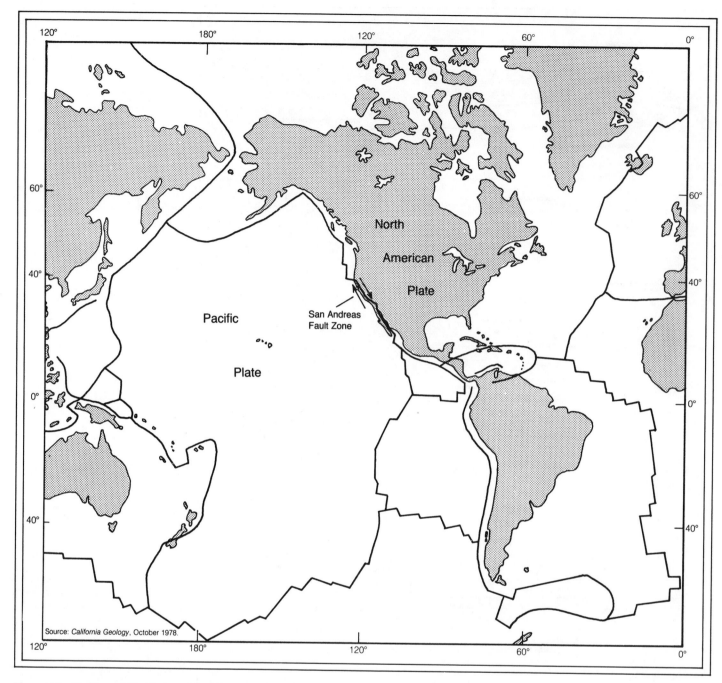

Figure 2.5 Pacific and North American Plates. (Richard Crooker)

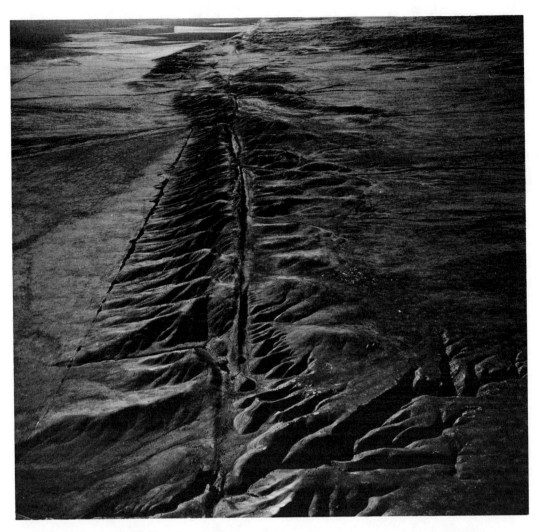

Figure 2.6 San Andreas fault. The marked linearity (or lineament) along the trace of the fault is quite apparent in this photograph. Where streams cross the San Andreas, their courses are offset or displaced to the right on the downstream side of the fault line. (U.S. Geological Survey, *Earthquake Information Bulletin*)

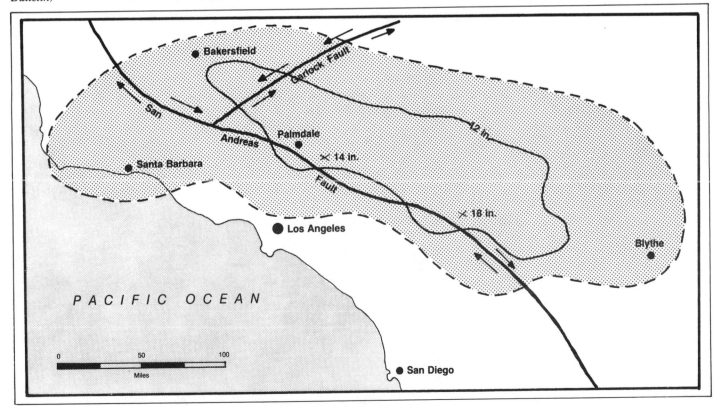

Figure 2.7 Palmdale Bulge. (Richard Crooker)

no Palmdale Bulge. In fact, the San Fernando earthquake remains the sole perpetrator of significant vertical motion in the southland in the last three decades. All the foregoing notwithstanding, there are those scientists who have rechecked the surveys and say that "the bulge is there."[8]

Now that we are more aware of tectonic activity on

both sides of the San Andreas rift, be it the eastern edge of the Pacific Plate, in the San Fernando Valley, or well within the North American Plate in the Mammoth Lakes area, let us turn our attention next to the landforms these tectonic forces have built. With a volcanic tableland in one part of California, block-faulted mountains in another, and a flat-surfaced, 25,000 sq mi valley in still another region, it is obvious that tectonics have created uniquely different landscapes, albeit ones that are none too steady. These landform or geomorphic provinces and their human settlements are the subject of the next chapter.

[8]Robert O. Castle and Barry Raleigh, both of the U.S. Geological Survey, countered Jackson's, Lee's, and Liu's findings, noting that the survey "errors were not crucial enough to explain the bulge away" (*Los Angeles Times*, December 26, 1980).

LANDFORM PROVINCES AND THEIR PEOPLE

Due in large part to the tectonic forces described in Chapter 2, California's landform diversity is unmatched by any other state in the "lower 48." The spectacular contrasts its physical landscape provides are reflected in the nine distinctively different landform or geomorphic provinces that comprise the Golden State. The scenic display begins along the 1,000 miles of coastline, where, from south to north, the granitic Peninsular Ranges, the east-west faulted Transverse Ranges, the sedimentary Coast Ranges, and the complex Klamath Mountains all front on the Pacific (see Fig. 2.1). Although they are not steeply truncated at an ocean's edge, the mountainous provinces of the interior also attain impressive heights, reaching upwards of 14,000 ft in the volcanic peaks of the Southern Cascades, the glaciated crests of the Sierra Nevada, and the up-faulted ridges of the Great Basin mountains. Down-faulted, below-sea-level basins give even greater vertical dimension to the Great Basin and southeastern deserts. Completing this array of landform contrasts are the volcanic tablelands of the Modoc Plateau in northeastern California and the down-folded, alluvium-filled Great Central Valley at the geographic heart of the state.

Given their dramatic diversity, California's landforms are a varied resource. Profuse reserves of petroleum lie trapped in the sedimentary formations of the Coast Ranges and offshore on the continental shelf. There is still gold in the hills of the Sierra Nevada and the Klamath Mountains. More significantly, the Sierras, Klamaths, and other high ranges capture and hold moisture from air masses blowing in from the Pacific while at the same time casting a vast rain shadow over Arizona and Nevada. These mountain watersheds assure the state of near self-sufficiency in water supply, perhaps its most vital natural resource. The Great Central Valley provides thousands upon thousands of square miles of the most productive farmland on the face of the earth. The mountains of the Great Basin yield high-grade metallic ores, and the intervening basins are rich in alkaline and saline minerals. And as an aesthetic resource, California's landform provinces (see Fig. 2.1) contain, in an area of 158,693 sq mi, just about as many scenic contrasts as one could ever hope to see, paint, or photograph.

Above all, though, the nine landform provinces of California provide a seemingly infinite array of human settlement sites. For reasons varying from the presence of spectacular seascapes and cool, breathable marine air to a relative abundance of certain biotic and mineral resources, the coastal provinces have proven perhaps the most attractive.

Archaeological evidence suggests that California's first cultural landscape took form along the Pacific shores of the Peninsular Ranges some 50,000 years ago. Beginning barely 200 years ago, European settlement displayed a decided preference for the seaward sides of the Peninsular, Transverse, and Coast ranges. Today, about four fifths of the state's 24 million inhabitants live in these three landform provinces. Most of these Californians reside in the San Diego, Los Angeles–Long Beach, and San Francisco–Oakland metropolitan areas within an hour's drive of the beach, and most would probably choose seaside residence were it not for prohibitive real estate costs, stringent environmental and zoning restrictions, remoteness from workplace, and other locational constraints. By the mid-1980s, one would be doing well to happen on a modest three-bedroom, two-bath house on a 60 × 100-ft ocean view lot for sale for under $500,000 in or near any of the coastal metropolitan regions.

Even California's contemporary Indians, though their ancestors were largely dispossessed of their coastal lands by the mid-nineteenth century and though today most of their reservations are found in the landlocked provinces of the interior, claim their largest holding—the Hoopa Valley Reservation and Extension of some 88,000 acres along the lower Klamath River—on the Pacific side of the Klamath Mountains. Yet the rightful aboriginal heirs to California have generally fared none too well in the allotment of lands in the interior.

By tradition, most California Indians were nomadic hunters and gatherers and thereby essentially did not participate in the sweep of agricultural settlement over the Great Central Valley, the mineral exploitation of the Great Basin, and the recent recreation-retirement rush to the Sierra Nevada. Thus, reservations in these inland provinces tend to be located off the beaten path on marginally productive land. Today's reservation Indians, nonetheless, are descendants of the first Californians and as such merit special mention in the following examination of the geomorphic provinces and contemporary settlement of the land.

THE PENINSULAR RANGES

The northwest-southeast trending Peninsular Ranges, the southernmost of California's four coastal landform provinces, is a northward extension of the peninsula of Baja California. As such, the province was at one time part of the continental plate and lay to the southeast of its present location. Then, several million years ago, the peninsular mass became welded to the northwest-tracking Pacific Plate and began rifting away from the mainland of Mexico. The waters of the Pacific filled the rift in the form of the Gulf of California, which in turn has steadily widened ever since. Today, the peninsula, whose batholithic backbone stretches discontinuously from the southern tip of Baja California 1,000 miles north to near Los Angeles, continues to inch northwestward and farther away from the continent.

Interior Highlands

The general structure of the Peninsular Ranges is that of a massive western-dipping granitic fault block[1] dramatically uplifted on its east side. The abruptness of the eastern escarpment culminates in Mount San Jacinto at nearly 11,000 ft above sea level in the northeast corner of the province. As Figure 3.1 reveals, internal faulting of the block along the San Jacinto, Elsinore, and other faults has helped shape a varying topography of northwest-southeast oriented mountain ranges of moderate elevation and intervening upland plains, plateaus, and small valleys. *Weathering* of rock, occasional *mass wasting* incidents (usually landslides triggered by earthquakes or excessive rainfall), and *differential erosion* (mostly by streams over rocks of differing resistance to erosion) have further sculpted these highland landforms.

The rugged terrain of the highlands has discouraged both agricultural and urban settlement, and has done little for recreational development. Although they attain impressive elevations in a few places, the higher mountain ridges are nowhere extensive enough in area to provide a significant recreational resource. For example, major ski resort complexes are precluded because of a dearth of slopes sufficiently high in elevation to assure long-lasting snowpacks. Idyllwild at the southwest edge of Mount San Jacinto State Park is the only genuinely "alpine" settlement in the Peninsular Ranges. Farther

[1]A *fault block mountain* is a block or part of the earth's crust that has been uplifted by vertical or normal faulting over an extended period of time, usually several million years. Although faulting can prevail on any side of a mountain range, fault block mountains in most of California's provinces are sharply faulted on their east sides (the scarp side or escarpment) and slope gently downhill to the west (the dip side).

south in the high back country of San Diego County, the small villages of Julian and Warner Springs provide a semialpine setting with the help of an occasional winter snowfall.

Rural, native California Indian settlement in the Peninsular Ranges, as well as in all the coastal landform provinces south of San Francisco Bay, is today almost exclusively found in the interior highlands of Riverside and San Diego counties. Here some 30 reservations comprising a quarter of a million acres accommodate a few thousand Indians. Actually, a majority of the southwestern California Indians live and work outside the reservations. The Morongo Reservation near Banning with some 32,000 acres is the fourth largest reservation area in California.

Agricultural settlement in the San Jacinto Basin and in the mountains to the west is much more extensive than in the eastern highlands because of the Basin's more suitable terrain, better soil conditions, and longer growing seasons. For example, in the coastward mountains of San Diego County from Fallbrook south to Escondido is found California's optimum environment for growing avocados; indeed, the region is first in avocado production in the state.

To the northeast, in the flatter San Jacinto Basin of Riverside County, all types of agriculture exist, including citrus orcharding, viticulture, truck farming, and field cropping. Many Basin towns such as Hemet, Perris, and Temecula originated as agricultural service centers, whereas in recent decades retirement, military, and other nonagricultural development has attracted people to the communities of Rancho California and Sun City and the March Air Force Base area. Murrieta Hot Springs and Lake Elsinore are among the Basin's principal recreational attractions.

Coastal Features

Westward toward the ocean, flat-topped but stream-dissected *marine terraces* (also referred to locally as *mesas*) pervade the landscape. Before the ice ages of the Pleistocene epoch, when sea level was much higher, subsurface ocean wave and current action planed off shallow seaward-sloping marine platforms. As the Pleistocene began and the Pacific retreated, a steplike pattern of marine terraces was revealed, with some rising above others because of vertical faulting. When ocean water became locked up in ice caps and glaciers, thus lowering sea level, streams cut *terrace canyons* or *barrancas* much deeper than they now appear.

Mission Valley, where today some of San Diego's newest regional shopping centers, hotel complexes, a stadium, and other urban attractions are located, is one of several such canyons that refilled with stream sands and gravels as sea level rose during interglacial periods. Mission Valley's broad alluvial surface enticed not only modern urban development, but also California's first Spanish mission settlement, San Diego de Alcalá. It is the gently sloping terraces, however, that have enabled San Diego, now the state's second largest city, to spread out many miles in nearly every landward direction from the central business district along San Diego Bay (Fig. 3.2). San Diego Bay itself, protected from winds and tides

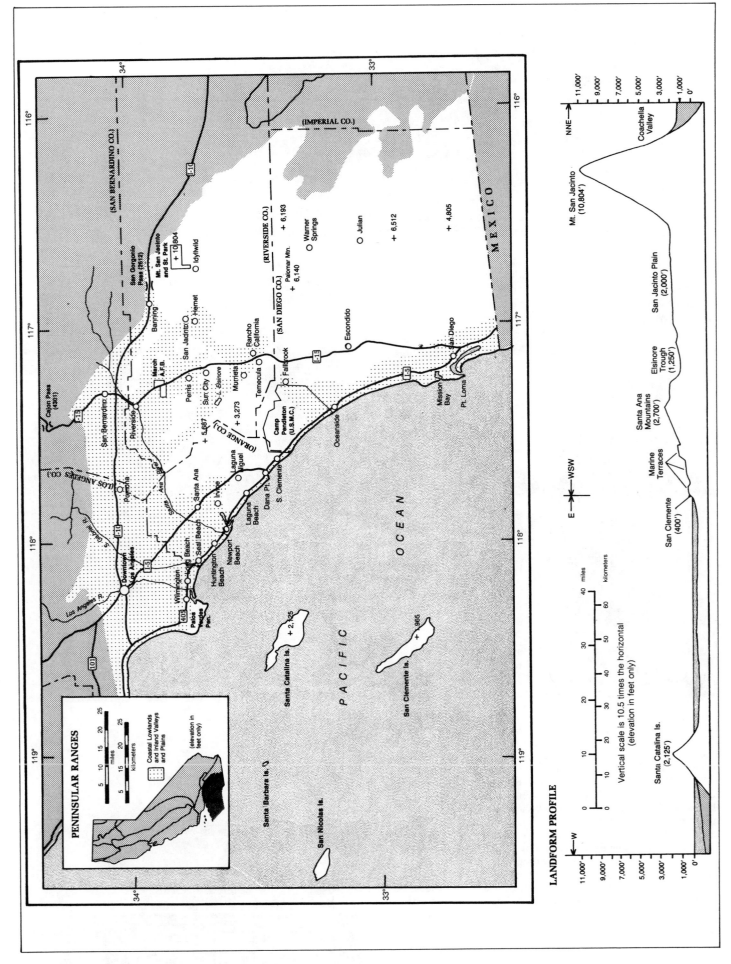

Figure 3.1   Peninsular Ranges and landform profile. (Richard Crooker)

A

B

Figure 3.2 San Diego. (A) A view of the city from space shows, from left to right, Mission Bay, Point Loma, North Island–Coronado Island, San Diego Bay and port facilities, city and suburbs, and a faint line (extreme right, or south) demarcating the border with Mexico. (B) San Diego's immediate bayside location and consequent cool, smog-free air help make the city second only to Los Angeles in tourism in the state. The view here is from the Harbor Island Marina. (C) San Diego is home to 800,000 people, the nation's largest tuna fleet, the West Coast's largest naval air station (North Island), and a large aerospace industry. The original 1769 Spanish settlement sites, including the mission up Mission Valley along the San Diego River and the military garrison on Presidio Hill, are several miles north of downtown. In the photograph, the San Diego skyline rises above the southern tip of man-made Shelter Island. (A: NASA; B: Port of San Diego; C: San Diego Convention and Visitors Bureau)

C

Figure 3.3 La Jolla beach, Scripps pier, and sea cliffs or palisades. A dozen miles northwest of downtown, yet well within San Diego's corporate limits, La Jolla (from *la joya,* "the jewel") is one of California's wealthiest residential communities. Scripps Institution of Oceanography, with aquaria and an onshore tide pool open to the public, graces the La Jolla shoreline while the University of California at San Diego and the Salk Institute for Biological Studies command a panorama of the Pacific from the terrace some 50 to 100 ft above sea level. (Crane Miller)

by Point Loma Peninsula, North Island–Coronado, and Silver Strand isthmus and used primarily by the United States Navy, is one of the Pacific coast's premier deep-water harbors.

The 118-mile coastline of Orange and San Diego counties is varied in both its geomorphological characteristics and its human use. In northern Orange County, the coast ranges in landform from tidal wetland at Seal Beach southward to wide, sandy beaches backdropped by low-lying *palisades* (cliffs) at Huntington Beach and extensive yacht harbors in Newport and Balboa bays. Sedimentary formations beneath Huntington Beach and offshore continue to yield petroleum, and so oil derricks, grasshoppers (oil pumpers), and drilling platforms pervade much of the landscape and seascape.

From the Newport-Irvine coast south through Laguna and Lagune Niguel, the beaches narrow appreciably and in some places are replaced by rocky tide pools and barely submerged rocks and reefs. This wave-battered shoreline is abruptly backed by steep coastal bluffs and marine terraces. Perched on these terraces is much of California's most expensive residential development; the Laguna coastline is often likened to the French and Italian Rivieras, and justifiably so! South of the Dana Point Marina and Doheny Beach, the San Clemente coastline presents a somewhat less dramatic and less densely developed version of the Laguna coast. This terrace landscape dissected by narrow beaches and bluffs continues intermittently down the San Diego County coast to La Jolla (Fig. 3.3) with major interruptions in the form of lagoons, estuaries, and tidal flats, such as those seen at Del Mar.

Several cities have grown up rapidly along this coast with the northernmost, Oceanside, the largest after San Diego. The large United States Marine Corps base at Camp Pendleton has spurred the growth of Oceanside, while acting at the same time as effective green belt separation between the Los Angeles–Orange and San Diego metropolitan areas. Mission Bay, a reclaimed tidal flat in the northwestern part of San Diego, is an outstanding recreational area with attractions such as Sea World and Vacation Island.

The diminishing supply of beach sand is the most pressing environmental problem facing shoreline inhabitants. Not only is there less and less area for sunbathers, surfers, beachcombers, and others, but also a narrowing buffer of protection for beachfront homes and sea cliffs against the periodic pounding of storm waves. The removal of beach sands by *longshore* (parallel to shore) or *littoral* currents to submarine canyons would normally not be of concern were it not for a decline in sand replenishment every time a new dam is built upstream from an estuary or an artificial harbor is developed. The California Coastal Plan, as mandated by state voters in approving Proposition 20 in 1972, addresses itself to saving this fragile shoreline recreational resource. But one wonders what will be left of the beaches, lagoons, and sea cliffs once coastal settlement has merged Los Angeles and San Diego into one megalopolis.

The Los Angeles Basin
The Peninsular Ranges Province extends northwestward to include the mostly densely settled portion of the Los Angeles Basin and the highly developed Long Beach, Palos Verdes peninsula, and Santa Monica Bay portions of the "South Coast." Several streams, including the Los Angeles, San Gabriel, and Santa Ana rivers and Ballona Creek, built the broad alluvial coastal plain surface that now accommodates California's largest urban population. Many of the channels have been lined with concrete to provide better flood control for the 9 million residents of the Los Angeles and Orange counties portions of the coastal basin.

Underlying the Basin's sedimentary fill to a depth of 31,000 ft below sea level is a giant downfold (*syncline*) of basement rock. The Basin's generally smooth surface (Fig. 3.7) is broken here and there by faults such as the Palos Verdes and Newport-Inglewood, which have uplifted Palos Verdes Peninsula, Dominguez Hills, and the Baldwin Hills. The folded and faulted sedimentary formations have yielded generously of petroleum, with the Wilmington oil field ranking first in production in California. This petroleum field underlies much of Long Beach and the fine manmade harbor seen in Figure 3.4.

The Islands
The Peninsular Province does not terminate at the Pacific's shores but rather submerges westward, forming a broad continental shelf with occasional mountain outliers in the form of several islands. San Clemente, currently restricted to naval use and otherwise uninhabited except by a unique population of flora and fauna, and Catalina, whose nearly 2,000 residents live in or around the tourist node of Avalon harbor, are the largest islands. Both islands project at their highest about 2,000 ft above sea level and have hilly surfaces underlain by igneous rocks with abrupt, palisaded coastlines and few sandy beaches. San Clemente appears as a fault block island dipping downward to the west with a steep eastern es-

Figure 3.4 Long Beach–Los Angeles harbors combine to form the nation's largest manmade harbor and the West Coast's largest container and commercial fishing ports. Nestled between San Pedro on the west, Wilmington on the north, and Long Beach on the east, Terminal Island is the centerpiece of the port complex and separates the inner and outer harbors. Reclaimed from the sea and Rattlesnake Island, Terminal Island now accommodates a naval shipyard, tanker terminals, fish canneries, and container facilities. (Port of Los Angeles)

carpment, whereas Catalina displays no particular surface symmetry. Both islands measure a few miles wide and are elongated more than 20 miles northwest-south. While Catalina is usually visible on a clear day from anywhere along the South Coast, San Clemente Island, at twice the distance (60 miles) offshore, is barely visible under the clearest of atmospheric conditions. Tiny Santa Barbara Island (part of the Channel Islands National Park) and somewhat larger San Nicolas Island are also not visible from the mainland and are uninhabited.

THE TRANSVERSE RANGES

The Transverse Ranges are Southern California's highest and most imposing mountains and, like the peninsular Ranges, reach westward into the Pacific in the form of several islands. Unlike the Peninsular Ranges, however, the axis of the Transverse Ranges is east-west rather than north-south. This position in the northern part of Southern California has led many to the opinion that the Transverse Ranges demarcate the southland from the rest of the state. For statistical and other purposes, the Kern and other east-west county lines are probably preferred, but the notion that Transverse Ranges are the real hurdle between north and south has many believers.

Onshore

The only major landform province oriented east-west, the aptly named Transverse Ranges, is the most rugged and, for the most part, the least densely settled coastal province. Seen in Figure 3.5 stretching from its west coast at Point Arguello eastward for 250 miles through the Santa Ynez, Topatopa, San Gabriel, and San Bernardino mountains, the Transverse Ranges steadily rise in elevation, attaining 11,485 ft in Mount San Gorgonio near their eastern end. Folding and faulting of sedimentary formations in the west and block faulting of metamorphic and igneous rocks in the east have created deep canyons lined with long, steep slopes throughout the Ranges. Drainage follows these tectonic features in some places, as for instance the east and west forks of the San Gabriel River along the San Gabriel fault.

Such topography is obviously not conducive to settlement; thus, only a small proportion of the province is intensively developed either to agriculture or urban uses: principally from the Santa Monica Mountains and San Fernando Valley (mostly incorporated in the City of Los Angeles) northwestward to the Oxnard Plain, lower Santa Clara River Valley, and along the coast to Santa Barbara. Mount Baldy village and Wrightwood in the San Gabriels and Green Valley (Fig. 3.6), Arrowhead Lake, Big Bear Lake, and communities between the lakes in the San Bernardinos all have small populations that are temporarily swelled during the skiing sea-

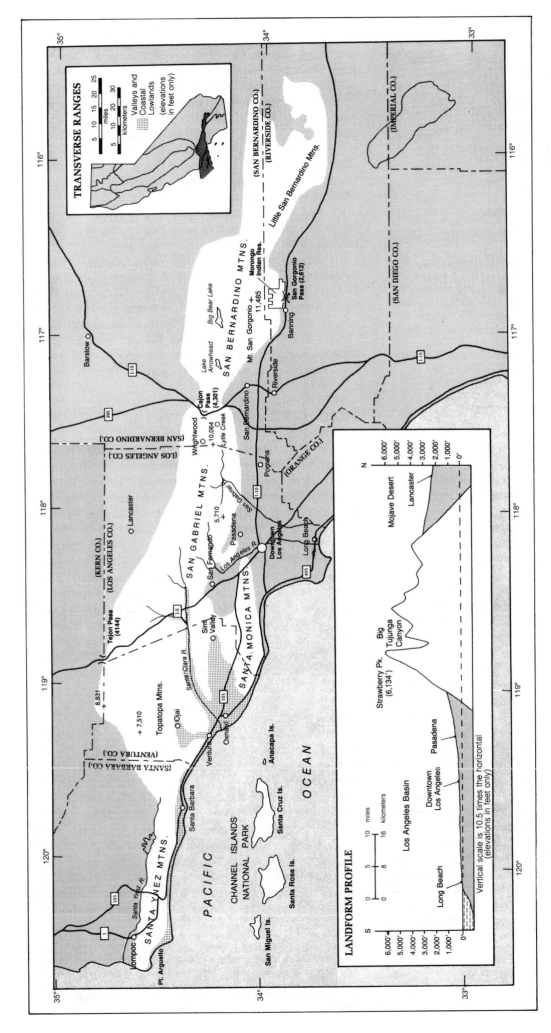

Figure 3.5 Transverse Ranges and landform profile. (Richard Crooker)

Figure 3.6 Green Valley and Lake, midway between Big Bear and Arrowhead in the San Bernardino Mountains. At about 6,845 ft elevation, Green Valley is "on top of the world" among Southern California's mountain resort-residential communities. Due to their more windward locations, Snow Valley (Slide Peak) and other nearby ski resorts receive more and longer lasting snow than Green Valley does. Arrowhead, Big Bear, and Green Valley lakes are all reservoirs, but surrounding yellow pine forests lend a natural alpine appearance. These resorts are about 2 hours by car from Los Angeles, which is one third the driving time and gas expense of going to Mammoth Mountain in the Sierra. Mammoth, however, offers a significantly longer season and superior skiing conditions in almost all regards. (Crane Miller)

son. Altogether, however, they represent only a few thousand permanent residents.

Although rugged and impressive in elevation, the Transverse Ranges lack the great coniferous forests and glaciated valleys and ridges of the Sierras and Klamaths. Not only are they scenically less attractive than other California mountain systems, but they occasionally act as an impenetrable landform barrier. During the heavy rains and snows of the winter of 1978, for instance, there were occasions when all surface routes northward from the Los Angeles metropolitan area were closed, with the Pacific Coast Highway blocked by mudslides and the Ridge Route (I-5) and Cajon Pass (I-15) closed by rock slides and/or snow.

Plate tectonics continues to involve the Transverse Ranges in a squeezeplay resulting in crustal compression and ongoing uplift, especially in the western ranges. In the eastern portion, the San Andreas fault slashes the ranges in two, forming the northern boundary of the San Gabriels but cutting southeastward through Cajon Pass to become the southern edge of the San Bernardino and Little San Bernardino mountains. Were it not for displacement along the San Andreas and San Jacinto faults, the San Gabriels and San Bernardinos would comprise one mountain range. Obviously, though, they will continue to pull farther apart as sections of two different crustal plates sliding laterally in opposite directions. Furthermore, the San Bernardinos are known to be a deeply rooted granitic mass that, along with the Sierra Nevada batholith, deflected the Pacific Plate and created the big bend in the San Andreas fault zone.

Offshore

Like the Peninsular Ranges, the Transverse Ranges also extend offshore in the form of several islands. These

islands form a single chain known as the Channel Islands and jut due westward into the Pacific as a prolongation of the Santa Monica Mountains. Geologically, they belong to the Santa Monica Mountains and were uplifted by folding and faulting along the east-west trending Santa Monica fault just a few million years ago. At that time, they were connected to the land as part of the Ancient Cabrillo Peninsula. Later, the peninsula began to subside and the chain separated from the mainland. Santa Cruz and Santa Rosa, at roughly the same size, height, and distance offshore as Catalina, became the largest of the islands.

Unlike Santa Catalina, however, neither of these islands has been developed to accommodate tourism, although there is existing military and pastoral use. Santa Cruz Island may permanently escape development by virtue of the sale by Dr. Garvey Stanton of most of the island to the conservationist Nature Conservancy and inclusion of the island in Channel Islands National Park, which was recently upgraded from national monument status. Somewhat smaller San Miguel Island and the tiny Anacapa chain (the other part of Channel Islands National Park) round out the Channel Islands group.

THE COAST RANGES

The Coast Ranges, easily California's largest and longest coastal landform province, measure some 400 miles in length from the Transverse Ranges northwestward to near the Oregon border and average 50 miles in width from the Pacific to the western side of the Great Central Valley. In fact, the San Andreas fault lies just west of the boundary between the southern Coast Ranges and the Central Valley,[2] the former sliding northwestward a couple of inches a year as part of the Pacific Plate. From San Francisco, the San Andreas runs northwestward along the Pacific side of the Coast Ranges until Point Arena, where it returns to sea. As Figure 3.7 shows, the San Andreas continues northwestward another 110 miles to a point offshore from Cape Mendocino, where it turns westward out into the Pacific.

Northern Faults

North of the Mendocino fracture zone (Fig. 3.7) another great fault zone, the South Fork Mountain, forms the eastern boundary of the Coast Ranges as they narrow down to only a few miles in width south of the Oregon border. The South Fork Mountain fault interfaces the granitic basement of the Klamath Mountains and the sedimentary and intruded Franciscan formation of the Coast Ranges, the latter formation having originally accumulated as ocean trench sediments washed down from the continental slope. Later, starting about 150 million B.P. and continuing until about half a million years ago, intensive folding and faulting uplifted the

[2]The eastern edge of the southern Coast Ranges, including the Temblor and some other low-lying ridges, is separated by the San Andreas from the main part of the range. Remember that the San Andreas fault zone rises from the Gulf of California and is oriented northwestward through several landform provinces, including the southeastern Coast Ranges.

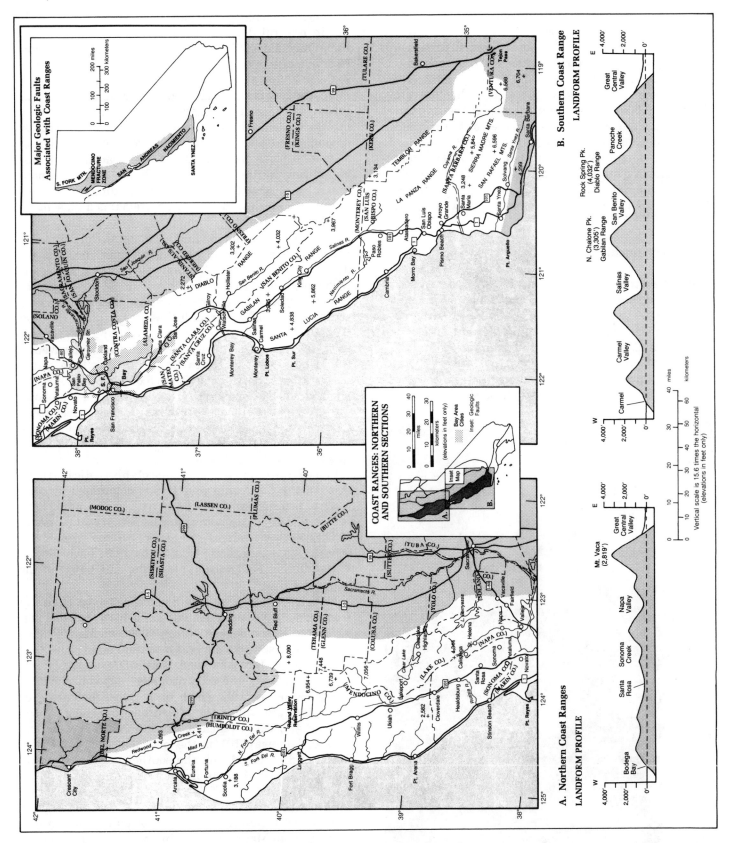

Figure 3.7 Northern and southern Coast Ranges and landform profile. (Richard Crooker)

Franciscan formation to prominence as a rock series throughout the Coast Ranges.

In the last few hundred thousand years, stream erosion and other gradational processes have surpassed tectonic processes, resulting in the wearing down of the Coast Range's highest ridges to maximum heights rarely exceeding 8,000 ft. The satellite view of the central Coast Ranges in Figure 3.8 shows the axes of the mountain ridges and intervening valleys as generally parallel to the major northwest-trending fault zones. This structural pattern dictates drainage of most of the rivers; for example, the Eel and the Mad in the north and the Salinas in the south flow northwestward into the Pacific.

Valley Settlement

Contemporary settlement of the Coast Ranges has favored the structural depressions, principally valleys fronting on coastal plains and embayments. Of course, the mildest coastal climate to be found anywhere in North America has also drawn people to the west side of California's Coast Ranges. But even though mild climate may be true of the entire length of the coast, these landform amenities are few and far between; thus, settlement has concentrated in the choicest of these locations.

Figure 3.8 Satellite view of central Coast Ranges focusing on, from north to south, Marin Peninsula and San Pablo Bay, San Francisco Bay and Peninsula, and the Santa Clara Valley. Golden Gate and Carquinez Strait (upper right or northeast), the latter carrying the Sacramento River into San Pablo Bay, are the only two gaps found in the entire 400-mile length of the Coast Ranges. These gaps permit the only penetration of ocean-going vessels deep into the interior of California. Unlike Landsat images seen earlier in this book, this picture is from a photograph taken with camera and film operated on board Skylab by an astronaut. (NASA)

Along this lengthy and rugged coast, singularly lacking in natural deepwater harbors, San Francisco–San Pablo Bay (Fig. 3.9) stands out as a dramatic exception. Nowhere else in California has nature provided so large, so deep, and so well protected an embayment. Furthermore, the Bay is flushed not only by ocean tides entering through the Golden Gate but also by freshwater from the Sacramento River flowing in from the northeast through Carquinez Strait. Thus, despite the activities of several ports and dozens of small boat harbors, past bay silting by the Sacramento River, and the sundry pressures of some 5 million people residing in nine surrounding counties, the Bay today remains a reasonably viable ecosystem supporting a variety of wildlife.

To both the north and the south of the San Francisco–Oakland–Vallejo metropolitan complex, the density of settlement thins out to two long strings of widely separated towns and small cities: one along the slow-going but eminently scenic State Highway 1 coastal route and the other through the interior along speedier U.S. 101. If one were to choose which direction to head from the Bay Area to escape congestion, however, it would be along the North Coast. For nowhere to the north is there a city of more than 5,000 inhabitants until far past where Highway 1 joins 101 and the Humboldt Bay cities of Eureka and Arcata are reached. Even these cities, with only about 40,000 residents between them, are small enough to fit the rural New England atmosphere of the North Coast.

Indeed, the economic landscape of this rustic northern third of the California coastline is dominated by commercial fishing, dairying, lumbering, and summer tourism (Fig. 3.10). Also adding to the settlement diversity of the northern ranges are several Indian *rancherías* (small village reservations) and the 18,543-acre Round Valley Indian Reservation along the east banks of the upper Eel River.

A southward exodus from San Francisco on Highway 1 will also leave urban congestion behind, but to a significantly lesser degree. After about an hour's drive south, the first of the several moderate-sized cities that ring Monterey Bay is reached. South of Carmel and Point Lobos (Fig. 3.11), the picturesquely rugged and nearly empty Santa Lucía Range abruptly fronts the Pacific for about 100 miles until the Morro Bay–San Luis Obispo area (Fig. 3.12) is reached. Southward from San Luis Obispo, Highway 101 is the principal route to Pismo Beach and Santa María, the southernmost city of any appreciable size (35,000) in the Coast Ranges.

In all, the counties of Santa Cruz, Monterey, and San Luis Obispo comprising the Central Coast region have a combined population in excess of half a million (excluding Santa María, which is in Santa Barbara County). The North Coast counties of Del Norte, Humboldt, and Mendocino, in contrast, have a total population of less than 200,000.

Landlocked Counties

Landform and settlement patterns in the sparsely populated eastern interior of the Coast Ranges may best be exemplified by contrasting two entirely landlocked counties within the province: Lake County in the north and

Figure 3.9 Inside the Golden Gate, looking north across the Bay towards Marin Peninsula and Angel Island from San Francisco Presidio. Where the ancestral Sacramento River originally cut its way to the Pacific through the Golden Gate, the Bay is 300 ft deep; much of its 400 sq mi, however, especially towards the southern end, is less than 10 ft deep at low tide. During a mid-Pleistocene interglacial period, long after the Sacramento had carved its way through the Coast Ranges to the Pacific, rising ocean waters flooded a structural depression created late in the Pliocene Period (11 to 4 million B.P.) and the Bay came into being. Because of bay filling and other human modifications, in the last 100 years the Bay has shrunk by some 100 sq mi to its present size. (Roger M. Rhiner)

Figure 3.10 The Russian River (here, near Guerneville) takes its name from the Russians who established their Fort Ross settlement (1812–1841) a few miles north of the river's mouth. The settlement served as a base for Russian and Aleut sea otter hunters as well as for crop growing until the sea otter was hunted into near extinction and the fort sold to a Mexican citizen of German and Swiss descent by the name of John Sutter. (Crane Miller)

Figure 3.11 Point Lobos near Carmel has been a State Reserve since 1933. Its 1,250 acres encompass dramatic coastal headlands and a forest of extremely rare Monterey cypress (*Cupressus macrocarpa*). Offshore rocks and sea are frequented by pelicans, sea lions, migrating grey whales, and the sea otter, the last having made a remarkable comeback (see Chapter 7). (Union Pacific Railroad)

Figure 3.12 San Luis Obispo countryside, south of town near the Madonna Inn. A few miles inland from Port San Luis and Pacific Gas and Electric's controversial Diablo Canyon nuclear power plant (nearby active faults pose potential problems), San Luis Obispo and its 35,000 residents enjoy a pastoral setting reminiscent of California's rancho days. One of the state's two polytechnic universities (the other is at Pomona) is located here. (Crane Miller)

San Benito County (Fig. 3.13) in the south. Each county has about the same area (125 to 140 sq mi) and population (20,000 to 30,000). Both are equally mountainous, with elevations exceeding 5,000 ft in places, and both are about equally distant from San Francisco.

But here the similarity ends. Whereas Lake County lives up to its name with Clear Lake (Fig. 3.14), the largest natural freshwater lake (85 sq mi) entirely within the borders of California, San Benito County is entirely lacking in natural lakes and must depend on reservoir and underground storage of water. Lake County lies well east of the San Andreas fault zone and is rarely affected by it; San Benito County, however, is adjacent to the fault and its towns, like Hollister, seem "to move a little bit each day." Conditions of milder and moister climate, lusher vegetation, and lesser seismic hazard appear to favor Lake County for tourism and future growth, although agriculturally San Benito County, with expanding orchard and vineyard acreage, may be catching up to Lake County and its famous Bartlett pears. Another drought could cramp San Benito County's agricultural development, but the prospect that nearby California Aqueduct water may become available diminishes this concern.

The southeastern Coast Ranges do enjoy one major economic advantage over the northeastern Ranges, namely, nearly all of the oil reserves found in the province. The upper Salinas and Cuyama valleys may be poor in local water resources, but they are rich in petroleum-bearing sedimentary formations.

Figure 3.13 The dry terrain of Pinnacles National Monument is typical of San Benito County. (Roger M. Rhiner)

THE KLAMATH MOUNTAINS

Although by no means the highest or largest of California's landform provinces, the Klamaths do claim the most complex physiography, vying with the Sierras for singularly spectacular terrain. As depicted in Figure 3.15, the Klamaths are many mountain ranges whose ridges are oriented in seemingly all different directions and whose upper limits approach 9,000 ft. Their outer bounds reach the Pacific in the west, extend into Oregon to the north, border the Southern Cascades in the east, and front on the Sacramento Valley to the south.

Compared to these surrounding provinces, the Klamaths are not only strikingly more rugged, but much older and exceedingly more complex in their geology. In the broad view, the Klamaths appear as an *upwarp* or arc of ancient metamorphic and *intrusive* igneous rocks (Fig. 3.16) that plunges downward under the much younger formations of the adjacent provinces. For instance, the Klamath Mountains are a northwestern extension of the Sierra Nevada, but the surface connection between the two provinces was buried by Quaternary lava flows emanating from the Southern Cascades.

Erosion and Deposition

In the last 60 million years, the Klamath Mountains have undergone extensive erosion. Many great rivers emanating both from inside and outside the province have incised steep "V-shaped" valleys and deep, sheer-walled gorges. Taken together, the Klamath River from the Columbia Plateau of southern Oregon, the Sacramento River from a spring at the base of Mount Shasta, and the Salmon, Scott, and Trinity rivers from within the Klamath ranges have created the most dissected mountain landscape for its size in all of California.

High above the narrow valley bottoms, Pleistocene glaciers (Fig. 3.16) sculpted the granitic and other erosion-resistant ridges of Castle Crags, the Marble and Salmon mountains, and the Trinity Alps into jagged peaks. Where the advancing alpine glaciers encountered serpentine and other rocks less resistant to the erosional work of ice, U-shaped valleys were formed. At the upper end or head of many of these troughs, concave *cirques* were scoured out by glacial erosion. Cirques and lakes at their bases are very much in evidence on north-facing slopes above 5,500 ft where *ablation* (melting or wasting of ice) is minimal. Down-valley and along the sides of the troughs, glaciers deposited piles of sand, gravel, rocks, and other eroded materials known as *moraines*. Since the last of the Pleistocene glaciers melted more than 10,000 years ago, many of the glacial landforms of the Klamaths have been modified beyond recognition by subsequent stream erosion, chemical and mechanical weathering of rock, mass wasting, and forest cover. Nevertheless, the various ranges of the Klamath Mountains still present spectacular glacial landscapes surpassed in California only by those of the Sierra Nevada.

Getting Away From It All

The high, rugged mountains and deep whitewater canyons that lure thousands of hikers, campers, and fishermen every summer at the same time deter all but the

Figure 3.14 Clear Lake looking south towards volcanic Mount Konocti (4,100 ft). The lake basin was formed by downwarping of the earth's crust several thousand years ago plus more recent damming brought on by volcanic activity. Although the lake is impressive to behold from almost any viewpoint, its shallowness and the indifferent commercial and seasonal residential development ringing it detract from Clear Lake's overall appeal. (Crane Miller)

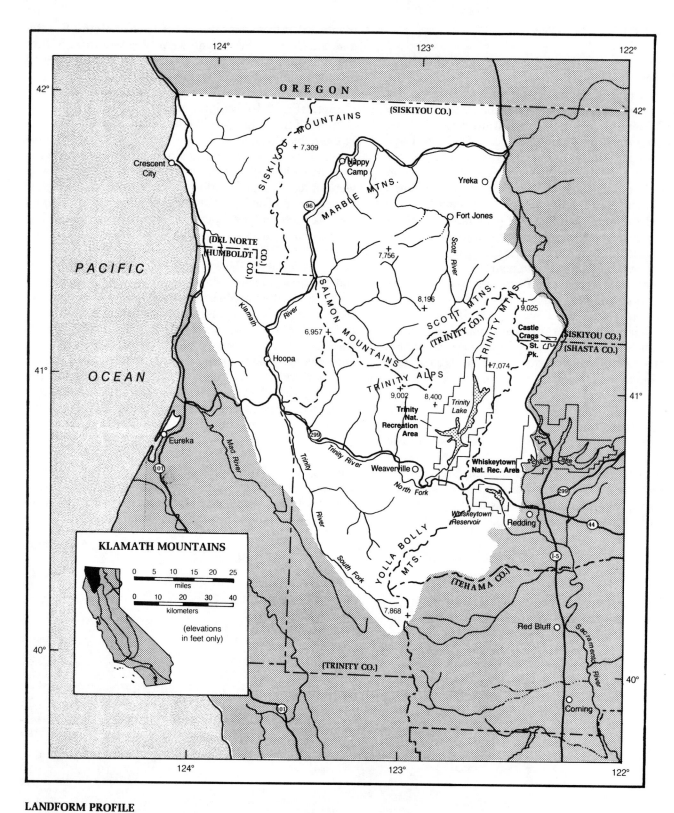

LANDFORM PROFILE

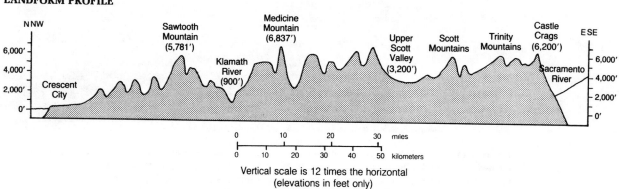

Figure 3.15 Klamath Mountains and landform profile. (Richard Crooker)

Figure 3.16 Castle Crags is a more than 6,000-ft high granitic formation radiometrically dated at +170 million B.P. At the time, magma *intruded* (lithified beneath the surface) what is now the southeastern edge of the Klamath Mountains province and later cooled beneath the surface to become a granitic batholith, of which Castle Crags is an exposed part. The present rugged appearance of the formation owes somewhat to the erosive work of ice during the relatively recent Wisconsin Age (60,000 to 15,000 B.P.). During this last cooling period of the Pleistocene, glaciers formed on the shady northeastern side of Castle Crags, and they in turn serrated ridges and scoured out small, U-shaped valleys along Castle Creek and some of its tributaries. Today, Castle Crags State Park is easily reached via I-5 about 40 miles north of Redding. (Crane Miller)

sparsest of permanent settlement in the Klamath Mountains. Lack of any interstate or other major highway or rail route through the region and its isolation from urban California also keeps would-be residents away. Although Interstate 5 skirts the eastern edge of the Klamaths, most of its travelers are only concerned with getting to and from the Pacific Northwest as quickly as possible. The two state highways that cross the region from I-5 to the Pacific are scenic forest-lined canyon routes along the Klamath and Trinity rivers, but both are narrow and winding and must be closed occasionally in winter because of heavy snowfalls.

For vacationers who want both easy driving access to campgrounds and a variety of sites to choose from, the Shasta-Trinity-Whiskeytown National Recreation Areas are favorite destinations. These U.S. Recreation Areas focus on three huge manmade lakes by the same names located in the southeast corner of the Klamath region. For the more ardent recreationist bent on hiking and fishing away from crowds, the Marble Mountain and Salmon-Trinity Wilderness Areas provide a chance to escape from it all in the high back country.

There are no cities as such in the Klamath Mountains. Towns (none with populations over 3,000) are few and far between. The lumber industry is the economic mainstay of many communities, but recreation and retirement are now the principal investment attractions in

the region. Lack of suitable terrain has limited agricultural settlement except in the alluviated, relatively flat Scott Valley, where ranching and hay farming are significant land uses. A few thousand native California Indians, who lay time-honored claim to the salmon and other fauna and flora of a bountiful natural environment, reside throughout the region both on and off reservations. The Hoopa Valley Reservation and its Extension, together comprising 88,165 acres along the lower Klamath River, is the largest (in area) and one of the most prosperous Indian settlements in all of California.

THE SOUTHERN CASCADES AND MODOC PLATEAU

Viewed in Figure 3.17 or from almost any vantage point in northeastern California, Mount Shasta at an elevation of 14,162 ft dominates the landscape. Except for Mount Rainier (14,406 ft) in Washington, Shasta is the highest of a long string of volcanoes, known as the Cascade Ranges, which extend from Mount Baker (10,750 ft) near the Canadian border southward through Washington, Oregon, and northeastern California to Mount Lassen (10,453 ft). To the east, Shasta overlooks the lava tableland of the Modoc Plateau, which is merely the southern tip of the vast Columbia Plateau. Shasta and

Figure 3.17   Mount Shasta blanketed in winter's first heavy snow. (Southern Pacific Railroad)

Lassen, by virtue of their great heights and composite massiveness, stand out visually in northeastern California, but the dividing line between the Southern Cascade Mountains and the Modoc Plateau is otherwise obscure and both landform provinces (Fig. 3.18) share recent volcanic origins.

Lava Almost Everywhere

The Southern Cascades and Modoc Plateau are the only provinces in California almost completely covered with young basaltic lavas and other *extrusive* igneous rocks, such as seen at Lava Beds National Monument in the northern portion of the region. Almost all of these extrusives erupted through vents and fissures in the region's surface only in the last few million years, and some, as in the case of Mount Lassen, as recently as the twentieth century.

It is noteworthy that intricate knowledge of the lava caves and other volcanic formations at Lava Beds enabled Captain Jack (Chief Kientepous) and his 50 Modoc warriors to hold out for more than three months in 1873 against a U.S. Army force with 16 times as many soldiers and superior armaments before being starved into surrender. Precedents for the Modoc War are examined in Chapter 8.

Evidence that volcanism continues to this day in the province can be seen in the steaming *fumaroles* (steam and gas vents), hot springs, and boiling mud pots of Las-

sen Volcanic National Park and felt in the occasional minor earthquake swarms that occur around Mount Shasta. Should these thermal and tectonic activities intensify, they may then be the precursors of another violent eruption of Lassen or Shasta. Both volcanoes, although considered dormant, are nonetheless active.

Another indication of the recency of volcanism in the Southern Cascades is the general lack of visible features of glacial erosion and deposition. Although five small glaciers exist on the upper slopes of Mount Shasta and signs of glacial scour can be seen in the Shasta Ski Bowl and U-shaped Avalanche Gulch, much evidence of the great glaciers that once emanated from Pleistocene Mount Shasta has been obliterated by recent volcanic activity. For instance, Shastina, Shasta's 12,336-ft satellite volcano, erupted and formed less than 250 years ago and in the process doubtless did away with preexisting glacial features.

Mount Lassen also mothered several late Pleistocene glaciers that converted V-shaped stream valleys into U-shaped glacial troughs. Since the time when Lassen Peak initally formed from eruption 11,000 years ago until the twentieth century, intermittent lava flows, cinder and pumice showers, and mudflows buried much of the evidence of earlier glacial erosion and deposition. Nevertheless, the glacially scoured sides of Mill Creek Valley, Blue Lake Canyon, Warner Valley, and other valleys in Lassen Volcanic National Park indicate that the ice exceeded 1,000 ft in thickness in some places.

Figure 3.18   (*Right*) Southern Cascades and Modoc Plateau, with landform profile. Magma that spills onto the surface, such as molten lava from an erupting volcano, eventually cools and lithifies to become *extrusive* igneous rock. As it is forming, extrusive rock is exposed to the elements on the surface and in the atmosphere and thus differs from intrusive rock, even though both types of rock are formed by fire (think of the cognate word "ignite" with regard to "igneous"). Typical of a plateau, the lava fields are flat surfaced, vertically faulted at their edges, and dissected by streams. (Richard Crooker)

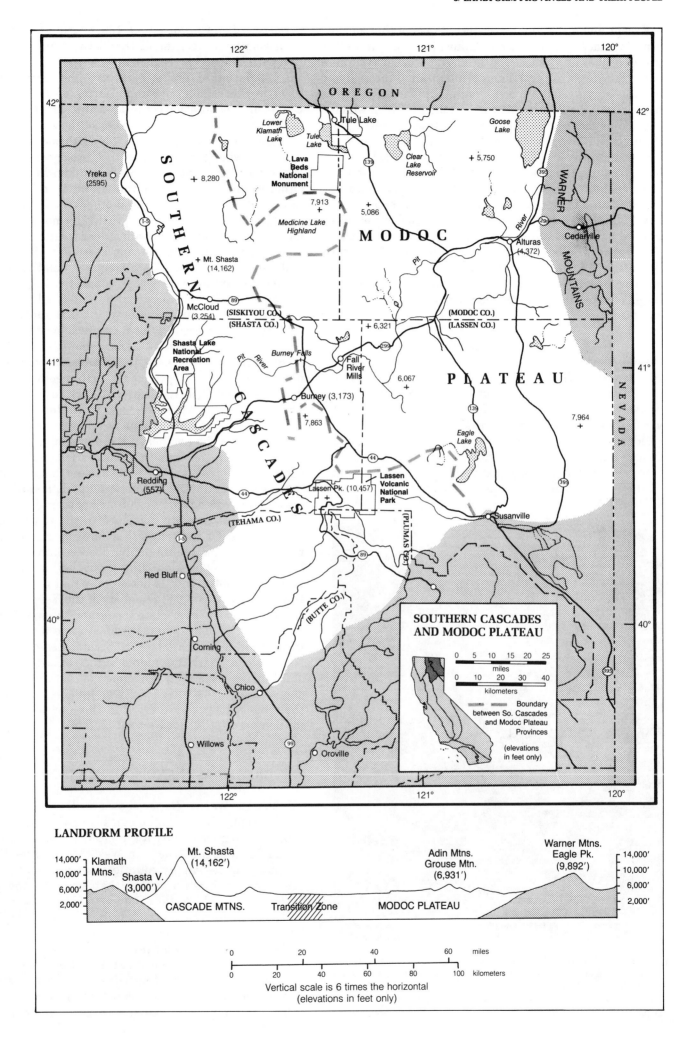

LANDFORM PROFILE

SOUTHERN CASCADES
AND MODOC PLATEAU

0 5 10 15 20 25
miles
0 10 20 30 40
kilometers

Boundary
between So. Cascades
and Modoc Plateau
Provinces

(elevations
in feet only)

Except along the higher western flanks of the Southern Cascades, northeastern California is not a well-watered land and consequently fluvial erosion is minimal. Compared to the Klamath Mountains, the region is noticeably devoid of rivers, lakes, and forests. Originating from the Warner Mountains, the Pit River, which cuts a diagonal course from northeast to southwest right through the lava plateau and mountains and into the Sacramento River at Shasta Lake, is the only relatively long stream in the province. Some of the so-called "short" streams, however, flow from among the largest natural springs found in North America. The springs above Burney Falls (Fig. 3.19) alone gush forth hundreds of millions of gallons of water daily from the plateau basalts. Yet Burney Falls is not the most prolific of several springs in the region. Like the Pit River, the larger streams flow into manmade lakes. Eagle Lake, the only large natural lake in northeastern California, is the exception.

People Almost Nowhere

Any way one drives through northeastern California, even along its western edge on busy I-5, one can't help but surmise that this is a land full of scenic wonders but virtually empty of people. Yreka, with less than 6,000 residents, is the largest town. It and the other towns strung out along the interstate highway service travelers and truckers mostly just passing through, as well as the local ranching and lumber industries.

Figure 3.19 Burney Falls in McArthur–Burney Falls Memorial State Park adjacent to the intersection of California 89 and the Pit River. The river forms Lake Britton here but flows on to Shasta Lake as a tributary of the Sacramento River. (California Department of Parks and Recreation)

Eastward on California 89, 139, or 299, the towns become smaller, fewer, and farther between until the junction with U.S. 395 is reached at Alturas. With about half the population of Yreka, Alturas is the second largest town in the region. In simple terms of distance from California's population centers, Alturas and its environs make up the most isolated corner of the state.

Scarcity of people living in the northeast is not hard to fathom when the previously discussed geomorphology of the northeast and its climate is taken into account. Other than a limited amount of arable land in the Tule Lake and Pit River basins and other small valleys, the volcanic landscape provides practically no opportunity for agricultural settlement and mineral extraction. Cold, dry winters and short growing seasons make farming and ranching all the less attractive. Relatively scant annual precipitation amounts coupled with past over-exploitation of virgin pine and fir stands allow for only a meager existing timber reserve. In all, the only natural resource that presently lures appreciable numbers of people to the northeast is 13,000 sq mi of magnificently scenic seclusion. Of course, these transitory tourist populations are attracted principally to the geothermal wonders of Lassen Volcanic National Park in summer and Shasta's long, snowpacked slopes in winter.

Although white settlement never reached land-rush proportions in the northeast, it did precipitate a decline in the native population that has carried on from statehood to the present. Several thousand Indians, representing four distinctively different linguistic stocks, once lived in the region. Today 1,000 or so of their descendants eke out an inadequate existence in the towns and on reservations. Of the tribes that have long since disappeared, the Yahi are probably the best known, thanks to an engrossing book and film about their last survivor, Ishi (see Chapter 8). It is noteworthy that in prehistoric times as many as 4,000 members of the Yahi and three other tribes spent every late spring and summer hunting and fishing in Ishi's "first world," in and around what in the year of his death in 1916 became Lassen Volcanic National Park. By the middle of the century, less than 400 Indians resided in the same general area. Similar depredations befell the Pit River Indians; members of their tribe, however, survive to this day to claim 3.4 million acres of Modoc Plateau land.

THE GREAT BASIN AND SOUTHEASTERN DESERTS

The basaltic Warner Range shown in all its lonely splendor in Figure 3.20 is lithologically part of the Modoc Plateau, but structurally it typifies the mountains of the Great Basin of the American West. The Warner Range is but one of seemingly countless north-south trending fault block mountain ranges that dominate the landscapes of several Western States, including the eastern and southeastern sides of California as mapped in Figure 3.21.

Between the uplifted ranges are downdropped basins of interior drainage from which the Great Basin Province derives its name: Mountain-born streams, usually dry except when filled with runoff from the rare winter storm or summer thundershower, drain down into the

Figure 3.20 Warner Range in the very northeast corner of California. The range is uplifted along north-south trending faults on its eastern side and therefore dips to the west, which is the side we see in this picture. With two peaks (Eagle and Warren) at nearly 10,000 ft elevation, the range captures enough precipitation from eastward-moving winter storms to feed the headwater forks of the Pit River and sustain coniferous forests and summer pastures. (U.S. Geological Survey, photo by W. A. Duffield)

sinks or *playas* (intermittent lake basins), never finding their way to the sea. The fine sediments that have accumulated in the basins in some cases yield high concentrations of borax, potash, soda ash, or other minerals of value to the playa mining industry. The heavier stream-eroded materials, such as rocks, sand, and gravel, are deposited as *alluvial fans* and *bajadas* (Fig. 3.22) sloping gently from the steep flanks of the surrounding mountains to the flat surfaces of the playas.

The geological history of the intermountain desert region of California is long and complex. The record as preserved in the surface rocks of the province indicates lengthy periods of invasion by the sea and consequent marine erosion and deposition, briefer periods of faulting and folding carrying on to the present, ancient granitic intrusion, more recent volcanic extrusion, and Pleistocene periglacial or *pluvial lake* formation (Fig. 3.23).

Focus on Death Valley

Nowhere in the Great Basin are geomorphic contrasts more forebodingly dramatic than in Death Valley. Imagine what the thoughts of 100 or so goldseekers were in December of 1849 when they first caught sight of the unfriendliest-looking piece of real estate they were ever likely to come upon. For one thing, they probably wished they'd never strayed from the makings of the Mormon Trail in an attempt to find a shortcut to the Mother Lode. For another, these Forty-Niners must have wondered where this below-sea-level, 140-mile valley ended, or whether there might be a passable gap in the 11,000-ft wall of mountains on its west side. Apparently making

matters worse, most of the argonauts realized that these mountains we know as the Panamints were not the Sierra Nevada—that even greater barrier still lay beyond. Even before venturing out from their Furnace Creek Wash viewsite to try to solve their quandry, at least some of the Forty-Niners must have already decided upon the morbid name they would give this barren valley.

To be strictly accurate, Death Valley is a basin rather than a valley. True, the Armagosa River does eventually come to rest in Death Valley, wherein lies its basin of interior drainage, but this is a down-faulted basin, not a stream-cut valley. In fact, these are adversary processes, the tectonic deepening of the trough surpassing its fluvial infilling. At 282 ft below sea level, Badwater (the little bit of standing water here in eastern Death Valley is undrinkable) will undoubtedly sink even lower as the basin continues its structural collapse.

Block faulting of the Panamints to the west and the Black Mountains to the east, right-lateral shifting along the San Andreas, left-lateral shifting along the Garlock fault, and right-lateral faulting elsewhere in the southern Great Basin have all contributed to the pulling apart of Panamint and Saline valleys, as well as of Death Valley (Fig. 3.24). Normal vertical faulting has been most intense in the last 3 million years, with fault scarps or traces thereof often appearing as the truncated middle or lower part of an alluvial fan.

It is hard to believe that in a basin where temperatures sometimes exceed 135° F in the shade and precipitation often evaporates before ever hitting the ground, there was once a 600-ft deep lake. Evidence of Lake Manly's

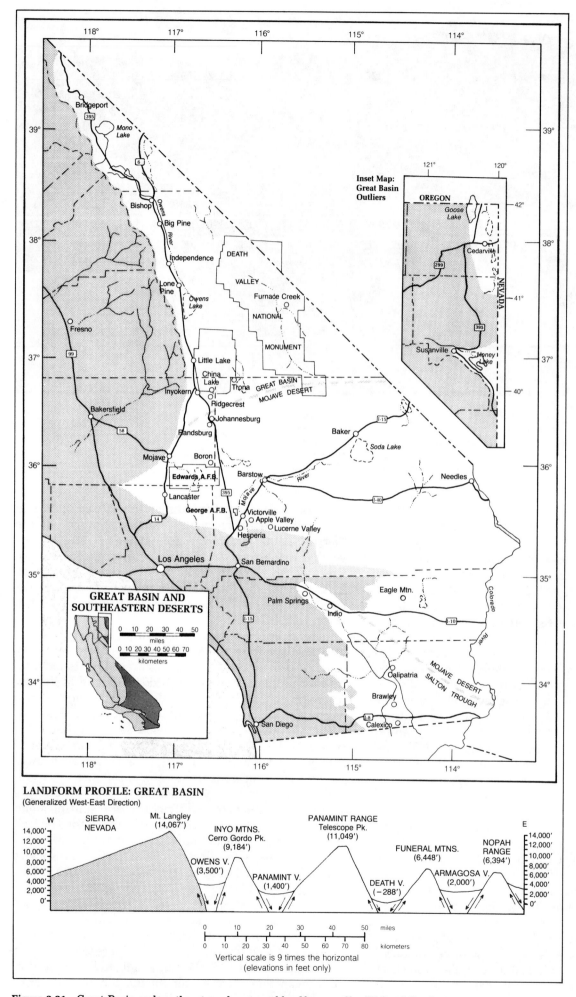

Figure 3.21 Great Basin and southeastern deserts and landform profile. (Richard Crooker)

Figure 3.22 Coalesced alluvial fans or *bajada* at the base of the eastern front of the Sierra Nevada in the foreground. At the base of the Inyo Mountains, in the background to the east, alluvial deposits are smaller and still preserve their fan shape. (Crane Miller)

Figure 3.23 Soda Lake: playa and pluvial lakebed near Baker and I-15 in the eastern Mojave Desert. Only for a short while after a cloudburst or abnormal winter precipitation is there likely to be any water in this and most other Great Basin playas. During the Pleistocene, however, annual precipitation was greater in the region, and eastern Sierran and other mountain glaciers sending their meltwater far out into the Great Basin created pluvial lakes such as Ancient Lake Mojave, of which Soda Lake was a part. Emanating from the San Bernardino Mountains, the Mojave River flowed into the ancient lake, but today its surface waters stop far short of Soda Lake and only its groundwater (Fig. 5.2) reaches all the way to Soda Springs on the western side of the playa. Dubbed Zzyzx Mineral Springs then, a health resort (note bath house and introduced palm trees in foreground) was built here a few decades ago. Clouded land title and delinquent income taxes helped bring about the resort's demise. For the last several years, the grounds and buildings have been under U.S. Bureau of Land Management control and used as a desert studies center by a consortium of the California state universities. (Crane Miller)

Figure 3.24 Death Valley lies between the Armagosa Range to the east and the Panamint Range to the west, the latter mountains including Telescope Peak at 11,049 ft above sea level. Erosion has created a badlands landscape that appears all the more stark for lack of vegetation. (National Park Service, photos by Richard Frear)

heyday 11,000 years ago has largely been lost in subsequent deposits of younger fan gravels. Some irrefutable signs of that last Pleistocene lake's presence, however, are still to be seen in Death Valley at: (1) Manly Bar, where longshore currents formed a gravel bar, (2) Mormon Point, where beach lines in alluvium are visible, (3) Shoreline Butte, a basaltic lava flow whose "steps" are actually wave-cut benches, (4) the mountains behind Badwater, where greyish bands of *tufa* (porous limestone or calcium carbonate) precipitated as a result of contact with an alkaline body of water, and (5) a shoreline terrace on a ridge of faulted gravels just north of the National Park Service residential area at Furnace Creek.

Considering the fact that even during the Pleistocene Death Valley was the hottest and driest place in North America, with the surrounding mountains providing the meagerest of watersheds, how did all that water get there? Its ultimate sources, in fact, were melting glaciers in the eastern High Sierra. Whenever climatic warming set in, such as during the waning millennia of the Pleistocene (15,000 to 10,000 B.P.) and in previous interglacial periods (for example, 65,000 to 60,000 B.P.), Great Basin valleys would begin to fill and then overflow with glacial meltwater: first Owens Valley, which would spill its excess into China and Searles lakes at lower elevations to the south, and they in turn into Panamint Valley. Once Lake Panamint neared a depth of 1,000 ft, it would send water gushing through Wingate Pass into Lake Manly.

Another pluvial lake system, whose waters originated in the San Bernardino Mountains and were carried via the Mojave River and Ancient Lake Mojave (now Soda

Lake; see Fig. 3.23), also replenished Lake Manly during the late Pleistocene. Much of Soda Lake's overflow may have drained eastward through Bristol and Danby basins into the Colorado River, however, with little left for Lake Manly.

Although essentially devoid of human settlement today, Death Valley has witnessed a long and varied parade of cultures occupying its landscape. While Lake Manly was still in existence, its shores were graced by the first culture in the region, that of the hunting, fishing, and gathering Nevares Spring People some 10,000 years ago. About 1,000 years ago, long after the lake had disappeared, the ancestors of the most recent aboriginal occupants of Death Valley arrived. Belonging to the Shoshone linguistic family and related to the Paiute Indians of Owens Valley, these nomadic peoples were gatherers, hunters, and pottery makers. Indians were known to frequent the region well into historic times but showed a decided preference for the cooler and wetter mountains as opposed to the hot and dry valley floor.

It was borate mining that ushered in the first semblance of non-Indian settlement in Death Valley. White mine and refinery operators and Chinese so-called "cottonball carriers" (bearers of calcium and sodium borate nodules) launched production of borax at Eagle Borax Spring, Cottonball Basin, and the Harmony Borax Works in the early 1880s. The refined borax was shipped by wagons driven by teams of 20 mules apiece 165 miles southwest to the railroad town of Mojave. Harmony folded in 1889, but borate mining continued off and on in the region for another four decades. For a time during the 1920s, the Death Valley area was producing 80 percent of all the borax consumed in the nation.

Eventually, though, discovery of borate deposits in the Mojave Desert near major rail lines and establishment of Death Valley National Monument in 1933 dealt death blows to the borax industry in the region. Since then, tourism has become the principal and only industry. In 1927, borax crew quarters at Furnace Creek Ranch were converted to resort use and construction began on luxurious Furnace Creek Inn. Although not originally intended as a tourist attraction, Death Valley Ranch, popularly known as Scotty's Castle, also was built during the Roaring Twenties. Since federal acquisition in 1970, Scotty's Castle and grounds, along with nearby volcanic Ubehebe Crater, are the major tourist attractions at the northern end of the National Monument. But Furnace Creek, with year-round accommodations, a Monument Visitor's Center, and Park Service headquarters, remains the focus of tourism and settlement in Death Valley.

A Manmade Sea

Unlike Death Valley's Lake Manly, the Salton Sea is an unusual case, for it is neither a vestige of the Pleistocene nor a cut-off extension of the Gulf of California, although the Gulf's waters did invade the Salton Trough several million years ago. Instead, the "Sea" is a manmade accident of the early twentieth century resulting from an ill-fated irrigation canal temporarily diverting the flow of the Colorado River into the Salton Trough instead of into the Gulf.

Currently, the Salton Sea is kept from evaporating away by inputs of used irrigation water from the Imperial Valley. The Sea acts as a sump for water that originates in the Colorado River and comes to the Imperial Valley via the All-American Canal. Before reaching the Sea and as part of the irrigation process, the water is *ditched* and *tiled,* as explained in Figure 3.25, so that crop-damaging dissolved salts are piped away and thus not allowed to accumulate in irrigated soils. Ditching and tiling in the Imperial Valley has not only maintained the Salton Sea but has also allowed agriculture to prosper where it would otherwise be impossible to exist.

Thinly Populated Deserts

Stretching discontinuously nearly 1,000 miles from Oregon down to Baja California and lying in the water-starved rain shadow of the Cascades, Sierras, Transverse Ranges, and Peninsular Ranges, the Great Basin and southeastern deserts of California are understandably a thinly populated land. The few cities of any appreciable size exist mostly in the western portions of the Mojave and Colorado deserts, where they are closest to the Los Angeles–San Diego metropolitan complex and where there is more level terrain and the mountain passes are less imposing.

Wedged in the apex where the Garlock and San Andreas faults join, the western Mojave's Antelope Valley contains the desert's largest city: Lancaster and neighboring Palmdale jointly claim some 50,000 residents, many of whom are connected with the local Lockheed plant or Edwards Air Force Base. The Antelope Freeway (California 14) puts these desert communities within an easy 45-minute drive of the San Fernando Valley. Another 50,000 people are associated by location with the Mojave River, Interstate 15, and the main Union Pacific-Santa Fe transcontinental rail lines in the communities of Apple Valley, Barstow, Hesperia, and Victorville. George Air Force Base, the Boron open pit borate mine, two Portland cement plants, light manufacturing plants, Solar One (the nation's first solar electric plant; see Chapter 5), and retail services broaden the employment base of the area.

Much larger in area and correspondingly smaller in population, the central Mojave sustains some 20,000 inhabitants. Most of them are retirees in the Yucca Valley–Twenty-Nine Palms area, but some work at Kaiser Steel's iron mines at Eagle Mountain (Fig. 3.26) and a U.S. Marine base.

Settlement of the eastern Mojave's 15,000 residents is almost entirely along the banks of the Colorado River in the agricultural service centers of Blythe and Needles and the Chemehuevi Valley, Colorado River, and Fort Mohave Indian reservations. Although most of the Colorado River reservation lies on the Arizona side of "The River," its 42,696 acres in California render it the third largest reservation in area in the state. Recreational development of "The River," notably upstream from where Parker Dam impounds Lake Havasu, currently provides the principal stimulus for the new settlement.

Though much smaller in area than the Mojave Desert, the Colorado Desert boasts a rapidly growing population

Figure 3.25 Ditching and tiling in the Imperial Valley. The checkerboard pattern (Fig. 3.40) of agricultural land use seen in the satellite view would likely not exist were it not for the removal of soluble salt from irrigation water accomplished by piping it away after use. Preparing the land for this involves digging a ditch, laying pipe (formerly tile, now porous plastic), and then filling the trench with sand and soil all in one operation. (NASA)

that now almost equals that of the entire Mojave region. The Coachella and Imperial valleys harbor most of the residents. Palm Springs, now a world-renowned winter resort and mecca for retired presidents and entertainers, is the largest city in the Coachella Valley. Combined with the agriculturally oriented cities of Indio and Coachella and other more modest resort towns, the valley's population now approaches 75,000.

South of the settlement void of the Salton Sea and the Anza-Borrego Desert, intensive irrigation agriculture of a variety of crops provides the major source of income for most of the Imperial Valley's 60,000 residents. The agribusiness centers of Brawley and El Centro and the border town of Calexico are the population nuclei. At the northern end of the valley, Calipatria, at −183 ft, can rightfully claim to be lower in elevation than any other

community of 2,000 or more residents in the nation. Underlying the Imperial Valley is one of the world's potentially most productive geothermal fields, and a test facility is already producing power from this natural source of steam energy.

Although a small tribe owns and occupies some valuable real estate within Palm Springs, Indian settlement in this area is mostly to the south on two Cahuilla reservations in the Coachella Valley and the Fort Yuma Indian Reservation in the irrigated Bard Valley of the lower Colorado River. The Yumas were among the few tribes of California Indians who practiced flood plain agriculture in prehistoric times. They have carried this tradition through to the present, but today the Yumas lease much of their land to outsiders and increasingly pursue nonagricultural endeavors.

Basin Settlement and Transient Tourism

North of the low deserts of the Colorado and the high deserts of the Mojave, the mountain ranges become more numerous, the basins smaller, the distance from Los Angeles greater, and the people fewer. Except for about 30,000 residents of China Lake, Inyokern, Ridgecrest, and Trona, many of whom are economically sustained by the China Lake Naval Ordnance Test Station as well as playa mining and processing operations at Searles Lake, there are no urban nodes in California's share of the Great Basin. The naval weaponry range itself is of course devoid of settlement and extends northwestward through most of the Coso Range almost to the Owens Valley.

The Owens Valley is the eastern gateway to the Sierras and as such maintains a population of several thousand in four communities strung out along U.S. 395. Bishop and Lone Pine, the largest towns, provide a variety of overnight accommodations for skiers heading for Mammoth or Tahoe, fisherman seeking trout from Lake Crowley or the lakes and streams of the eastern Sierras, and other vacationers. The Los Angeles Department of Water and Power, which owns much valley land and most of the water reserves, the California Department of Fish and Game, the U.S. Forest Service, the U.S. Bureau of Land Management, and other government agencies employ many local residents. Indians, mostly Paiutes, live on reservation land both in and outside the towns and are employed by the local service industries and governments. Mining and ranching are relatively insignificant employers of the local working force.

Settlement north of the Owens Valley to the Nevada border, although a distance of more than a hundred miles on U.S. 395, is limited to a few tiny communities. Towns like Leevining and Bridgeport service travelers on the lonely but magnificently scenic stretch of highway.

Mountain settlement in the Great Basin has come and mostly gone. A century ago, gold and silver drew thousands of miners to boom towns like Bodie in the mountains east of Bridgeport and Cerro Gordo ("Fat Hill") high in the southern Inyo Mountains. Darwin in the Argus Range southeast of the Inyos and Randsburg (Fig. 3.27) and Johannesburg in the Rand Mountains of the northern Mojave are of more recent vintage, but they too appear to be on the brink of becoming ghost towns.

In those two tongues of the Great Basin that project from northwestern Nevada into northeastern California, Susanville is the only community of significant size. The city's several thousand residents derive income from lumber mills, retail stores, a state penal facility and other government functions, the railroad, agricultural and livestock service industries, motels, and auto service stations. In short, Susanville is a service center for a remote part of the state and is culturally more closely tied to Reno, Nevada, than any large city in California.

THE SIERRA NEVADA

By any dimension, the Sierra Nevada is more impressive than any other landform province in California. Late in the last century, naturalist John Muir calculated the Sierras to be "about 500 miles long, 70 miles wide, and

Figure 3.26 Eagle Mountain mine, whose eventual closing was announced by Kaiser Steel Corporation in November 1981, produced hematite and magnetite. Each containing some 70 percent pure iron, both these iron ores are considered high grade. Magnetite possesses magnetic properties that permit it to be concentrated even further by magnetic separators (pelletized) at the mine. After processing, the ores were transported by rail 150 miles west to Kaiser's Fontana plant for conversion into steel. With the phasing out of primary steelmaking but the continuing of steel finishing operations at Fontana, in the future raw steel is likely to come from outside the state. (Crane Miller)

Figure 3.27 Randsburg mines, located a mile off of U.S. 395 in the Rand Mountains of eastern Kern County, produced more than $10 million worth of gold between 1895 and the end of World War I. Gold-bearing quartz veins in granitic rocks were the source of the precious metal. The towns of the Rand district, including also Atolia, Johannesburg, and Red Mountain, have also serviced silver and tungsten mining operations. (Crane Miller)

from 7,000 to nearly 15,000 feet high." Partly because of Muir's vivid descriptions of the Sierras, tens of millions of visitors have since ventured into this massive expanse of mountains where "glaciers are still at work in the shadows of the peaks, and thousands of lakes and meadows shine and bloom beneath them, and the whole range is furrowed with cañons to a depth of from 2,000 to 5,000 ft, in which once flowed majestic glaciers, and in which now flow and sing a band of beautiful rivers."[3]

John Muir's portrayal of the Sierra Nevada ("Snowy Mountains") is just as reliable as it is graphic, save for

[3]John Muir, *The Mountains of California* (Berkeley, Calif.: Ten Speed Press, 1977), pp. 2–3. The quotations are from this facsimile edition of John Muir's original 1894 classic.

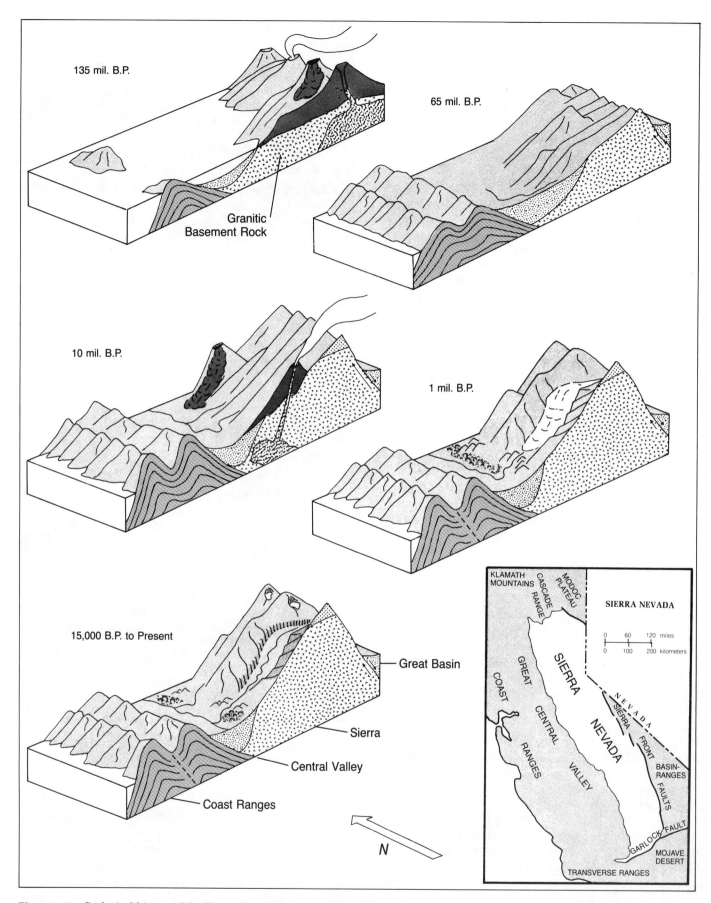

Figure 3.28 Geological history of the Sierra Nevada in cross-section. (Richard Crooker)

an exaggeration in length of about 100 miles by his inclusion of the Southern Cascades. His description is all the more remarkable in that he wrote it nearly a century ago without benefit of either aerial or satellite information. Obviously, though, he had lengthy firsthand experience in the Sierras and knew the range perhaps better than any other person in recorded history. Muir's favorite spot was Yosemite Valley and it was his decades of intimacy with the landscape that first prompted him to suggest glacial origins for the deep, sheer-walled valley. John Muir was not a geologist by training and his view ran counter to the then-prevailing theory that the valley was downdropped by normal faulting. But Muir was eventually proven correct, and as a consequence we know the Sierra Nevada as one of the most glaciated mountain ranges in the world.

Ancestral Formations

Pleistocene glaciation was merely the latest of a series of major geological events that gave birth to the Sierra Nevada that we know today. Figure 3.28 traces that history from 135 million years ago while the ancestral Sierras were emerging from 300 million years beneath the sea. Indeed, the oldest rocks now found in the Sierras date from about 435 million B.P., when they first formed at the bottom of the sea. Figure 3.29 shows one of the few places in the Sierras where these ancient rocks can be seen: in this case, overlying younger granitic rocks forming a *roof pendant*. One would expect that these roof pendants contain fossils since they originated in a sea basin teaming with life. But the heat and pressure later exerted by granitic intrusion from below transformed marine fossils, other sedimentary rock materials, and

even submarine volcanics into metamorphic rocks: for example, shale and basalt metamorphosed into schist, shale into slate, sandstone into quartzite, and limestone into marble. The metamorphosis also caused gold, silver, scheelite (tungsten ore), and molybdenite (ore of molybdenum, a steel alloy) to form at contact points between the older rocks and the granitic intrusion.

About $3 billion worth of these valuable minerals has been extracted from the Sierras. Gold, mined from placer stream deposits and *lodes* (gold-bearing quartz veins, for example), accounts for the bulk of this value; but today it is only of historical interest (see Chapter 8). The steel alloy ores, on the other hand, are presently mined in the eastern Sierras, notably at the nation's largest molybdenum-tungsten mine near Pine Creek, west of Bishop.

Granitic Intrusion

The next great episode in the building of the Sierras was the intrusion of a massive granitic batholith that would eventually become the rock core of the entire range. Presently, 10,000 sq mi of the Sierra region is covered by this speckled, off-white crystalline mass. But 135 million years ago and before, the mass was largely fluid magma convecting upward and intruding into the older surface rocks that by now were being exposed to atmospheric weathering and erosion as the sea retreated.

In the ensuing 70 million years, most of the magma cooled beneath the surface to become granite, although some extruded onto the surface as volcanoes and lava flows. The Yosemite Valley granites seen in Figure 3.30, for instance, lithified about 80 million B.P. As erosion ravaged the overlying rocks, more and more granite became exposed. Mild uplift from normal faulting raised

Figure 3.29 Roof pendants in the eastern Sierra. On a few peaks and high ridges where they have not been removed by erosion, older, darker-colored rocks overlie the exposed granitic batholith of the Sierra. West of Crowley Lake on Mount Morgan, the pendants appear both as the remnants of a roof on top of the mountains and as horizontal bands intruded with lighter-colored granite down the east side of the mountain. (Crane Miller)

Figure 3.30 Yosemite Falls, which drops 2,425 ft, marks the point where Yosemite Creek cascades over the granite walls that nearly surround Yosemite Valley. Starting tens of millions of years ago while the Sierran batholith was being uplifted and tilted ever more steeply to the west, rivers incised their way through sedimentary rocks and into the underlying granites to form the range's first stream-cut valleys. In the case of Yosemite Valley, it was and still is the Merced River that cut its way through the valley floor. But only in the last million years have valley granites encountered the considerably greater erosive power of glaciers and the subsequent broadening and deepening of the valley. Tributary glaciers, occupying formerly stream-cut tributary valleys feeding into Yosemite Valley, also scoured out U-shaped, hanging valleys, many of which would become the sources for today's waterfalls. (National Park Service, photo by Richard Frear)

the ancestral range to about 3,000 ft above sea level but the constant erosion of a tropical climate kept the highest peaks from surpassing these heights. Gold veins were also exposed as streams and rivers carried the precious metal downstream to the placer deposits of the western foothills.

Following the relative quiescence of ongoing stream erosion from about 65 to 30 million B.P., a period of violent volcanism set in that has persisted until almost the present time. At first, volcanic explosions rocked the northern Sierras, scattering steam, ash, and *bombs* (rocks and other volcanic debris falling from the sky) over the landscape. The erupting volcanoes spent themselves and eventually disappeared, but outcrops of their light-colored rhyolitic ash can still be seen near the western and northern edges of Lake Tahoe, in Donner Pass (Figure 3.31), and intermittently northward to the Cascades.

Over the next several million years, ash falls gradually gave way to outpourings of lava that mixed with water and earth materials to form steaming hot volcanic *mud flows*. The mud flows solidified as grayish-appearing andesite, which is much in evidence in the region immediately south of Tahoe, especially through Sonora Pass. The andesite flows covered upwards of 10,000 sq mi of the northern Sierra at one time or another between 20 and 5 million B.P. Thereafter and into the ice ages, the focus of volcanism shifted southward to the Mammoth-Mono area, where a huge lava flow left Devil's Postpile (Fig. 3.32) in its wake and a series of nearby eruptions gave birth to an 11,034-ft mountain that would

Figure 3.31 Donner Pass and Lake were both carved out of local *plutonic* (intrusive) and volcanic rocks by advancing glaciers with extensive glacial deposits being left behind on the flanks of the lake. Donner Summit is 7,239 ft above sea level and carries one of the few all-year highways (I-80) across the Sierra. In this view toward the lake, a fresh spring snowfall had closed the pass earlier in the day. Winter snows can accumulate in drifts 100 feet deep and close the pass indefinitely, as the George and Jacob Donner party of 87 men, women, and children found out in 1846–1847. The Donner Party was snowed in at the lake from November through April, and some of its members reportedly resorted to cannibalism to stay alive. Eventually, the ordeal in and across the Sierra would take 40 lives. Today, modern snowplows usually clear the pass within hours of even the worst of winter snowfalls. The long white lines on the slopes south of the lake are snow sheds for the transcontinental rail line. (U.S. Geological Survey, photo by H. S. Gale)

A

B

Figure 3.32 Devil's Postpile is part of a 600,000-year-old lava flow that originated a few miles to the southeast near Mammoth Mountain. All other things being equal, the volcanic basalt (possibly andesite) of the pile weathered and eroded into nature's most efficient geometric shapes: six-sided columns (A). The top of the formation (B) was subsequently planed off by late Pleistocene glaciers, whereas a *scree* or *talus pile* of broken rock has accumulated at the base. (A: Union Pacific Railroad; B: Jim Ralph)

become a skiers' paradise, namely, Mammoth Mountain. There have been no eruptions in the twentieth century, but hot springs at the base of the Postpile, lying 25 miles east in Hot Creek, as well as elsewhere tell us that volcanism is far from dead in this part of the Sierras.

Block Faulting

Although uplift from faulting has been continuous in the Sierras since the earliest granitic intrusions over 200 million years ago, only in the last 10 million years has uplift of the batholith so exceeded its erosion that the highest crests of the range finally rose more than 10,000 ft above sea level. In fact, vertical displacement (mountains rising and valleys dropping) of nearly 20,000 ft has occurred in the southern Sierras in the last 3 million years alone. Almost all of the recent faulting, including that of the 1872 Lone Pine earthquake, originated in the Sierra Nevada fault zone along the steep eastern escarpment of the Sierras. The 1980 series of strong earthquakes near Mammoth are further evidence of the Sierras' dynamism.

In essence, the granitic batholith is still in the process of being block-faulted so that it rises sharply on its eastern edge and tilts or dips downward ever so gradually on its western side, giving the Sierras an asymmetrical profile (see the cross-section in Fig. 3.28). The long western slope is the one exposed to moisture-bearing storms coming from the Pacific. Consequently, numerous great rivers have incised steep V-shaped valleys up and down the range's length. The eastern slopes, because of their abruptness and rain shadow location, handle only a small proportion of the Sierran drainage and thus have short whitewater streams but no long rivers. Erosion by ice and wind, weathering of rock, and mass wasting are also wearing down the granite fortress, but uplift continues apace and keeps the Sierras a young and growing mountain range.

Pleistocene Glaciation

The great alpine glaciers of the Pleistocene have come and gone on several occasions over the last million years in the Sierras, and they may even return again in the not-so-distant future. Whatever happens, the valley glaciers have already made their mark more obvious than any other agent of erosion or weathering affecting the Sierras. Glacial landforms are ubiquitous today on both sides of the Sierras, from the 5,000-ft elevation all the way up to the summits of 14,000-ft peaks.

In sheer size, the U-shaped troughs and their tributary *hanging valleys,* now the conveyers of the nation's highest waterfalls, are the most impressive products of glacial scour. Glaciers thousands of feet thick and dozens of miles long carved Yosemite, Hetch Hetchy, Tenaya, and other previously V-shaped stream valleys ever more deeply and broadly into the granitic batholith. The best examples of valley glacier scour, including these three valleys, are found within the boundaries of Yosemite National Park.

The erosion potential of a glacier depends on a number of factors, not the least of which is the structure of the rock beneath and on the sides of it. The more closely *jointed* the granite a glacier is overriding, the more rock will be eroded. For instance, as Tenaya Glacier advanced parallel over and along closely spaced joints in granite, it scoured Tenaya Canyon some 2,000 ft deeper than if all those fractures had not been there.

Interspersed between the glaciations, which lasted tens of thousands of years, were equally long *interglacial periods* when warming trends set in and glaciers retreated. As the glaciers wasted away, they left in their wake *lateral* and *terminal moraines, erratics, glacial lake beds,* and other depositional landforms shown in Figure 3.33.

By about 10,000 B.P., the last of the great Pleistocene glaciers had melted away in the Sierras. There have been three minor glaciations since then, however, the

Figure 3.33 East Sierra moraines, such as this one along McGee Creek west of Crowley Lake, resulted from glaciers depositing rocks, gravel, sand, and other unsorted earth materials they had originally eroded up valley and then carried down valley. The till deposits accumulated along the sides of the glaciers as *lateral moraines,* at the point of farthest down-valley advance of the glaciers as *terminal moraines,* or at glacier retreat points as *recessional moraines.* (The French word *moraine* refers in fact to an unconsolidated heap of rubble.) The McGee Creek moraine and till, seen here at an age of 2.5 million years, may be the world's oldest glacial deposit from the Quaternary period. The steepness of the eastern side of the Sierra and its drier climate, the latter contributing to *sublimation* (moisture converting from a solid to a vapor state) of ice, help explain the prevalence of moraines on the east rather than the west side of the Sierra. The large boulders are Sierran glacial erratics. Like glacial erratics found any place in the world where glaciers have come and gone, the boulders are plucked out of rock formations by the glacier and then carried varying distances by the moving ice. Once the ice thins out or the glacier stops advancing, the boulders are dropped. Wherever they come to rest, erratics usually appear somewhat out of place compared to the native rocks of the area. (Crane Miller)

most recent being the "Little Ice Age" barely 200 years ago. The five dozen or so tiny glaciers found today in the Sierras owe their origin to that eighteenth-century cooling-off period. They owe their continued existence to high elevation—most are above 10,500 ft—and their exposure away from the sun, which diminishes ablation. Figure 3.34 shows the Sawtooth Ridge–Matterhorn Peak group of glaciers prospering under these geographical advantages.

These and some other Sierran glaciers appear to be gaining additional benefit from the cooling trend of the last 20 years. For instance, some of the heavy snowpack of the 1977–78 winter survived the following summer's melt season to become *firn,* and in turn glacial ice, because of the early coming (in October 1978) of the next winter snows. It is too early to tell whether or not the Sierras' glaciers are building noticeably more rapidly than they are ablating. But we do know that the current cooling trend has resulted in substantial growth of hundreds of much larger glaciers only some 600 miles away in the Northern Cascades of Washington.

Long before and long since the Pleistocene, a type of mechanical weathering of rock known as *exfoliation,* or the "peeling away" of granite, has characterized the wearing down of the Sierras almost as uniquely as has glaciation. The back side of Half Dome in Yosemite National Park, Moro Rock in Sequoia National Park, Tehipite Dome in Kings Canyon National Park, and other *exfoliation domes,* which look like giant onions with their skins peeling off, are almost as common a sight in the Sierras as are glacial landforms.

Why the domes weather the way they do is not fully understood, although alternate freezing and thawing of moisture in the rock joints, unloading or removal of overlying rock layers, and the crystalline structure of granite are all known to contribute to exfoliation. The weathered rock heaps up at the base of the formation into a *talus pile* or a more gentle *talus slope.*

Recreation and Retirement

It is obvious from the physiography thus far described that, save for the western foothills, the Tahoe Basin, the Mammoth Lakes area, and Yosemite Valley, the 25,000 sq mi Sierra Nevada does not provide a terrain conducive to human settlement. Yet its great dimensions and mountainous landscape make the Sierras the premier alpine playground of California. People come and go in the Sierras by the millions the year around. The greatest influx of vacationers is during summer, when the national parks and forests seem overrun by campers, boaters, fishermen, sightseers, and the like. Even higher up on the popular back country trails like the John Muir, the Pacific Crest, or the Mount Whitney, one is apt to encounter dozens of other hikers on any clear summer day. Of course, there are also still the less frequented trails, forests, wilderness areas, streams, lakes, meadows, and mountain summits where one is likely to see only wildlife.

Fortunately for its conservation, almost all of the Sierran high country is not accessible by motor vehicle. Most of the Sierras' more than 2,000 glacial lakes, for in-

Figure 3.34 Matterhorn–Sawtooth Ridge glaciers along the northeastern boundary of Yosemite National Park. These and other existing Sierran glaciers occupy *cirques* scoured out by much larger Pleistocene glaciers that had disappeared by 10,000 B.P. Palisade Glacier, nestled in the cirque of 14,242-ft North Palisade Mountain 70 miles to the south of this scene, is California's largest existing glacier and it measures only a scant square mile in area. Today's Sierran glaciers are pitifully small by comparison with those of the Pleistocene, when ice covered nearly 300 miles of the length, 30 miles of the width, and up to 1 mile of the depth (Yosemite Valley glaciers were probably more than a mile thick) of the range. (U.S. Geological Survey, photo by W. D. Johnson)

stance, are at least a day's hike from a roadhead. In fact, from the southern end of the range at Walker Pass (California 178, 5,250 ft) northward over 200 miles to Tioga Pass (California 120 out of Yosemite, 9,945 ft), there is no way to cross the crest of the Sierra except by foot or on the back of an animal. Furthermore, Tioga, Sonora, and Ebbetts passes are routinely closed in winter, seasonally extending the impassable crest of the Sierra another 100 miles northward almost to the Tahoe Basin.

But despite winter's severe imposition on access to the High Sierras, the more snow there is, the more downhill and cross-country skiers there are. Ski resorts, often discouragingly crowded from autumn's first snows until the spring thaw, are scattered throughout the High Sierras in such areas as Donner-Tahoe (Figs. 3.35 and 3.36), June Lakes, and Mammoth in the eastern part of the range, and Badger Pass (in Yosemite National Park), China Peak, and Mount Riba (Bear Valley) on the western slopes. Expansion of facilities at these and other existing ski resort areas continues.

Environmentalists' concerns, however, over the negative impacts of building more access roads, manicuring slopes, waste disposal, wildlife depredation, and other modifications have mounted to the point of thwarting development of new winter, and even all-year, resort sites. Mineral King, just south of Sequoia National Park and closest of any proposed Sierran sites for skiers from the Los Angeles metropolitan area, and Independence Lake, north of Donner Pass and convenient to vacationers from the Bay Area, Sacramento, and Reno, are notable casualties among recent year-round resort proposals.

The seeming inability of the government agencies and commissions involved to expedite decisions also contributed to the frustrations connected with these proposals. Perhaps such recreational development proposals would be more expeditiously served if left to local voters to decide. Paradoxically enough, voters in Nevada County, in which Independence Lake is located, defeated one measure on the November 1978 ballot that would have limited population in unincorporated areas to 50,000 by

Figure 3.35 North Lake Tahoe ski area. Manicuring slopes, such as done here, exposes soil organic materials that are then washed into the lake, thereby increasing algae content. (Roger M. Rhiner)

Figure 3.36 Truckee River and town. At 5,820 ft, Truckee, with a population of 1,400, services transcontinental travelers and truckers from I-80 and provides quick access to Tahoe via California 89 and 267. (Crane Miller)

1990 and another that would have imposed a moratorium on new land divisions until a new county general plan was adopted. Voters to the south in El Dorado County turned down a measure that would have reduced the number of building permits to 600 in 1979 as compared to some 3,000 issued in 1978. El Dorado County fronts on Lake Tahoe and it is here that impacts from the defeat of growth and development control measures are likely to be most keenly felt. We shall return to the subject of environmental impact and Lake Tahoe in Chapter 7.

Other than the Tahoe Basin, the only significant growth area in the eastern Sierra is Mammoth Lakes. Although Mammoth Lakes is a year-round alpine playground, Mammoth Mountain is the area's main attraction, with two gondolas, three surface lifts, and sixteen chairlifts. Mammoth is the nearest ski resort of these proportions to Southern California's estimated 500,000 skiers. Of the 10,000 skiers likely to be on the mountain on any Saturday during the season, most are from the Los Angeles metropolitan area. The skiers are weekend visitors, but their presence swells the semipermanent seasonal population by another few thousand—the people who operate the lifts, restaurants, inns, motels, gas stations, and stores. To accommodate both weekenders and semipermanent residents and beat the first snows of winter, the building of condominiums and other housing units has been going on at a fever pitch during the offseason, especially since the local water district secured the rights for additional water from Lake Mary that resulted in the lifting of a building moratorium in 1978.

This is the latest, and perhaps biggest, of several building booms to affect the area over the last quarter century and it is certain to keep Mammoth Lakes on the road to becoming one of the Sierra's largest and most congested cities. Lack of sufficient housing and parking facilities, inadequate access from U.S. 395, sewage disposal problems, and negative environmental impacts of all sorts are flies in the ointment of expansion that can be overcome with viable regional planning; but another drought like that of the mid-1970s, when there was hardly enough snow to ski on, would halt the boom no matter what else was done.

Recent development at Mammoth and Tahoe notwithstanding, most of the Sierras' permanent population remains situated in numerous towns and small cities strung out along the length of the western foothills. From Paradise, Quincy, and other Feather River Country towns in the north through Nevada City, Grass Valley, Auburn, Placerville (formerly Hangtown), and Sonora in the Mother Lode Country to small southern foothill recreational centers like Bass Lake, Shaver Lake, and Lake Isabella, no single community claims more than 20,000 residents and most far fewer than half that number. Many of the Mother Lode communities originated as mining camps during the Gold Rush, faded into obscurity once local placer deposits ceased yielding gold (Fig. 3.37), and then revived in the present century as agricultural, lumbering, retail trade, retirement, and tourist centers. Away from the towns are increasing numbers of homes occupied by retirees and urban workers who commute to such cities as Sacramento.

Sierran Indian populations are small and scattered almost exclusively along the western foothills in several rancherías and in the Tule River Indian Reservation, with 54,116 acres, the state's second largest reservation in area, situated southwest of Sequoia National Park. Two hundred years ago, upwards of 150,000 Indians lived in the Great Central Valley and the Sierran foothills. But in the wake of sweeping agricultural development, the hunting and gathering Maidu, Miwok, and Yokuts vacated the valley for the hills. Water, oak acorns, other seeds, fish, and game were plentiful in the foothills and became even more so as domesticated crops and livestock invaded the valley and forced the native fauna to seek refuge in the hills.

One of the few remaining vestiges of aboriginal use of the natural landscape is at Chaw'se Indian Grinding Stone State Park in the Mother Lode Country, where oak acorns are still ground by Miwok Indians in holes hollowed out of limestone outcroppings. The 135-acre site is the only one in the state park system devoted to Indian culture.

THE GREAT CENTRAL VALLEY

Forty to 80 miles from east to west and 400 miles from north to south, the Great Central Valley's dimensions match those of the Sierra Nevada. Any other way one views the two landform provinces, though, they bear no resemblance. The Great Valley, Central Valley, or Sac-

ramento–San Joaquin Valley(s), as this heartland of California is variously called, is flat as a pancake—on a typical hazy day not unlike Iowa or Nebraska, where mountains are nowhere in sight. The two great river systems that drain the Central Valley give it even more of a Midwestern look, with the Sacramento from the north and the San Joaquin from the south meandering along in some appearances like the mighty Mississippi or the wide Missouri.

Whatever the Great Valley lacks in scenery compared to the Sierras or in size compared to the Midwest, however, it more than makes up for in its agricultural landscape. For no other single area of 25,000 sq mi in the nation—or the world, for that matter—can come close to matching the Great Central Valley in terms of value of agricultural output, variety of crops grown, and crop yields per acre. And, as if this were not enough, the valley is rich in hydrocarbons—oil and natural gas.

Fold and Fill

The geologic explanation for the existence of this broad, productive valley plain in the midst of the Pacific Mountain System begins some 200 million years ago with formation of a deep structural trough in the earth's crust. What is now the Great Central Valley was then a deepening geosyncline underlying the submarine western continental shelf of the North American Plate. As shown earlier in Figure 2.3, the volcanic predecessor of the Sierra Nevada and the Klamath Mountains next began to rise from the sea, sending ever-increasing amounts of eroded materials into the downfold. Marine sedimentation helped fill the trough to great depths—more than 40,000 ft below sea level in some places.

In time, the ancestral Coast Ranges were uplifted by the onslaught of the Pacific Plate; the Sierran granitic batholith tilted ever closer from the east; the last of the seas retreated (about 3 million B.P.); the great rivers covered the surface with alluvium and glacial outwash brought down from the mountains; and the sediment-filled trough became the contemporary Great Central Valley depicted in map and cross-section in Figures 3.38 and 3.39. Today, the alluvial soils provide an essential

Figure 3.37 Empire Mine, Grass Valley. This northern Mother Lode mine produced nearly $1 billion worth of gold. Nearby Grass Valley lies along busy California 49; its population recently passed the 6,000 mark. (Crane Miller)

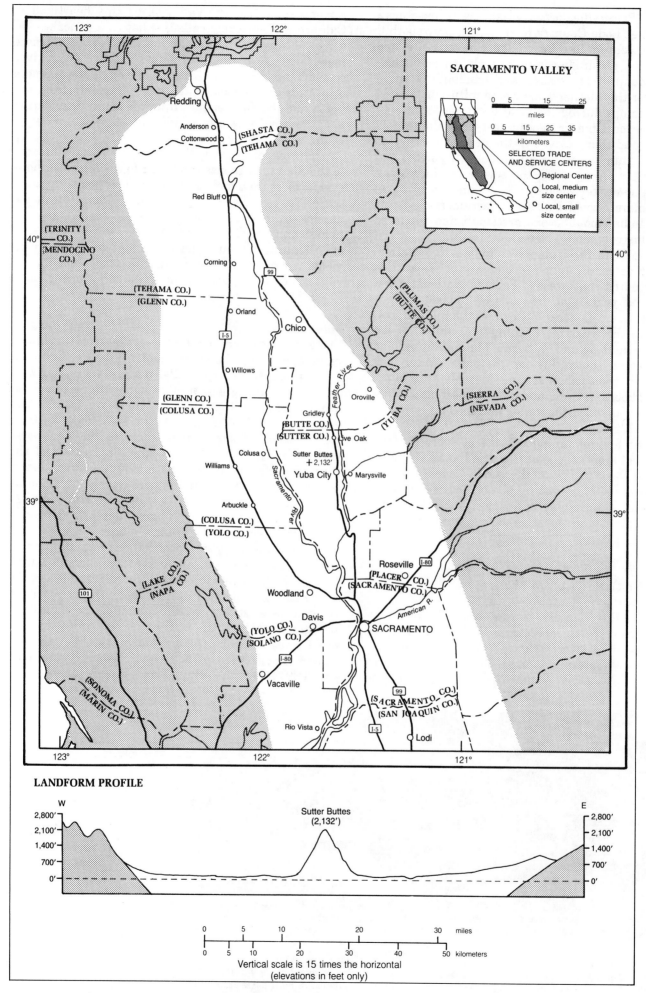

Figure 3.38 Sacramento Valley and landform profile. (Richard Crooker)

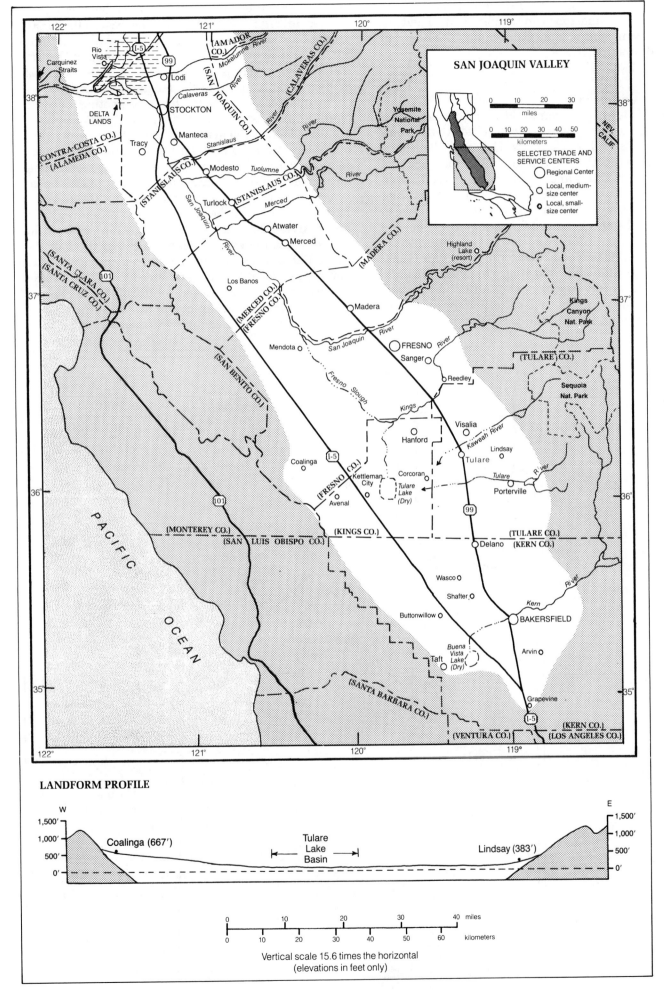

Figure 3.39 San Joaquin Valley and landform profile. (Richard Crooker)

basis for the world's most productive agriculture, and the older marine sandstones and shales yield oil and gas in amounts sufficient to keep California in the forefront of national production.

California's Cornucopia

The Great Valley is predominantly a land of prosperous, irrigated farms and large and small cities that accommodate some 3 million residents. Urban settlement is strung out mostly along California 99 in the middle of the San Joaquin Valley and the newer I-5 and California 99E on both sides of the Sacramento Valley. Away from the beaten paths, small farm towns too numerous to mention dot the checkerboard farmscape seen from the air.

The parallel and perpendicular county and state roads, fence lines, windbreaks, irrigation channels, property lines, and utility line easements are all uniformly laid out in accordance with the grid pattern of the township, range, and section lines of the U.S. Rectangular Land Survey. The 160-acre *quarter section* homestead, explained in Figure 3.40, became the basic unit for the original agricultural subdivision of the valley. At present, legal title to virtually all the farmland in the Central Valley as well as elsewhere in the state (Fig. 3.25) is identified according to the rectangular survey.

The quarter section is the basis for another, quite different form of federal regulation, namely, the 1902 statute that places a 160-acre limitation on the use of federal irrigation water. To keep farm prices from rising out of sight as well as for other reasons, quarter-section holdings have been consolidated into larger units in the last several decades throughout much of the Great Valley. This runs counter to the old law if federal Central Valley Project irrigation water is used by the larger farms. Recent interest in reviving enforcement of the long-dormant 160-acre limitation has stirred up considerable controversy, for if farmers are forced to sell their excess property and/or revert to greater use of privately owned well water, the rural character of the Great Central Valley will undoubtedly change. Furthermore, food prices

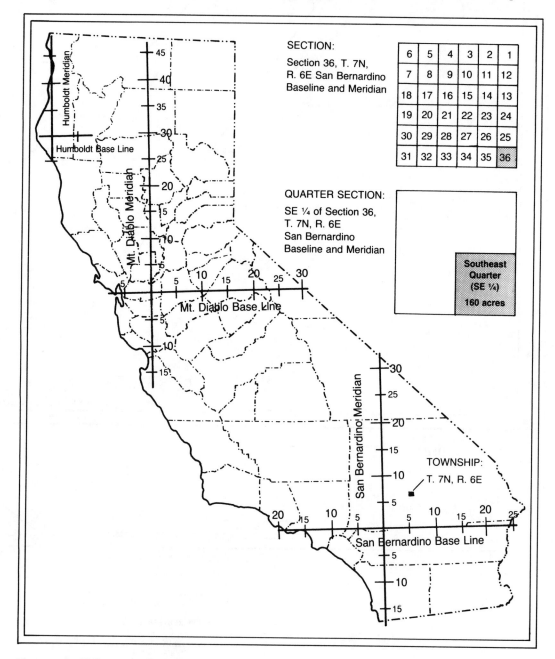

Figure 3.40 U.S. rectangular land survey. (Richard Crooker)

may climb as the economies of large-scale farm operation diminish. A fuller discussion of the Central Valley Project and the ramifications of greater groundwater use follows in Chapter 5.

The river systems, as well as the road and railroad networks, have profoundly influenced urban settlement patterns in the Great Valley. The preference for riverside sites is seen in cities from north to south in the valley: Redding and Red Bluff along the upper Sacramento River; Yuba City and Marysville opposite each other on the tributary Feather River; and Stockton on the navigable lower San Joaquin River—now including the Port of Stockton with the help of the manmade Stockton Deep Water Channel. Both the Sacramento (Fig. 3.41) and San Joaquin rivers drop only about 500 ft on their long gentle courses through the valley and thus afford countless opportunities for navigable access to the sea.

Nowhere, though, are the advantages of riverside location better displayed than at the confluence of the Sacramento and American rivers. It is here that Sacramento, with a population now approaching 275,000 within its corporate limits and 1 million in the greater metropolitan area, grew to become the Central Valley's largest city. Since its beginnings as the boat landing for Sutter's Fort (Fig. 3.42), Sacramento has enjoyed access by seagoing vessels via the Sacramento River. Navigable access to San Francisco and the Pacific, coupled with the city's juxtaposition between the Bay and the Mother Lode and selection as the state capital during the Gold Rush, gave Sacramento quick and permanent ascendancy. Barely above sea level, riverfront Sacramento suffered the ravages of seasonal flooding until levees were built.

Old Town Sacramento eventually gave way as the central business district to an area several blocks east of the river, where the capitol building and a park were built. The river likewise relinquished commercial prominence as transcontinental railroad lines came on the scene starting in the 1860s, followed by twentieth-century U.S. and interstate highways; although the river indirectly experienced revival with development of the Sacramento Deep Water Ship Channel and the Port of Sacramento (Fig. 3.43), both just west of the city and the river. Seen in Figure 3.44 as the transportation hub of California's prosperous heartland, the confluence of two great rivers, and possessing a wealth of developable land, Sacramento has earned a place of preeminence among the state's outstanding cities.

Except for Stockton, which claims third place in valley population ranking with 300,000 metropolitan area residents (including the city of Lodi), San Joaquin Valley cities have developed with little or no dependence on river transportation, although the Merced, Tuolumne, Stanislaus, and other Sierran tributaries of the San Joaquin River have figured prominently in the development of irrigation agriculture in the region. Fresno, for instance, grew up a dozen miles south of the San Joaquin River as the food processing and distribution center of the San Joaquin Valley. Its metropolitan area, which

Figure 3.41 Sacramento River and Sutter Buttes, about an hour's drive north of Sacramento. The buttes are actually volcanic plugs surrounded by tightly folded sedimentary rocks. Stratigraphic traps in the latter now yield significant amounts of natural gas. (Crane Miller)

Figure 3.42 Sutter's Fort in Sacramento was built by John Sutter during the Mexican era. The headquarters for Sutter's New Helvetia rancho, it was sought out by most new settlers to California as a place to rest and recuperate after a long, arduous trek across half the continent. (California Department of Parks and Recreation)

Figure 3.43 Port of Sacramento is the terminus of the Sacramento Deepwater Ship Channel (in the center of the aerial photo). Rice (see Chapter 11), timber products, and other goods move by boat and barge out of the port. (NASA)

includes all of Fresno County (the nation's most productive agricultural county by value), contains the Great Central Valley's second largest population, nearly half a million. Fresno's central location in its own county, the San Joaquin Valley, and the state affords it many advantages as well as agribusiness fame. The city is also prominent as a trucking, rail, and air terminal, and it is a convenient stopover and even residence for Californians who frequently travel north and south. And, as Californians who pay federal income taxes well know, Fresno is now an Internal Revenue Service Center.

The city functions as a western gateway to Kings Canyon–Sequoia (California 180) and Yosemite (California 41) national parks, China Peak and Huntington Lake (California 168), and other Sierran resort areas. Unlike Sacramento, though, Fresno has no direct access through the Sierran landform barrier to the interior Great Basin states. Fresno's Highway 99 neighbors to the north, principally Modesto with 100,000 metropolitan residents and the smaller cities of Merced (30,000) and Madera and Turlock (17,000 each) perform agribusiness, light industrial, retail, and other urban functions similar to those found in the larger city, but on a smaller scale.

None of the three counties—Kern, Kings, and Tulare—south of Fresno are naturally drained by the San Joaquin River system; rather, water spills out of the southwestern Sierra via the Kaweah, Kern, Kings, and Tule rivers into irrigation canals, groundwater basins, and basins of interior drainage. Buena Vista and Tulare lakes catch what is left of surface runoff, although some flow of the Kings River is diverted away from Tulare Lake into the San Joaquin River via the Fresno Slough. In times of excessive runoff, as in the winters of 1969 and 1978, the Kings River has surmounted manmade levees and temporarily made Tulare Lake the largest freshwater lake in the state. Though important to irrigated agriculture, these rivers were obviously never thought of as routes to the Pacific or even anywhere

closer and thus their transportation significance was nil. Nevertheless, the southern San Joaquin Valley's largest city, Bakersfield, was founded over a century ago along one of these rivers—the Kern. Here it joined with two pioneer wagon and cattle trails (from Los Angeles via Tejon Pass and from Mojave via Tehachapi Pass, both over the Tehachapi Mountains) and a railroad (also over Tehachapi Pass). The waters of the Kern, now diverted upstream into Kern River Canal, were then vital to Bakersfield's early growth as a cattle and railroad town.

Very late in the nineteenth century, the Kern River oil field began production and others in the vicinity soon began to produce, converting Bakersfield into an oil town. Agricultural development followed on the heels of petroleum discovery and the city became a service center for both industries, reaching a present-day corporate population of 80,000 and a metropolitan area population of 200,000. Other southern San Joaquin Valley cities are numerous but modest in size, with Visalia (40,000) being the largest and fastest growing.

Anyone who has ever taken the long, boring drive on I-5 knows what to expect from the west side of the San Joaquin Valley: much newly irrigated cropland, highway patrol cars, some oil fields, an aqueduct or two, a few scattered gas station–coffee shop–fast food clusters, and no cities. To some drivers, the flat land east of the highway and the low rolling hills of the Coast Ranges to the west add up to millions of acres of nothing. This lack of scenery and settlement continues up to the Delta lands, where the San Joaquin and Sacramento rivers meet.

If one leaves the dreariness of I-5 and ventures into the Delta lands, however, the sights improve: The *distributaries* (two or more rivers originating from a single river) of the two rivers have created myriad small, flat islands where truck farming takes place on reclaimed land and small boat landings serve fishermen, hunters, and water skiers. Seasonal river flooding occasionally

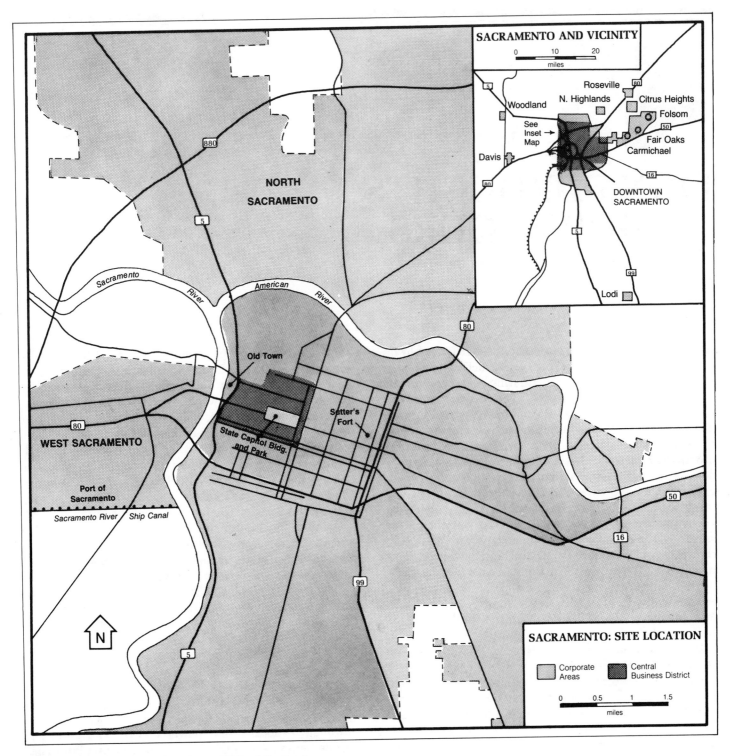

Figure 3.44 Sacramento and environs. (Richard Crooker)

causes crop and property damage and tidal bores increase ocean saltwater intrusion, but except for the narrow Carquinez Strait gap, the unique inland delta is protected by the Coast Ranges from direct exposure to the sometimes stormy Pacific.

Led in population by Rio Vista with some 3,000 inhabitants, towns in the Delta are few and small. A producing natural gas field at Rio Vista broadens the economic base of the town. Natural gas fields in the valley extend from the Delta lands northward to Sutter Buttes in the upper Sacramento Valley.

Of California's pre-1769 native population of perhaps 300,000 or more, the Yokuts of the San Joaquin Valley comprised one of the largest tribes with upwards of

15,000 members. As mentioned earlier, however, the spread of agricultural settlement all but did away with the native landscape and its people (the modification of flora and fauna and its impact on aboriginal populations will be examined in Chapter 7). By 1910, the state's total Indian population had declined to a scant 17,000 and the Yokuts to barely over 500.[4] As for the San Joaquin and Sacramento valleys, there are no extensive Indian landholdings left except for the western part of the Tule River Indian Reservation and a few rancherías.

---

[4]Today, Indians statewide number more than 100,000, but many of them are from out of California and less than 10 percent reside on reservations and rancherías.

4
FROM DROUGHTS TO DOWNPOURS

Anyone living in California during the 1970s could no doubt recall some of the many interactions among a changing climate, wildly fluctuating water resources, and an uncertain energy supply. The decade started out normally enough, with the atmosphere providing predicted amounts of precipitation each winter and clear skies during the summers. There was plenty of water for producing hydroelectricity, irrigating crops, meeting industrial and recreational demands, watering lawns and gardens, washing cars, and even filling restaurant waterglasses. Energy was cheap and seemingly abundant as hydroelectric output met about 30 percent of the state's power needs and fossil fuels took care of most of the rest. And clean-burning natural gas, what little of it was required in California's normally mild winters, heated homes, offices, factories, and classrooms ever so economically. In all, California's climate, water supply, and energy production were performing about as expected and the future appeared promising.

By mid-decade, however, California was in the throes of both a drought and an energy crisis. The outlook had turned bleak. Admittedly, the energy crisis was fashioned by international events, but the drought aggravated the problem in California. For as rivers and reservoirs dried up, so did hydroelectric production. Hydro's share of the state's total electrical energy production years ago was predicted to decline to about 10 percent by the year 2000, but certainly not to less than 5 percent as early as 1977. The unforeseen change in California's climate that caused hydro's demise could not have come at a more inopportune time: Petroleum imports and prices were skyrocketing; local reserves of natural gas were dwindling to near exhaustion; geothermal development was struggling along at a snail's pace; and advocates of coal, liquefied natural gas (LNG), and nuclear power seemed an eternity away from resolving their differences with environmentalists.

To make matters worse, the drought threatened to ruin California's number one industry—agriculture—as well as to seriously debilitate most nonagricultural enterprise. Even the best-laid schemes of water resource experts offered little solace as communities resorted to importing water by truck when municipal reserves disappeared and the 400-mile California Aqueduct ceased carrying the precious liquid from a once water-surplus Northern to a usually water-deficit Southern California. As the drought wore on, California's legendary self-contained water resources seemed precisely that.

But in the winters of 1978 and 1979, rain miraculously returned to the state and in unprecedented amounts. Almost as if to compensate for earlier shortcomings, weather conditions had once again radically changed during the decade. The hydro picture brightened, water rationing ended, and the skiing industry revived. The record Sierra snowpack assured Californians that water would be available for a while and residents once again returned to their former profligate use of the resource.[1]

Meanwhile, California's most abundant climatic resource—sunshine—came into sharper focus in the 1970s as an alternative energy source. Collecting solar energy for water and space heating was nothing new to some California homeowners, but by the end of the decade ways of directly converting the sun's energy into electricity by *photovoltaic* and other means for mass distribution seemed closer at hand. What better place is there in the nation than California's sun-drenched deserts, after all, to locate solar power plants? And an energy fringe benefit exists in the atmospheric circulation patterns of the deserts as wind power.

Hopefully, solar and wind power technologies will evolve to the point of competing commercially with coal and nuclear developments as the principal surrogates for oil, gas, and hydro energy sources. Together, these last three now meet some 65 percent of the state's power needs but are projected to provide only 20 percent by the end of the century. Given a rapidly changing energy picture, an environment long plagued by air pollution, a warm and sunny climate, a population outnumbering that of any other single state by millions, and an increasingly automated way of life, it is abundantly clear

---

[1]Here it is pertinent to note that a short animated film titled "Water Follies: A Soak Opera," was produced by the City of Denver (Colorado) Water Department. It is suitable for all ages and gets the water conservation message across in a unique yet effective way.

that California must make haste to develop its unique solar energy resource to the fullest potential.

THE LURE OF MILD CLIMATE

Placed against this mixed backdrop, the traditional lure of the Golden State has relied not upon availability of water and energy, but rather upon the irresistible draw of mild climate and a romantically embellished image. As Chapter 1 detailed, the romance of California has been promoted by many people for many reasons. A persistent element of this mystique, however, has remained in the notion of "forever summer" weather. Rightly or wrongly, it has provided a consistent measure of value for the immigrant to this state.

The Legacy of Horace Greeley

When Horace Greeley issued the now-famous dictum "Go west, young man, go west," he could not have hit upon a more appropriate theme for California.[2] In addition to economics and adventure, however, climate proved to be a dominating motive drawing tourists and immigrants to the state, and especially to the southern portion. To a native of upstate New York or Minnesota, the weather was a source of amazement and delight, producing a sense of wonder that was conveyed in letters, books, advertisements, and lectures. Some went so far as to proclaim marvelous cures for all ailments that would soon accrue to the pilgrim if he or she would but bask in the climate of the state.

Thus, by the early 1900s, Southern California had acquired a reputation as Shangri La and paradise on earth for the infirm, invalid, and afflicted. As Carey McWilliams recalled, the classic, if somewhat cynical, motto of the times became: "We sold them the climate and threw in the land." This draw of climate and claims of health benefits constituted one element of the westward appeal of California to the rest of the nation. More than health considerations alone drew many immigrants to the state, however.

Midwestern Graffiti

Various scholars and observers have concluded that Southern California generally owes its particular ambience to the dominant influence of displaced Midwesterners. Indeed, as early as the 1930s, a popular saying identified Southern California as the western seacoast of Iowa. The saying might well have substituted Illinois, Ohio, Nebraska, or any other of the Middle Western states, since the number of native-born Californians seldom accounted for a very large percentage of the total compared to such immigration sources. Annual Iowa-day picnics or Ohio-day reunions were common occurrences in the state, providing these former Buckeyes and

Hoosiers, Hawkeyes and Boomers an opportunity to swap reminiscences of life back on the prairie. Such reunions became less common after the late 1950s. If the picnics declined, however, the immigration patterns certainly continued.

An interesting cultural effect derives from the fact that this migration has been rather constant. The continual flow of new residents into the state has created a layered form of cultural identity wherein the newcomers strive to develop characteristics which may be attributed to the "California personality," but in the process create an overall sense of never-ending growth and development with a Midwestern twang.

The Grapes of Wrath

California's role as a key agricultural state has also contributed to its steady appeal. Frequently, when poor weather or economic conditions created untenable situations in other parts of the country, California came to be viewed as an escape—a sunny, Mediterraneanlike setting where food could at least be grown most of the year and the earth and sky would be gentle in the meantime. Having lived through brutal winter blizzards or scorching dust storms, was it any wonder that immigrants to the area saw a chance for improvement of their lives? The exaggerations of the fecundity of the soil and climate were misleading and often extreme, but there was just enough truth in the myths to encourage people to continue to see California as the answer to unrealized dreams. Steinbeck's *Grapes of Wrath* (movie and book) partially questioned the popular image of California, but for the most part the seekers of dreams persisted in chasing their dreams to the West. In fact, the trend of American immigration into California had a curious twist.

Initially seen as a resort for the rich, increasingly the state came to be considered a land of opportunity also for the less affluent—an image promoted by land companies, railroads, and others. Throughout the early 1900s, this in-migration occurred at a respectable rate, with occasional swells in the level of movement. The Depression years, for example, brought well over 350,-000 persons across the country in old cars and trucks. As time progressed, the lure of California expanded to include working-class people from such diverse places as Ontario and other parts of Canada, West Texas, New York, and Oklahoma. Much of this continual flow, however, could still be traced to the small towns and farms that looked to California as an enchanted land where orange and palm trees grew in abundance and even country folk could share in some of the magic.

The Resort Mentality: A Place in the Sun

California as a new home and destination for permanent residence is one of the realities that has influenced the culture of the state. There is another facet to the lure of mild climate, however. With its ideal and varied weather, myriad tourist attractions, and wealth of geographic wonders, California has also been a prime setting for those who wish to escape the harsher climate of their native areas for a short time only.

[2]Greeley borrowed the phrase from J. B. L. Soule, who had first published that advice in the *Terre Haute Express* in 1851. Due to Greeley's greater prominence, however, his restatements of this advice became better known and credited, especially since he was able to publish it through the pages of the *New York Tribune*. Thus, Greeley is more widely credited with this directive than is Soule.

Many parts of the state have catered to a transitory population by providing the atmosphere, amusements, and diversion sought by this clientele. Palm Springs is widely known for its winter appeal; San Diego has created a tourist haven of hotels, aquatic and wildlife parks, commercialized beaches, and golf courses; San Francisco is a mecca for visitors with its well-known Chinatown, Fisherman's Wharf, and Golden Gate Park; Lake Tahoe is a tremendous draw; and the growth of time-shared condominiums at the seashore and on the ski slopes has brought a new meaning to the term "resort community" in California.

The continuing appeal of the state as a goal for migration or recreation persists. Such influence is clearly not a one-way phenomenon, however. With ever-increasing demands on its resources, power, and environment, the people of the state face the challenge of living with and understanding the limits as well as the abundance of nature. They must learn to understand and utilize the regions and elements of the climatic system.

CLIMATES, MICROCLIMATES, AND CONTROLS

California is commonly spoken of as having a Mediterranean climate. This reputation, which has lured millions of people to California, holds true only for the relatively small coastal portion of the state where most of these millions have settled. Examined closely, California can be seen to have innumerable climates, varying from dry summer-subtropical and alpine-arctic *macroclimates* to highly localized *microclimates,* such as those found deep in a forested valley or high up on a north-facing mountain slope.

To add still more variety, California's climates have seasons—contrary to the belief of many outsiders—and they are not all "seasons in the sun." Indeed, every summer the northwest coast is fogbound and cool while the interior deserts, despite frequent thundershowers, swelter in the continent's hottest temperatures. Winters offer equally stark contrasts, with the Sierras and Klamaths often buried by record snowfalls while the lowlands never see snow. Spring and fall have their extremes as well, when a hot, dry Santa Ana blows through the Los Angeles Basin on the same day that tule fog paralyzes the San Joaquin Valley.

Although Figure 4.1 depicts six climate zones (arid, semiarid, warm summer–Mediterranean, cool summer–Mediterranean, highland, and alpine), the true detail of California's climates and microclimates cannot be adequately described in a one-page map. Thus, a more localized look at the state's climatic diversity is presented here in terms of the geographic features that control it. These *climate controls* include altitude, latitude, oceanic influences, air pressure systems, and winds.

Altitude and Air Masses

Whenever air changes altitude, it changes temperature. This in turn causes a change in the temporary state of the atmosphere, or what we call the "weather," climate being the long-term condition of the atmosphere at a particular location. Remembering that air has weight and therefore exerts *air pressure,* consider that as an air mass rises, the pressure upon it lessens and the air expands and cools. If an air mass loses altitude, on the other hand, the pressure around increases and the air compresses and consequently heats up. The *air mass* we speak of may be *maritime polar* air (mP) from the Gulf of Alaska or *continental polar* air (cP) from Canada or *maritime tropical* air (mT) from the Pacific. Whatever its source, the incoming air will be forced to rise as it encounters California's mountainous terrain and mountain-caused or *orographic lifting* (Fig. 4.2) will take place. *Frontal lifting* (Fig. 4.3), where lighter, warmer air is forced up and over heavier, colder air, and *convectional lifting* (Fig. 4.4), where warm surfaces (usually deserts) radiate heat up into a cooler atmosphere, also cause air mass ascent. The latter two are more common in states with less varied topography than California's.

The temperature changes resulting from lifting occur without any infusion or subtraction of heat from the air mass and are termed *adiabatic.* When unsaturated or "dry" air (actually in a *vapor* state) ascends or descends, it changes temperatures at a *dry adiabatic rate* (DAR) of 10° C per km or 1,000 m (5.5° F per 1,000 ft). Once rising air has cooled to its *dew point* (temperature at which the air begins to *condense* or convert from a vapor to a liquid state) it will continue to cool at a reduced *wet adiabatic rate* (WAR) of about 3° C/km (3.2° F/1,000 ft), assuming further ascent.[3]

Condensation causes the formation of water droplets, which in turn accumulate to form clouds. Exhaling in chilly air produces the same effect; the moist breath is rapidly lowered in temperature by the cold air to its dew point and forms a cloud for an instant. Of course, the cloud produced by a human breath *evaporates* (from a liquid to a vapor state) almost as quickly as it formed.

The water droplets in the atmospheric cloud, however, may continue to grow and become heavy enough to fall to earth or *precipitate.* If the dew point of the air mass is above freezing, the precipitation will be in the form of rain; if it is at or below 0° C, the cloud will precipitate snow. Cloud formation or condensation generally precedes precipitation, but the two can occur simultaneously.

Condensation also releases *latent heat of condensation* in the air mass, causing the slowdown of adiabatic cooling from the DAR to the WAR. Eventually the air mass will begin a descent throughout which it will heat by compression at the DAR. Figure 4.5 illustrates these adiabatic processes at work as a winter storm tracks eastward over the Coast Ranges, Central Valley, Sierra

---

[3]Although television, radio, newspapers, and other media still widely use the Fahrenheit (F) system of measurement, the metric Celsius or Centigrade (C) temperature scale is gaining favor, and the reader should be familiar with its use in studying climate. Thus, the Celsius scale is employed in this section, in Figure 4.2, and occasionally elsewhere in Chapter 4. Formulas for converting from one scale to the other are:

From °F to °C: °C = 5/9 (°F − 32°)
From °C to °F: °F = 9/5°C + 32°

The most used distance and area conversion equivalents are: 1 km = .62 mi, 1 mi = 1.61 km, 1 m = 3.28 ft, 1 cm = .39 in, 1 in = 2.54 cm, 1 sq km = .386 sq mi, and 1 sq mi = 2.59 sq km. The Federal Metric Conversion Act of 1975 calls for conversion to the metric system; but there is no mandatory deadline, so it may be a while yet before California "metrifies."

Nevada, and Great Basin. The significance of the Sierra Nevada as a producer of *orographic precipitation* is evident from a comparison of the annual windward and leeward precipitation data given in Figure 4.5. Figure 4.6 also shows rain shadow conditions stemming from leeward descent of air masses.

Mountains exert an extremely localized influence on precipitation wherever they abruptly border a broad lowland or a large valley. For instance, Mount Wilson at an elevation of 5,709 ft receives an average of 36 inches precipitation annually, whereas at the base of the mountain and just a few hundred feet above sea level, Pasadena gets less than half that amount each year. Both places receive almost all of their precipitation in winter; at Mount Wilson, however, it often falls as snow, whereas in Pasadena and throughout the Los Angeles Basin it is almost always as rain. Obviously, temperature differences are caused by elevation differences and they also account for differences in the forms of precipitation emanating from a particular winter storm. It would be grossly misleading to say that it never snows in Southern California, but it would be close to climatic fact to state that it never snows in the Los Angeles Basin. Seven million people who live in the basin like the idea of no snow in their backyard but still available less than an hour's drive away.

Latitude and West Coasts

California's latitude of from 32.5° to 42° north (N) and its position on the western coast of the continent place it in a unique climatic position in North America. Throughout the earth's continents, wherever there is a west coast between about 30° to 40° N or S there will also be found a Mediterranean climate. This dry summer–wet winter climate occurs in only two relatively small regions of the Northern Hemisphere: here in California and in the southern European and North African lands peripheral to its namesake, the Mediterranean Sea. There are four even smaller and more widely scattered Mediterranean climate areas south of the equator in Chile, South Africa around Capetown, and Australia in the Adelaide and Perth regions.

In all, Mediterranean climates, including California, occupy only a scant 2 percent of the world's land surface. It is noteworthy, too, that no such mild climate exists between 30° and 40° latitude on the east coasts of any of the continents, including North America. Why this type of climate exists solely on west coasts will be explained in the sections on oceanic influences and pressure and winds.

A latitudinal range of nearly 10 degrees, coupled with a mountainous topography, carries California through a gamut of subtropical and mid-latitude climates and local variations. For example, coastal locations near the 42nd parallel (Oregon border) are overcast most of the year, receive winter rainfall approaching 100 inches, and seemingly never experience heat or cold waves (Fig. 4.7). On the other hand, the San Diego metropolitan seashore area, at about 33° N, has clear days more than half of the year, less than a dozen inches of winter rain, and an occasional hot spell. San Diego experiences the drier climate largely because it lies well to the south of the main

Pacific winter storm track while the northwest coast is usually right in the midst of it.

In the middle of the coastline, at about 38° N, is the San Francisco Bay region, which experiences moderate winter precipitation and pleasant year-round temperature conditions. But the Bay Area also has microclimates that vary from foggy to dry because of the presence of several mountain ranges, a huge bay, and a large river. The general pattern from the southern to the northern end of the state is one of progressively wetter and cooler climates, with the Bay Area striking a happy medium between the extremes.

California's great latitudinal range also allows for some regional modification of the generally pervasive dry warm season–wet cool season precipitation regime. The exception to the rule is the desert southeast, where meager annual precipitation tends to be concentrated in summer rather than winter. Tropical air masses from as far away as the Gulf of Mexico and the southeastern Pacific bring in the summer moisture. Because they usually track considerable distances over land, these tropical air masses usually drop most of their moisture long before crossing the Colorado River or the Mexican border into California. There is usually enough unspent moisture in them, however, to be convected (by the rising desert surface heat) and condensed into towering cumulus clouds. The thunderheads in turn often produce thundershowers that are sometimes locally heavy enough to cause destructive *flash flooding*.

On occasion, which is usually only once in three or four years and then in August or early September, a *chubasco* will come into southeastern California from the Pacific and the Gulf of California with the force of a hurricane. Such storms have been particularly devastating in the Imperial and lower Colorado River valleys, where they take lives, destroy crops, and wash away roads and bridges. *Sonoras*, named after the Mexican state over which they travel, track in from more southeasterly directions and more distant origins but can be as destructive as chubascos. Besides high winds, these storms bring short but often drenching rains that can lead to flash flooding.

Oceanic Influences

More than any other single climatic control, the Pacific Ocean can be said to keep the California coast cool, but not cold, throughout the year. The marine air is cooled by one of the world's major cool ocean currents, the 400-mile wide California Current, which taps the cold waters of the Arctic Ocean, Bering Sea, and Gulf of Alaska. Ocean currents, like the California, are among the great exchangers of heat and cold between the tropical and polar latitudes and are essential in sustaining *heat balances* in the global environment. In the case of California, the current literally imports coolness from colder climates and keeps coastal California from getting too hot.

Ocean currents result from a number of phenomena. They are set in motion by prevailing surface winds—the westerlies, in the case of California. The moving air pushes and pulls (drags) the surface water of the currents. Differences in the *density* (or weight) of water will

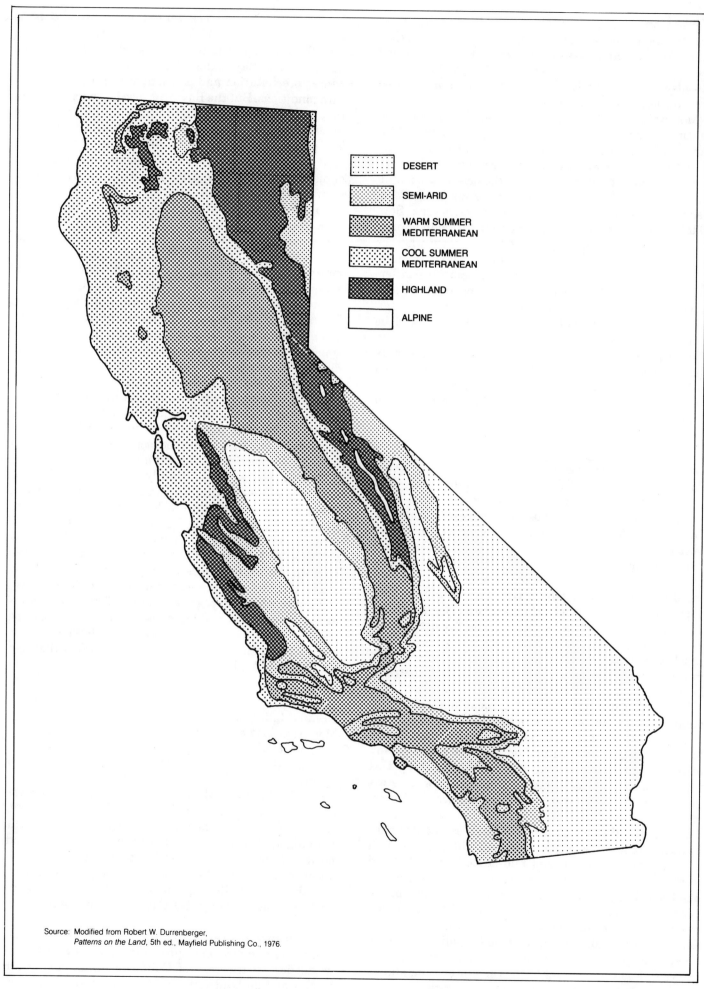

DESERT

SEMI-ARID

WARM SUMMER
MEDITERRANEAN

COOL SUMMER
MEDITERRANEAN

HIGHLAND

ALPINE

Source: Modified from Robert W. Durrenberger,
Patterns on the Land, 5th ed., Mayfield Publishing Co., 1976.

Figure 4.1 California climates. (Richard Crooker)

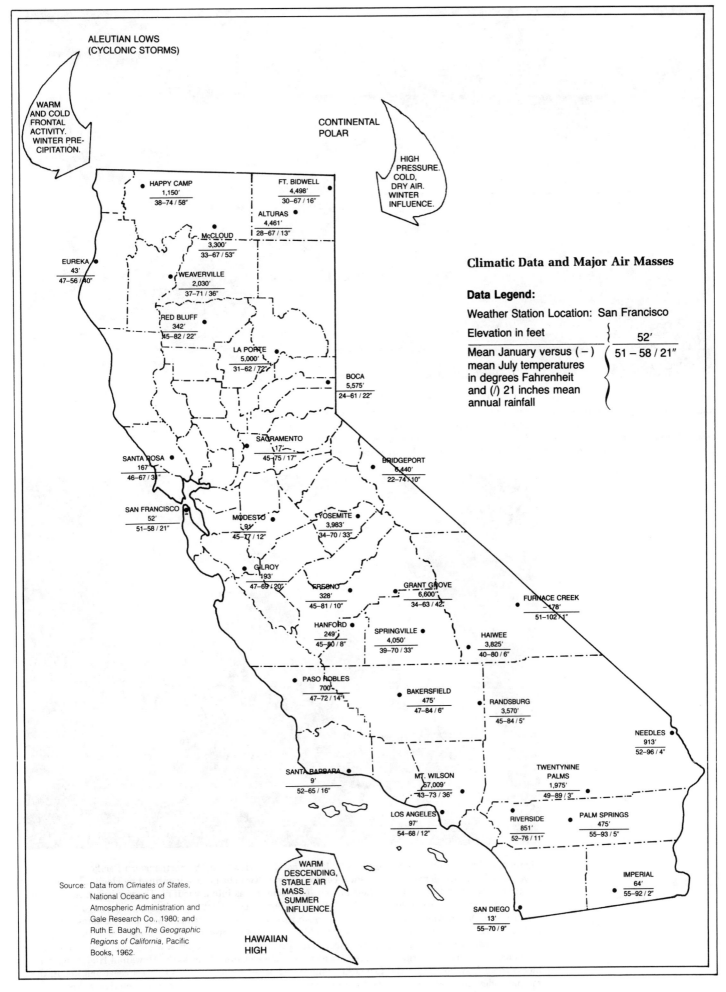

ALEUTIAN LOWS
(CYCLONIC STORMS)

WARM
AND COLD
FRONTAL
ACTIVITY.
WINTER PRE-
CIPITATION.

CONTINENTAL
POLAR

HIGH
PRESSURE.
COLD,
DRY AIR.
WINTER
INFLUENCE.

Climatic Data and Major Air Masses

Data Legend:

Weather Station Location: San Francisco

Elevation in feet — 52'

Mean January versus (−) mean July temperatures in degrees Fahrenheit and (/) 21 inches mean annual rainfall — 51 − 58 / 21"

HAPPY CAMP 1,150' 38–74 / 58"
FT. BIDWELL 4,498' 30–67 / 16"
ALTURAS 4,461' 28–67 / 13"
McCLOUD 3,300' 33–67 / 53"
WEAVERVILLE 2,030' 37–71 / 36"
EUREKA 43' 47–56 / 40"
RED BLUFF 342' 45–82 / 22"
LA PORTE 5,000' 31–62 / 72"
BOCA 5,575' 24–61 / 22"
SACRAMENTO 17' 45–75 / 17"
SANTA ROSA 167' 46–67 / 31"
BRIDGEPORT 6,440' 22–74 / 10"
SAN FRANCISCO 52' 51–58 / 21"
MODESTO 9' 45–77 / 12"
YOSEMITE 3,983' 34–70 / 33"
GILROY 193' 47–69 / 20"
FRESNO 328' 45–81 / 10"
GRANT GROVE 6,600' 34–63 / 42"
FURNACE CREEK −178' 51–102 / 1"
HANFORD 249' 45–90 / 8"
SPRINGVILLE 4,050' 39–70 / 33"
HAIWEE 3,825' 40–80 / 6"
PASO ROBLES 700' 47–72 / 14"
BAKERSFIELD 475' 47–84 / 6"
RANDSBURG 3,570' 45–84 / 5"
NEEDLES 913' 52–96 / 4"
SANTA BARBARA 9' 52–65 / 16"
MT. WILSON 57,009' 43–73 / 36"
TWENTYNINE PALMS 1,975' 49–89 / 3"
LOS ANGELES 97' 54–68 / 12"
RIVERSIDE 851' 52–76 / 11"
PALM SPRINGS 475' 55–93 / 5"
IMPERIAL 64' 55–92 / 2"
SAN DIEGO 13' 55–70 / 9"

WARM DESCENDING, STABLE AIR MASS. SUMMER INFLUENCE.

HAWAIIAN HIGH

Source: Data from *Climates of States*, National Oceanic and Atmospheric Administration and Gale Research Co., 1980; and Ruth E. Baugh, *The Geographic Regions of California*, Pacific Books, 1962.

Figure 4.1 *continued*

Figure 4.2 Orographic lifting over the White Mountains in eastern Mono County near the Nevada state line. Orographic precipitation can be seen occurring here on the western flanks of White Mountain (14,246 ft) and other peaks of elevations higher than 12,000 ft as a moisture-laden air mass moves from west to east (left to right) and must rise over the mountains. Note the increase in clouds and rainfall eastward as the air mass rises, cools, and condenses. Figure 4.5 diagrams the orographic process. (Crane Miller)

Figure 4.3 Frontal lifting over the Pacific. In the satellite view over the northeastern Pacific (the clouds have parted over California and the snow-covered Sierra), two storms are identified by clouds swirling counterclockwise and inward into their low pressure centers, as into a vacuum. The northernmost cyclone is associated with the Aleutian Low (Fig. 4.9), which pumps out moist, cold air masses destined for the west coast of North America. Westerly winds push the storms southeastward, with many coming onshore in California in a normal winter. When such cold air invades an area of warm air and forces the warmer air to rise, cool, condense, and perhaps precipitate, a *cold front* occurs. Such a winter cold front (and the attendant wind-driven storm surf) intensify as they come onshore. Because the Hawaiian High (Fig. 4.9) blocks them from entry into California in summer and because the state is on a west coast and lies in the mid-latitudes, tropical *warm fronts,* where warm air invades zones of colder air, are relatively rare occurrences. (NASA)

Figure 4.4 Convectional lifting occurs where a land surface is being intensely heated, such as in a desert in summer, and warm, relatively light air rises into an upper layer of moist, unstable air. The rising air *adiabatically* (by expanding) cools to its dew point temperature (Fig. 4.5), condenses, and often precipitates violently. Cloudbursts, sometimes causing flash floods, are most common in the southeastern deserts in summer. In both of these summer views, one (A) of the Owens Valley with Mount Whitney (14,495 ft) in the background and the other (B) of interior Los Angeles County, tropical moist air from the south has condensed into towering cumulus thunderheads. (Crane Miller)

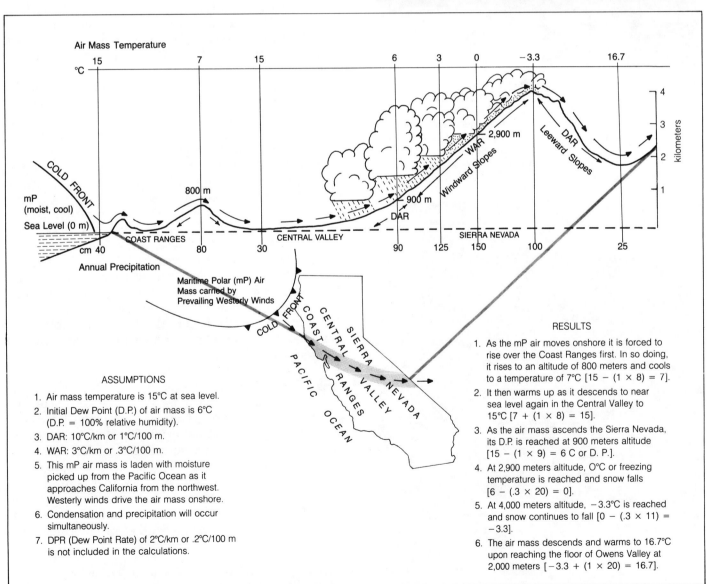

ASSUMPTIONS

1. Air mass temperature is 15°C at sea level.
2. Initial Dew Point (D.P.) of air mass is 6°C (D.P. = 100% relative humidity).
3. DAR: 10°C/km or 1°C/100 m.
4. WAR: 3°C/km or .3°C/100 m.
5. This mP air mass is laden with moisture picked up from the Pacific Ocean as it approaches California from the northwest. Westerly winds drive the air mass onshore.
6. Condensation and precipitation will occur simultaneously.
7. DPR (Dew Point Rate) of 2°C/km or .2°C/100 m is not included in the calculations.

RESULTS

1. As the mP air moves onshore it is forced to rise over the Coast Ranges first. In so doing, it rises to an altitude of 800 meters and cools to a temperature of 7°C [15 − (1 × 8) = 7].
2. It then warms up as it descends to near sea level again in the Central Valley to 15°C [7 + (1 × 8) = 15].
3. As the air mass ascends the Sierra Nevada, its D.P. is reached at 900 meters altitude [15 − (1 × 9) = 6 C or D. P.].
4. At 2,900 meters altitude, 0°C or freezing temperature is reached and snow falls [6 − (.3 × 20) = 0].
5. At 4,000 meters altitude, −3.3°C is reached and snow continues to fall [0 − (.3 × 11) = −3.3].
6. The air mass descends and warms to 16.7°C upon reaching the floor of Owens Valley at 2,000 meters [−3.3 + (1 × 20) = 16.7].

Figure 4.5 Orographic lifting and adiabatic processes. (Richard Crooker)

Figure 4.6 Rain shadow conditions on the leeward slopes of the eastern Sierra Nevada. Here sage, rabbitbrush, and other high desert scrub are found at the 6,500-ft elevation, whereas at the same elevation on the windward slopes of the Sierra there are rich coniferous forests. Also as seen here, clouds often stop forming once an air mass begins its leeward descent because: (1) descending air warms by compression, and (2) most of an air mass's moisture has precipitated in its windward ascent. (Crane Miller)

also cause it to move in currents, as when colder, heavier polar seawater sinks to the ocean floor, spreads equatorward, and displaces warmer, lighter tropical water. *Coriolis force,* which on a counterclockwise rotating earth involves the tendency of objects, winds, and ocean currents to veer to the right of their path of movement in the Northern Hemisphere, also contributes to the motion and direction of the currents.

Along continental west coasts like California's, winds and coriolis force often combine to displace surface water seaward from a southeastward-flowing current. Colder water from the depths then moves up to the surface to replace the removed water in a process known as *upwelling.* The colder surface water in turn may drop the temperature of the air above it to its dew point and condensation may take place in the form of fog. Whenever northwesterly winds (blowing toward the land) prevail, which is off central and Southern California in late spring and along the northern coast throughout summer, fog is carried onshore.

It is noteworthy that upwelling sustains a significant nonclimatic resource for California as well: its ocean fishery. Upwelling brings nutrients from the cold depths of the sea to the surface where they are vital to the growth of *phytoplankton* (microscopic plants) and *kelp* (seaweed). The sea plants are the foundation of a marine *food chain* which involves the phytoplankton being eaten by small fish and they in turn being consumed by larger fish.

Marine air buildup is sometimes amplified by an abrupt change in the coastline's shape or directional orientation, such as south of Point Conception in the Catalina embayment. Here the conformation of the coastline and islands cause a counterclockwise swirl or *eddy* within the main air currents. This Catalina Eddy can deepen the fog layer to several thousand feet and cause drizzle in the Los Angeles Basin in the normally dry months of May and June. Water-filled gaps in coastal landforms, such as the Golden Gate and Carquinez Strait in the central Coast Ranges, allow marine air (sea breezes) to penetrate deep into the interior. Sacramento and Stockton, for example, benefit from their positions downwind from Carquinez Strait by enjoying somewhat cooler summers than cities elsewhere in the Great Central Valley. Overall, though, the coastal mountain barrier prevents marine influences from affecting the climates of interior California.

The surface waters of the California Current generally range from 50° to 70° F throughout the year and, although never icy cold, they never seem warm enough to satisfy the swimmer who has experienced the 85° waters of Hawaii or Florida. The surfer (Fig. 4.8), on the other hand, commonly wears a wet suit and couldn't care less about water temperature as long as the waves are right. For either person, the best beach weather is in August, when both air and water temperature hover around 70° F and the late spring fogs have long since gone their way, at least from along the Southern California coast.

Figure 4.7 Heavy rainfall and moderate temperatures make Redwood National Park along the northern coast a lush habitat of giant trees and ferns. (National Park Service, photo by Richard Frear)

Figure 4.8 Surfing in Santa Monica. Storm surf, the surfer's delight, results from storms either far at sea or coming onshore locally. Wind speed, duration, direction, and *fetch* (areal extent of water body) generally determine wave size, except where tidal waves (from tides, not earthquakes) or *tsunamis* (from earthquakes, not tides) are involved. Waves generated by sea-floor earthquakes are also referred to as seismic sea waves. (National Park Service, photo by Richard Frear)

The fact that the warmest weather starts about six weeks after the first day of summer (June 21 or the *summer solstice*) is explained by the relatively long *seasonal temperature lag* produced by the Pacific Ocean: It takes large bodies of water much longer to absorb the sun's heat energy (*shortwave solar radiation*) and reradiate it (*longwave earth* or *terrestrial radiation*) than it does dry land surfaces. Consequently, this time lag is somewhat longer along the coast than inland from the sea, where maximum temperatures are reached only about four weeks after the maximum high sun date of June 21 in the Northern Hemisphere.

The same lag occurs in winter, but in reverse, when maximum loss of earth radiation and thus the coldest temperatures occur in late January, or about a month after the low sun *winter solstice* of December 21. Most of us are probably more familiar with *daily temperature lag*, when the warmest part of the day is at about 2 p.m., or a couple of hours after the sun has reached its highest angle in the sky at high noon. The principles of radiation not only govern the weather but are the key to understanding solar energy, a subject that will be explored in Chapter 6.

Air Pressure and Winds

Air exerts an average pressure of 14.7 pounds per square inch at sea level. An atmospheric physicist would refer to this air pressure as 1 atmosphere (atm); a meteorologist would say it is the equivalent either of 29.92 inches of mercury or 1,013.2 millibars (mb). But air pressure varies from place to place with changes in temperature, altitude, and other atmospheric conditions. For instance,

sea level air pressure will usually vary from *low pressure* of 980 mb to *high pressure* of about 1,040 mb, depending on differences in air temperature. Along the equator, where temperatures are relatively high, the surface air is made lighter with warming and therefore rises, creating a zone of *equatorial low* pressure. As the air ascends, it cools off; as it becomes colder, it also becomes heavier. Once the air reaches higher altitudes, the atmosphere acts as a heat exchanger (much as ocean currents do in maintaining global heat balance) by forcing the tropical air poleward about 30°, where its heaviness causes it to sink down into regions of *subtropical high pressure*. In the Pacific between Hawaii and California (Fig. 4.9), the mass of descending air is known as the *Hawaiian High*. And it is this clockwise-swirling *high pressure cell* that takes precedence over any of the controls heretofore mentioned in determining California's climates.

Because the subsiding air of high pressure cells (circular-shaped, spinning outward) and *ridges* (air masses that are more elongated in shape) warms by compression and thus in a sense dries out, such high pressure systems are associated with clear, stormless weather. When high pressure hovers over an area for several months every year, such as the northeastern edge of the Hawaiian High does over California every summer and sometimes longer, mild climate prevails. In fall, the Hawaiian High usually begins to weaken and move away from California as it follows the sun southward—the Hawaiian High is normally strongest during the summer, when the sun is high, and weakest in the winter, when the sun is low. As winter approaches, the retreating ridge dissipates to the point of allowing low pressure cells (circular-shaped,

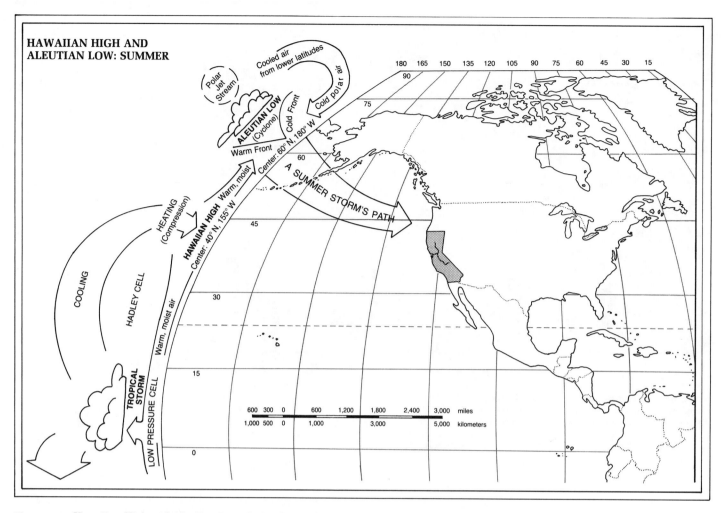

Figure 4.9 Hawaiian High and Aleutian Low. (Richard Crooker)

spinning inward) and *troughs* (more elongated in shape) to migrate into California. These systems of rising, condensing air usually bring rain if they originate in the central Pacific as mT air masses, or rain and snow if they are pumped out of the *Aleutian Low* (Figs. 4.3 and 4.9) as mP air masses. By spring, the Hawaiian High starts to reestablish itself in the North Pacific and in so doing pushes the storm tracks northward of California.

In some winters, the Hawaiian High happens not to leave the state's shores and as a consequence California suffers through a drought. During the unusually dry winters of 1975 and 1976, the Hawaiian High not only did not weaken as expected, but it teamed up with a continental high pressure cell. Together the two cells became a *blocking high,* rerouting Pacific-born storms far to the north and east of the western United States. The results were record snows back East and drought out West. But no sooner had the state begun to prepare for prolonged drought than the Hawaiian High again changed its movements, allowing countless storms accompanied by record precipitation to hit California in the waning winters of the decade.

The behavior of the Hawaiian High is difficult to predict, let alone explain. But if some answers can be found—for example, through further study of the relationship of sunspot activity to changes in atmospheric pressure—we will be closer to more accurate prediction of long-term climatic change as well as better forecasting of day-to-day weather.

Differences in air pressure from one place to another—as, say, from the Hawaiian High at 1,030 mb in the Pacific Ocean to a thermal low at 990 mb over the Great Basin—provide the basis for the horizontal surface circulation of air or winds. In the previous example, the sinking air of the ocean high is spreading out towards the heated, rising air of a desert thermal low. The low pressure cell acts like a vacuum as it pulls air counterclockwise (in the Northern Hemisphere) into its center. The resultant wind, however, does not flow in a straight line directly from high to low but instead moves roughly parallel to *isobars* (lines of equal barometric pressure such as that at 1,030 mb) because of coriolis force's counterbalancing of the *pressure gradient.* California's prevailing resultant winds, the *westerlies* (winds are named after the direction from which they come), emanate throughout most of the year from the dry northeast side of the Hawaiian High.

The Hawaiian High and its westerly winds are augmented in their effort to keep coastal California mild by the *sea breeze.* The sea breeze is especially welcome in summer, when it is often strong enough to penetrate well inland. A typical summer day will start out with the land heating up more rapidly than the ocean. A heat or thermal low deepens over the land while high pressure builds over the water. The cool California Current and subsiding Hawaiian High increase ocean air pressure all the more; by mid-morning, the sea breeze is beginning to flow *onshore,* as illustrated in Figure 4.10. At night,

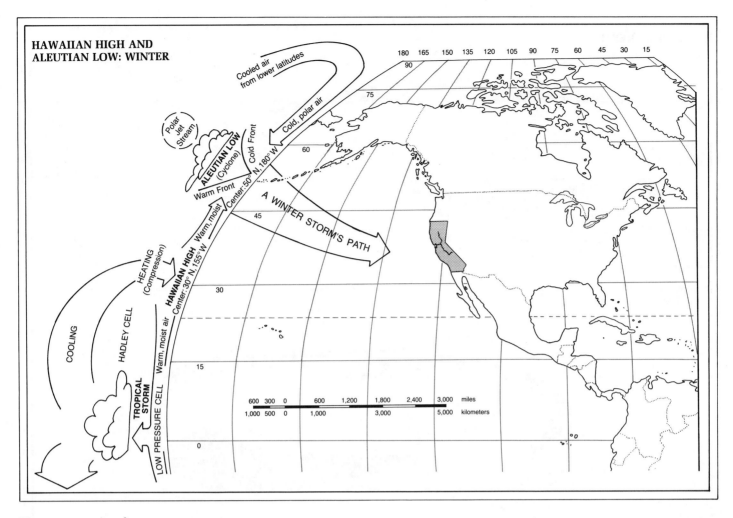

Figure 4.9 *continued*

the local pressure cells reverse position as the land cools off at a faster rate than the sea. The *offshore* flow is known as a *land breeze.*

The most significant deviation from the prevailing westerly wind and sea breeze circulation pattern occurs with the advent of the *Santa Ana,* a hot, dessicating *easterly* wind that sweeps down from the high deserts of the Great Basin into the Southern California coastal lowlands. Although Santa Anas can happen any time of the year, they are most common during fall, when the Great Basin begins cooling off and the Hawaiian High starts to lose its strength. These seasonal atmospheric changes allow high pressure to build in the dry western interior of the continent and low pressure to deepen offshore. Local mountainous terrain also plays a major role in bringing the Santa Anas to the South Coast. The east-west orientation of the Transverse Ranges and the passes through and between these and the Peninsular Ranges literally let the Santa Anas into the lowlands, which are open to the sea. Beside flowing from higher to lower pressure, the winds also lose about 4,000 ft in altitude on their way to the sea. This means downslope compressional heating at the DAR, as exemplified in Figure 4.11. It is typical during an autumn Santa Ana for beach city temperatures to be in the nineties while desert locales are in the seventies. In winter, colder Santa Ana-like winds usually follow the passage of storm fronts, but they occur anywhere in the state where high pressure ridges in behind departing low pressure.

Southern Californians regard the Santa Ana as anything from an ill wind to a dissipater of smog. Relative humidity in a Santa Ana is usually less than 20 percent, which brings on everything from the misery of dried-out sinuses to crops needing more irrigation. The greatest hazard posed by the dry wind, though, is for homes located in or near fireprone *chaparral,* tall, dense evergreen shrub, a topic examined in Chapter 7. Often gusting over 50 knots (nautical miles per hour), Santa Anas not only spread fires quickly but also blow down trees and power lines. On the brighter side, a Santa Ana usually blows the smog out to sea and affords unlimited visibility as well as breathable air. Santa Anas generally last for two or three days before there is a return to the normal onshore flow of hazy marine air. In drier years, when high pressure seemingly stalls over Nevada or Utah, they occur in longer episodes and with greater regularity.

The antithesis of the steep pressure gradient and resulting high winds and clear skies of a Santa Ana is the stagnant air and near zero visibility of a *tule fog.* It seems a paradox that both weather phenomena happen about the same time of the year and close to one another. The tule fog season starts in the San Joaquin Valley a little later in fall than when the Santa Anas commence south of the Tehachapis, but the two have been known to be in full force on the same day. Since there is not much to see in a tule fog, a better perspective of its average areal extent is gained from the satellite view in Figure 4.12.

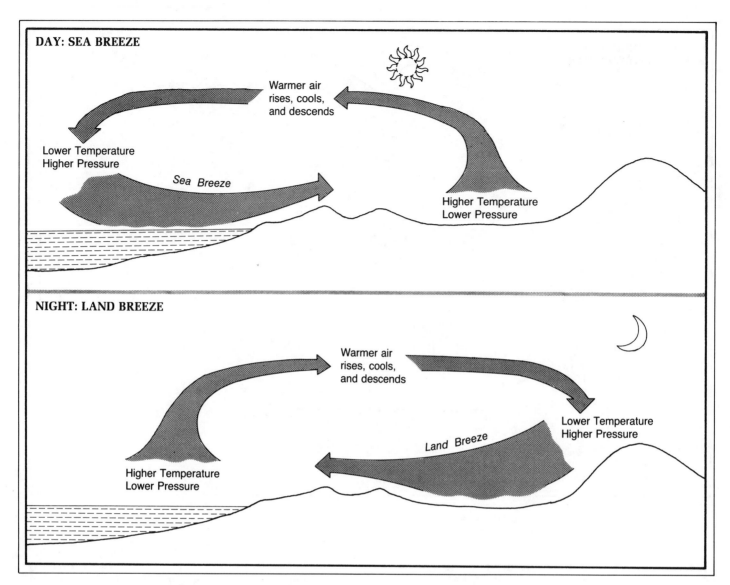

DAY: SEA BREEZE

Warmer air
rises, cools,
and descends

Lower Temperature
Higher Pressure

Sea Breeze

Higher Temperature
Lower Pressure

NIGHT: LAND BREEZE

Warmer air
rises, cools,
and descends

Lower Temperature
Higher Pressure

Land Breeze

Higher Temperature
Lower Pressure

Figure 4.10 Sea and land breezes. (Richard Crooker)

Tule fogs derive their name from the tule reeds or cattails that grow in the swamps and deltalands of the Great Central Valley; early nineteenth-century Spanish explorers first dubbed the southern San Joaquin Valley the "Land of the Tulares" after the tule reeds that surrounded the then huge Tulare Lake. The lake has since disappeared, but not the fogs that shroud cities like Bakersfield, Fresno, and Stockton anywhere from 20 to 40 days a year. The tule is a radiation fog that forms on cold nights when the ground is rapidly losing heat (radiation cooling) and there is little or no wind. Vertically, the fog may thicken to 2,000 ft in this way. Horizontally, it is so blinding that multivehicle crashes on the highways are inevitable.

The pressure and wind conditions mentioned so far occur in the lower atmosphere or *troposphere,* which extends from the earth's surface up to the *tropopause* at an altitude of about 12,000 m or nearly 40,000 ft; however, an upper atmospheric wind known as the *jet stream* occasionally has a profound effect on California's weather. The *polar jet stream* develops at about 50° N, where the tropopause drops sharply to some 7,000 m in altitude and a steep pressure gradient is created by heavy polar air mixing with lighter tropical air.

Since the jet stream is far above the highest mountains and the friction of the lower troposphere, coriolis and pressure gradient forces balance out to produce a west-to-east airflow that sometimes exceeds 350 km/hr in winter. Consequently, jet aircraft flying in the polar jet stream will gain or lose ground speed depending on which way they are going. In some winters, the rapidly moving stream of cold air oscillates in a wavelike motion far to the south of its normal course. When such a jet stream *wave* and its attendant upper troposphere ridge and trough dip down over California and the southwest, temperatures plummet to record lows as dry, polar air rushes in.

Los Angeles was the victim of one of these arctic outbreaks late in 1978 when, for the first time in a December since 1897, subfreezing temperatures were recorded. The freeze played havoc with tropical garden plants and citrus and avocado crops, especially in interior valleys where the cold air remained trapped several days, and even weeks in some locations, after a warming trend set in along the coast. Once in a great while, a lower-level storm will develop under the jet stream and snow will fall down to sea level—as it did from Palm Springs to Seal Beach late in January 1979.

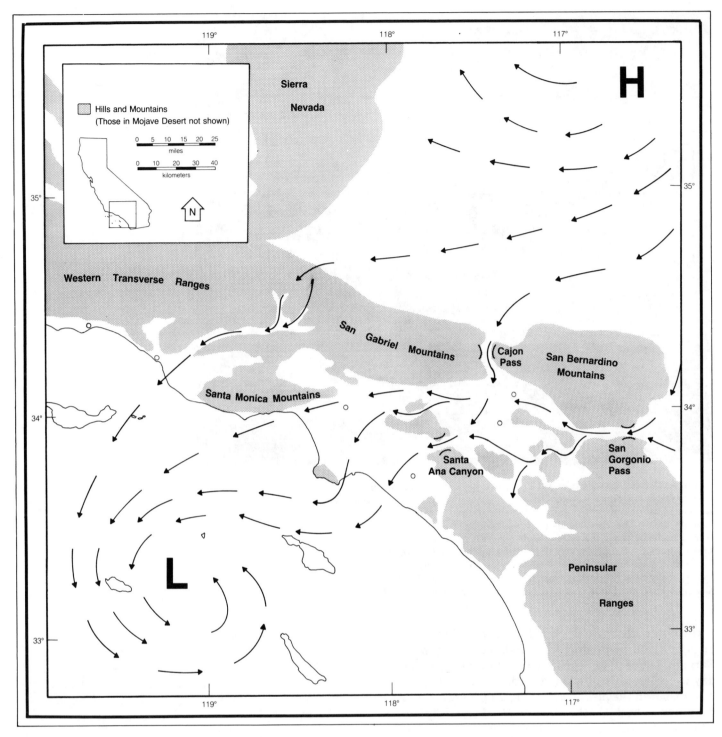

Figure 4.11 Santa Ana winds. (Richard Crooker)

Significant climatic change in California would obviously result from any increase in the wave pulsations of the polar jet stream or from a southward shift of its present course. The state's winters would become colder, drier, and longer. On the other hand, there exists another jet stream—the *subtropical jet stream*—to the south of California that could have quite the opposite climatic effect if it were to change its spatial pattern. A northward shifting of the subtropical jet stream would be likely to bring warmer, wetter, and longer summers to California. As it is, Southern California sometimes gets a taste of the tropics when an upper-level wave from the jet stream spurs a chubasco or a sonora or just several days of humid, muggy weather.

Colder or hotter, drier or wetter, California's climatic future in large part will be determined by how the jet streams behave. In the meantime, the upper atmosphere continues doing its part in exchanging the heat of the tropics and the cold of the polar latitudes, with California somewhere in between.

WEATHER MODIFICATION

Artificial weather modification takes different forms, some accidental and others deliberate. Air pollution is perhaps the best, or should we say worst, example of the former; rainmaking, when it works, is a good example

Figure 4.12 Satellite view: Central Valley tule fog and Southern California Santa Anas. Note the lack of clouds typical of a Santa Ana condition throughout most of the scene. Some clouds, however, are seen to the southwest (lower right corner) over the Pacific and to the north (middle left) over the southern San Joaquin Valley. The ocean clouds mark the location of the low pressure system that is attracting the Santa Ana or easterly winds; the valley clouds comprise an infamous tule fog. The latter is protected from being broken up by the Santa Anas by the insurmountable north-south barrier of the Sierra Nevada. Thus, a landform barrier and a wind reversal (from the prevailing westerlies) reduce air circulation in the valley to practically zero. Meanwhile, gaps in the east-west oriented Transverse Ranges, such as Cajon Pass, San Gorgonio Pass, and Santa Ana Canyon, allow easterly winds easy access to the coastal lowlands. (NASA)

of the latter. We obviously don't want smog, but it seems an inevitable by-product of a high-technology society. Perhaps increasingly sophisticated technology will one day overcome this unwanted modification of the atmosphere, but in the meantime progress appears to be painfully slow at best. On the other hand, when precipitation results from the seeding of clouds, we are supposedly getting what we asked for from the heavens above. We say "supposedly" because sometimes induced precipitation gives us more than we bargained for—floods may occur, property may be destroyed, and lives may be lost.

Unintentional: Smog

Unfortunately, California's climatic vernacular includes the word *smog,* which has been portrayed as everything negative from an animated monster to a toxic gas. People departing jet planes at Los Angeles International Airport say it brings tears to their eyes. Vacationers returning via I-5 say they get all choked up as they drive into the San Fernando Valley. Even those 100 miles away in the desert say they can smell it coming. There is little question that smog elicits few kind words, but certainly a mix of emotions and symptoms. What's

worse, smog destroys crops and forests and aggravates human respiratory ailments by the score.

As for who or what causes smog, the blame rests on a combination of topographic, climatic, and cultural features existing in a given region. Such regions in California are predominantly urban and include the San Francisco Bay Area (particularly the East Bay and Santa Clara Valley cities), the larger cities of the Great Central Valley, and the Los Angeles Basin and neighboring coastal plains and valleys. We shall focus on the interactions among the three principal elements of smog in the Los Angeles Basin. Perhaps it is a poetic injustice, but the basin is also known by the acronym SCAB (South Coast Air Basin) which includes some 6,500 square miles in Los Angeles, Orange, Riverside, and San Bernardino counties. Nevertheless, it is here, more than anywhere else in the state, that we find the optimum (or worst?) combination of natural and manmade elements that make smog a threat to life, limb, and property (as if Southern Californians didn't already have enough to worry about with earthquakes).

It has long been said with regard to the health hazards posed by air pollution that the basin topography of the Los Angeles region makes it the worst possible place to locate several million people. Except during the wind reversal of a Santa Ana or the high winds following a storm front passage, air pollutants are trapped by mountain barriers in the basin and the valleys that front on it. Another look at Figure 4.11 shows the three-sided containment posed by various sections of the Tranverse and Peninsular ranges. Three valleys, San Fernando, San Gabriel, and San Bernardino, are almost completely surrounded by hills and mountains and as a partial consequence suffer more smog alerts than other parts of the basin. Sometimes smog builds up so heavily in the basin (Fig. 4.13) that it spills out through the mountain passes into the deserts. Fronting as it does on the ocean, the basin and valley topography is also conducive to temperature inversion, which is discussed next.

The purveyors of smog are the very same climatic conditions that give coastal Southern California its mild climate—namely, the Hawaiian High and the sea breeze. They team up to produce the *temperature inversion,* which involves warmer air aloft overriding cooler air nearer the ground. Normally, temperature decreases with increase in altitude, but occasionally atmospheric conditions produce an inverse situation in which temperature increases as altitude increases. Such a temperature inversion occurs within an *inversion layer,* a layer of air that is warmer than the air beneath it.

Figure 4.14 illustrates how the warm subsiding air of the Hawaiian High meets with the cool marine air of the Pacific to form an inversion layer that on most summer days tops out at about 2,000 ft altitude. The inversion layer then acts like a lid over the cooler, denser surface air layer, allowing no vertical movement of any pollutants. Horizontal movement of the contaminants is also thwarted: by mountains and hills to the north, east, and south and by the onshore sea breeze from the west. Besides keeping smog from escaping out to the ocean,

the sea breeze, which rarely exceeds 11 or 12 knots and then only in the afternoon, carries pollutants far into the interior of the basin. Thus, 10 million people in a sense become hermetically sealed in the SCAB pot to await their fate.

Of course, that fate will to a large degree rest on the source, kind, and amount of atmospheric pollutants that diffuse throughout the basin. Although the percentage has declined with wider use of emission control devices, about 65 percent of SCAB's smog is still produced by internal combustion engines in various types of vehicles. Actually, it is Southern California's abundant summer sunshine that photochemically catalyzes vehicle exhausts (oxides of nitrogen and hydrocarbons) to form the eye-smarting, gagging, foul-smelling main component of smog, *ozone* (O_3). People living anywhere in the South Coast Air Quality Management District (SCAQMD) are asked to restrict outdoor exercise and driving whenever ozone levels exceed two tenths of 1 part per million (ppm) of air for one hour or more. Such first-stage smog alerts occur on an average of 100 times a year, mostly in summer and mostly in the east San Fernando, San Gabriel, and San Bernardino valleys.[4] Although restrictions broaden to get more people and cars off the streets during stage 2 (.35ppm) and stage 3 (.5ppm) alerts, the former occur with less than one tenth the frequency of stage 1 alerts and the latter rarely, if ever, in an average year.

[4]The SCAQMD issues smog forecasts for various communities according to its Pollutant Standard Index (PSI), which lists four levels of air quality on a scale of 0–500: good (0–100), unhealthful (100–200), very unhealthful (200–300), and hazardous (300–500). Besides ozone, other pollutants considered in a PSI forecast include carbon monoxide, nitrogen dioxide, lead, sulfur dioxide, sulfates, and suspended particulate matter. It is noteworthy that these valleys experienced their worst-ever siege of stage 1 alerts in the first two weeks of October 1980. Under the PSI during the same episode, air quality ranged from unhealthful (100–200) to very unhealthful (200–300).

Figure 4.13 Smog in the Los Angeles Basin all too often makes misnomers out of streets named Valley View Road or Skyline Drive. (Jan Seaman)

Within the valleys suffering the most stage 1 and 2 alerts, there has been a dramatic shift eastward of smog incident frequency in the last 10 years, from the Pasadena-Arcadia area of the San Gabriel Valley to the Upland-Fontana Area of the San Bernardino Valley. Before the Kaiser Fontana steel mill shutdown in 1983, it and the sea breeze, as well as more cars and trucks, teamed up to render San Bernardino Valley smog perhaps the worst in the state: The ozone produced locally by motor vehicles and imported by the sea breeze may have combined with *sulfur dioxide* (SO_2) particulate matter from coal (coke) burning of the steel manufacturing operation to form a substance more hazardous to health than either of the ingredients by themselves.[5] Vehicle emissions of invisible, odorless *carbon monoxide* (CO) further amplified the health hazard.

Besides the component of smog we can smell and taste, there is one we can see. This is *nitrogen dioxide* (NO_2), which gives California smog its characteristic amber-beige appearance. As with ozone, NO_2 forms in sunlight from nitrogen oxide (NO) emitted mostly by motor vehicles. Incidents of unhealthful levels of NO_2 are fewer and farther apart in a normal year in the basin than with ozone alerts. Although both oxidants may contribute to emphysema and lung cancer, the relatively low levels of NO_2 normally in the air on smoggy days have been shown in laboratory experiments to destroy lung cells taken from humans and animals.

Perhaps the fact that, in the case of SCAB smog, some 7 million motor vehicles are the worst offenders is a blessing in disguise. For cars and the like don't burn coal. And it is the oxidants of coal burning that can bring on a killer fog such as the one in 1952 that contributed to the deaths of several thousand residents of London, England. The sources of SO_2, sulfates, H_2SO_4 (yes, sulfuric acid!), and other air effluents Londoners were breathing were largely industrial, although it was December and heavy use of coal for domestic and commercial heating was underway. The topographic contribution of that disaster was the shallow Thames River Valley and the meteorological input came from a subsiding mass of cP air. In Southern California, meanwhile, the use of coal for space heating and firing thermal electric plants was, and hopefully will continue to be, taboo. Even in heavy industry, with the exception of metals manufacturing, utilization of coal is practically nil in the basin.

There is, however, another source of SO_2 and sulfates in the basin that is cause for mounting concern: petroleum, which inherently contains sulfur. The energy industry is expanding use of oil to fire its thermal electric power plants, especially in light of shrinking local reserves of natural gas, fluctuating import quotas of natural gas by pipeline, and lack of an LNG terminal. When SO_2 and sulfates reach unhealthful levels in the basin, which is now an average of 30 days a year, power plants are asked to switch to natural gas, which produces about 1/100 the SO_2 of so-called low-sulfur fuel oil. On such

"sulfate days," which may go on for a week or so if there is persistent heat, sunlight, humidity, and stagnant air, air conditioners and fans are widely used and consequently the demand for electrical energy skyrockets to record levels for the year. In the afternoons of some summer days, demand can exceed 15,000 megawatts (1 MW = 1 million watts) in the basin.

By itself, natural gas is unable to support these levels of electricity production, but to avoid a potential air pollution disaster that might accompany increased fuel oil use, electricity is imported on lines from far outside the basin. Other stationary sources of sulfur oxidants and particulate matter, including refineries and petrochemical and metals plants, are also ordered by the SCAQMD to curtail operations on sulfate days. And the unloading of oil from tankers is altogether prohibited.

In all, it would appear that the edicts and actions of private industry, the federal Environmental Protection Agency (EPA), the state Air Resources Board (ARB), and the local SCAQMD are beginning to pay off in the form of better air quality in the basin. Starting with the banning of backyard incinerators in 1957 and proceeding to the present era of unleaded gas, obvious progress has been made in controlling both the stationary and mobile sources of smog. It appears that levels of many air pollutants are now lower on the average in the basin than they were in the 1970s and two previous decades. But will more cars, trucks, buses, and factories and lack of implementing clean energy alternatives obviate this progress? Will opting for cleaner air over new industry depress the regional economy? As it is now, some large manufacturers, who have already spent considerable sums of money on their own air quality control, foresee the possibility of what they regard as unduly stringent governmental regulations forcing them into laying off large numbers of employees or even abandoning the basin. In any case, the EPA, under the Clean Air Act, has the power to cut off federal highway funds and halt industrial growth in cities that fail to reduce smog.

It appears now that SCAB cities are several years away from meeting the federal standard of .12 ppm ozone and must ask for more time to clean up their air. Moreover, many drivers have "poisoned" their autos' catalytic converters by using leaded gasolines instead of the required unleaded gas and thus may be increasing overall air pollution. Perhaps by the end of this decade, the public and private sectors will somehow be able to join forces in such a way that breathing Los Angeles Basin air will no longer be likened to smoking so many cartons of cigarettes in a year.

Acknowledging the fact that vegetation at the same time contributes to and helps alleviate pollution of the air,[6] certain species of both natural and cultivated plants are suffering from manmade smog. The principal natural vegetation association affected is the commercially

---

[5]In December 1981, Kaiser Steel Corporation announced the 1983 shutdown of its coke ovens, blast furnaces, and steelmaking furnaces due to competition from foreign steel manufacturers. Kaiser Fontana will stay in operation but will convert to finishing purchased steel slabs and becoming a steel supply and service center, relatively smog-free operations in comparison with steelmaking.

[6]Plants exude hydrocarbons, such as pollens and terpenes, into the atmosphere to help form haze. Other natural air pollutants include volcanic dusts, blowing dust and sand, smoke and brush and forest fires, salt from breaking sea waves, and bacteria and viruses. On the other hand, *photosynthesis* in plants, whereby oxygen and carbohydrates are formed from chemical reaction among water, carbon dioxide, and light or solar energy, helps maintain the oxygen content of the atmosphere. The formula for photosynthesis is: $H_2O + CO_2 + $ light energy $= $ —CHOH— $+ O_2$.

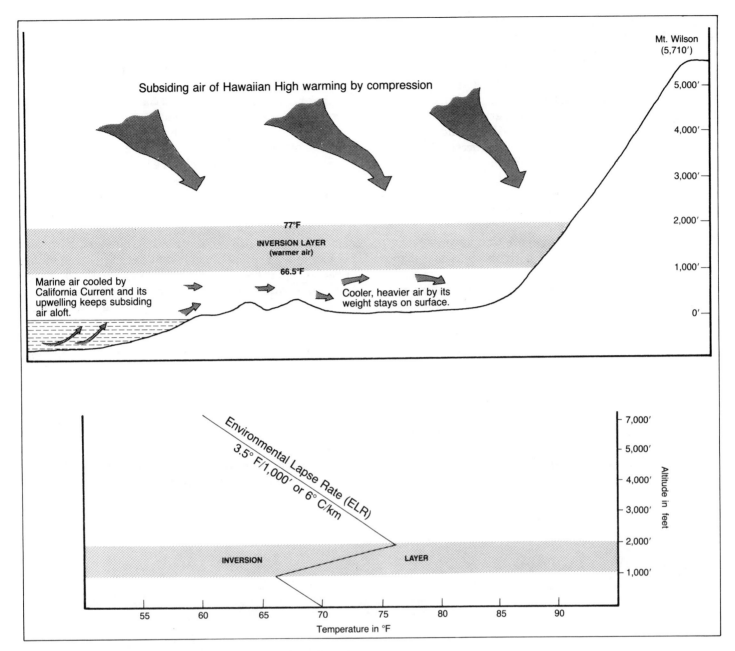

Figure 4.14 Temperature inversion in Los Angeles. (Richard Crooker)

important Ponderosa pine forest of the San Bernardino Mountains. Smog, mainly ozone, has caused a decline of nearly 50 percent in wood volume from yellow or ponderosa pine (*Pinus ponderosa*) trees in the San Bernardino National Forest since 1950. Conifers and shrubs that are relatively resistant to smog have replaced the dominant ponderosa in many parts of the forest, but they are mostly species of little or no value to the lumber industry as well as ones that raise the fire hazard. Evidently, smog weakens yellow pines to the point of nonresistance to the ravages of the bark beetle and other pests.

Smog damage to farm crops poses a much more serious situation than with forests because it is more widespread in the state and the economic loss is greater. The loss averaged tens of millions of dollars annually by the mid-1970s in Southern California, Bay Area, and Central Valley agricultural counties alone. Ozone and peroxyacyl nitrates (PAN) do most of the damage; mainly to leafy vegetables such as spinach and lettuce, although

SO_2 also "burns" leaves and eventually renders plants unfit to send to market. The sources of these crop and forest killers are the same mobile and stationary ones discussed earlier, which should make residents wonder how far out into rural California they have to go to escape smog.

Intentional: Rainmaking

As the drought of the mid-1970s wore on into its second winter, Californians increasingly gave thought to how the few storm clouds that now and then passed overhead could be made to give up their moisture. Clearly, it seemed, the time had come for somebody to do something more about the weather than just talk about it—lest the state run out of water entirely. Yet neither drought nor rainmaking to combat it were new to California. Actually, the forerunner of modern cloudseeding methods may be said to have been developed by one Charles M. Hatfield just after the turn of the century in Southern

California. Hatfield's technique involved filling evaporating tanks with a supersecret chemical formula that was supposed to induce rain. Nowadays, such formulas usually include silver iodide and/or dry ice that supercool ice crystals in clouds, causing them to gain weight and fall to earth. Twice, in 1904 near Los Angeles and in 1915–16 in San Diego, Hatfield experimented with his rainmaking formula (probably not silver iodide) and in both cases apparently met with rousing success—at least the downpours that followed would seem to indicate that he did. Nobody really knows whether or not Hatfield's experiments actually produced rainfall, but a measure of his success is the fame he gained that later won him contracts in Canada, Honduras, and Texas.

Charles Hatfield and many more contemporary rainmakers have had to contend with the paradox of too much success in the form of floods following their work. The deluge that accompanied Hatfield's rainmaking in San Diego caused that city's Morena Reservoir to overflow and send floodwaters downstream to wash out a dam and inundate city streets and buildings, as well as cause several drownings. Hatfield's original contract with the city called for his rainmaking to fill the reservoir and not much more. The city council refused payment of his $10,000 fee on the ground that the results of his efforts far exceeded those stated in the contract. Hatfield sued the city and the city demanded that he pay for all the flood damage. The whole mess eventually wound up a draw, with neither party realizing financial recovery.

Subsequent legal storms resulting from apparently excessive rainmaking—for instance, in a suit filed by victims of the 1955 Yuba City flood and contemplated legal action by victims of the February 1978 floods in Los Angeles County—have made even modern-day weather modification a risky and costly business in more ways than one. Accurate weather forecasting is obviously one way of reducing the risks inherent in cloud seeding, but wind direction and air mass temperature and moisture content often change instantly and without warning. Knowing when to seed or not to seed clouds is tantamount to knowing when the weather is going to change—and that is trying to predict the unpredictable.

There are economic and environmental benefits to be gained from intentional weather modification, however. For example, a recently completed 14-year cloudseeding project over the San Gabriel Mountains produced nearly 100 billion gallons of precipitation over and above what normally would have fallen. The additional water, which encouraged a heartier watershed vegetation cover, was valued at more than $3 million above the total cost of the cloudseeding operation. In another project, starting in the late 1970s and running into the present decade, research on winter cloudseeding to augment the Sierra Nevada snowpack is being carried on as part of the Sierra Cooperative Pilot Project. The SCPC's principal aim is to increase runoffs in both California and Nevada. If successful, the project could be of inestimable value in furnishing additional hydroelectric energy and irrigation water for the two states.

WATER: THE CONTROVERSIAL RESOURCE

Few, if any, of California's natural resources stir more innovative responses as well as controversy among the state's citizens than water. Innovation is seen in the great aqueduct systems that crisscross the state, carrying water from where it is the most plentiful to where it is most needed. While such water-sharing schemes are of priceless benefit to recipient cities and farms, they often have an irreversible negative impact on the environments that give up the water in the first place.

Thus do the waters of controversy begin to flow, as the people losing the water and the environment it supports wage legal and political battles with the people who gain the precious liquid and all its benefits. On occasion, water rights disputes have even boiled over into armed conflict. Works by such authors as Carey McWilliams[1] and Morrow Mayo,[2] as well as Remi Nadeau's *The Water Seekers* and even a full-length motion picture, *Chinatown,* have bubbled forth from the bottomless well of water conflict in California. But when all has been litigated, written, said, and done, the all-too-familiar doctrine of "the greatest good for the greatest number" seems to hold sway as large farms grow larger and big cities get bigger with water imported from somewhere else.

WATER RESOURCES:
AN UNEVEN HYDROGRAPHY

California's surface stream systems supply an average of 76 million acre-feet of water annually (1 acre foot, or AF, is the equivalent of 1 acre of land 1 foot deep in water), but, as shown in Figure 5.1, nearly 75 percent of the natural streamflow occurs in the northern third of the state. This uneven distribution of natural fresh-

water resources assumes significance when considered together with the fact that about 80 percent of annual water consumption takes place in the southern two thirds of the state. A review of Chapter 4 and the climatic controls that render the north wet and the south dry essentially explains the geographic disparity of water supply and demand in California.

When the hydrography depicted in Figure 5.1 is viewed in comparative terms, the Sacramento with its tributaries like the Pit, Feather, Yuba, and American stands out among individual river systems, supplying about one third of all of the state's streamflow. The river systems of the northwest, including the Smith, Klamath, Mad, Eel, Noyo, and Russian, combine to supply about 42 percent of total streamflow. Of the 25 percent of natural streamflow found in the southern two thirds of the state, the San Joaquin River and its tributaries contribute about half of it.

Most of the south's remaining surface runoff comes from the interior-draining rivers of the southern San Joaquin Valley, the multitude of smaller streams rushing out of the eastern Sierra, and the "exotic" Colorado River, whose sources are entirely outside the state. There are numerous central and south coast streams emptying into the Pacific, as well as interior-draining water courses in the southern deserts, but the aridity of the south renders their flow *intermittent* rather than *perennial* and thus of minor consequence in the overall surface water supply picture of California. Fortunately for the total surface water supply, California's streams and rivers are relatively free of pollution compared to those in some Eastern states, although heavy use of fertilizers and herbicides tends to obviate some of the benefit of minimal waterway pollution from mining and manufacturing industries in California.

[1]Carey McWilliams, "Water! Water! Water!" in *Southern California: An Island upon the Land* (Santa Barbara and Salt Lake: Peregrine Smith, Inc., 1973), pp 183–204.
[2]Morrow Mayo, "The Rape of Owens Valley," in *Los Angeles* (New York: Alfred A. Knopf, 1933), pp. 220–246.

WATER CONSUMPTION AND DROUGHTS

Overall consumption of water by all users in California now averages about 28 million acre-feet (MAF) a year.

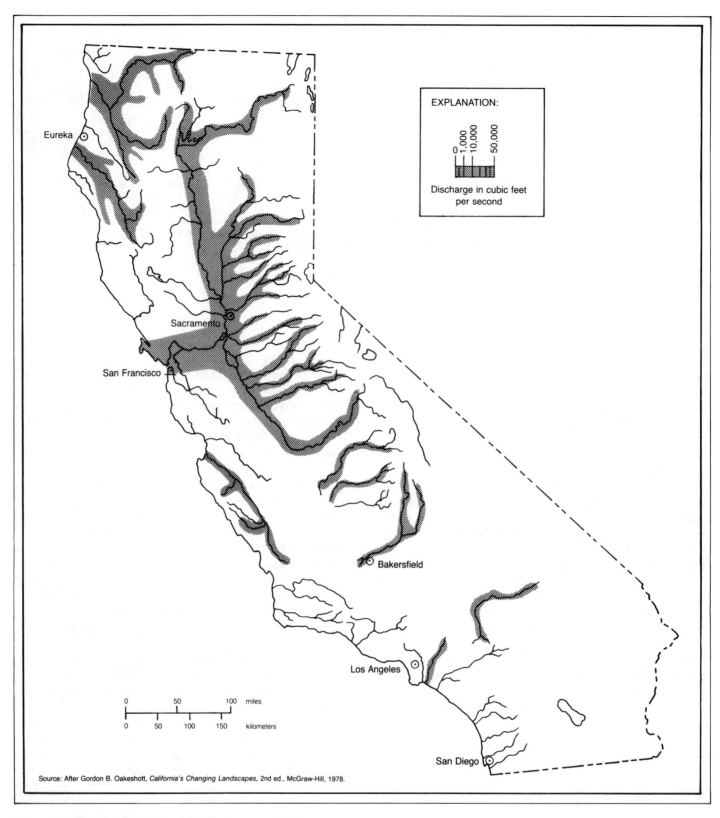

EXPLANATION:

0 1,000 10,000 50,000

Discharge in cubic feet
per second

Eureka

Sacramento

San Francisco

Bakersfield

Los Angeles

San Diego

0   50   100   miles

0   50   100   150   kilometers

Source: After Gordon B. Oakeshott, *California's Changing Landscapes*, 2nd ed., McGraw-Hill, 1978.

Figure 5.1 Hydrography. (Richard Crooker)

This represents about a 2 million acre-foot increase in each of the three decades since 1950, when annual consumption was approximately 22 MAF. In view of the fact that California's population has more than doubled since 1950, this modest increase in consumption seems of little concern until recent changes in allocation of the "unconsumed" 48 MAF (76 MAF − 28 MAF = 48 MAF) are considered. When we have deducted the 3.4 MAF required for salinity repulsion in the Sacramento Delta, the 18 MAF for preserving natural streamflow mostly in the northwest (in keeping with the Scenic and Wild Rivers Act of 1972), and the 1 MAF for the U.S. Supreme Court's reduction of California's claimed share of the Colorado River supply from the total 48 MAF, less than 27 MAF remains uncommitted. To muddy the picture even more, about half of the 27 MAF is unavailable as a developable resource because the runoff is situated in remote areas or occurs as uncontrollable floods.

This leaves California with a surface water resource development potential of about 13.5 MAF a year. Even if dams, reservoirs, diversion tunnels, and aqueducts are built to tap every ounce of this potential, California will still have precious little hedge against a prolonged drought. For, as illustrated in Figure 5.2, water in reservoirs doesn't simply lie around waiting for us to use it; instead, it evaporates into the atmosphere as an inextricable part of the *hydrologic* or *water cycle*. In fact, in the sunnier parts of California, even in years of normal precipitation, there exists a *water budget* deficit; evaporation from water bodies and *evapotranspiration* from plants and soil far exceeds precipitation. In dry years, the deficit can spread to the four corners of the state.

Drought or no drought, annual water consumption of 28 MAF is not likely to diminish unless a mass exodus of California's agricultural industry occurs. Irrigation agriculture alone accounts for about 85 percent of all water consumption and other agricultural and food processing activities for another several percentage points. For instance, production of just 1 pound of beef from the time it starts out as irrigated alfalfa for cattle feed until it reaches the dinner table requires 2,500 gallons of water. And beef is just one of thousands of varieties of foods and fibers requiring varying amounts of water for growth and processing. Of the 10 percent or so of strictly nonagricultural consumption of water, residential and industrial users share most of it. A family of four uses an average of 360 gallons a day or 130,000 gallons a year for everything from drinking and dishwashing to flushing toilets and watering lawns. Examples of industrial consumption in California range from 25 gallons of water needed to produce 1 gallon of gas to 60,000 gallons required to make 1 ton of steel.

By virtue of being the greatest water consumer, agriculture is one of the biggest losers whenever drought strikes. This has been true almost since the time large-scale commercial agriculture started in California. Barely a decade and a half after statehood, the drought of the mid-1860s all but wiped out a burgeoning beef industry by destroying more than 2 million head of cattle. In modern-day droughts, such as the one that occurred in the mid-1970s, losses are sustained not from cattle perishing on the range from starvation and thirst, but rather from their being sold prematurely because pasture lands have dried up and feed prices have inflated. Their forced sales, in turn, add downward pressure to cattle prices. Falling cattle prices contributed $500 million of an estimated $800 million total agricultural loss in the last year (1977) of the drought. Farmers growing *rain-fed* crops incurred much of the remaining $300 million loss because they depended on natural rainfall, which was less than 40 percent of normal in some *dry-farming* regions of the state. In all, the drought caused about a 17 percent drop in California's net agricultural income in 1977.

Had the drought continued beyond 1977, irrigated agriculture as well would have felt the water pinch despite the availability of well water. Even in years of normal precipitation, unwanted salts accumulate on irrigated land wherever deep percolation of water is restricted by a *perched water table*, as illustrated in Figure 5.2. The problem is especially acute in the San Joaquin Valley, where some 400,000 acres of crop land may return to desert in the 1980s if saline tailwater is not somehow flushed out of the region. Presently some irrigation drainwater is discharged into the San Joaquin River, Tulare Lake evaporation ponds, and a holding reservoir near Merced via the San Luis Drain. Besides the need for an outlet to the sea, much more fresh water will be required to avoid *desertification* (also see Chapter 3 regarding desertification in the Imperial Valley).

Drought-induced losses suffered by nonagricultural sectors of the California economy were in some cases more severe than those experienced by the farming community. Hydropower losses alone, if quantified for the

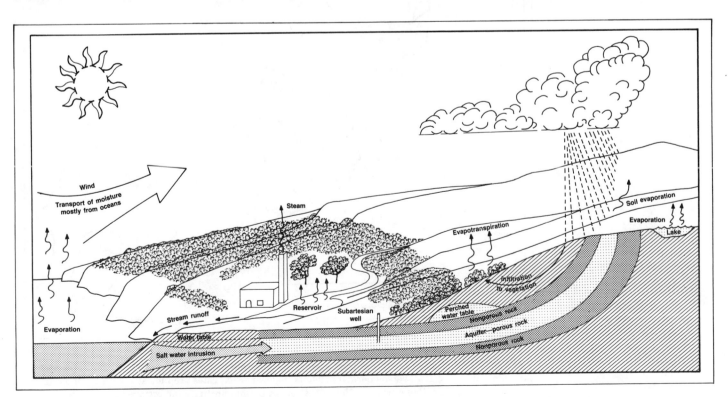

Figure 5.2 Hydrologic cycle and groundwater. (Richard Crooker)

worst years of the drought (1975–1977), probably far exceeded those of agriculture, not only because relatively expensive fuel oil was imported to prevent an electricity shortage, but also because of the inestimable costs to the environment and the health of residents posed by substituting a "dirty" energy source (fossil fuels) for a relatively "clean" one (hydropower).

The geography of the hydroelectricity shortage appears in Figure 5.3, where most of the Sierra Nevada and Klamath Mountains watershed is shown receiving less than 40 percent of normal precipitation in 1976. This watershed holds most of the state's hydroelectric dams, and by the fall of 1977 many of its reservoirs had gone dry. Imported hydroelectricity—for example, from the Columbia River via the Pacific Intertie line—was also in diminishing supply because the drought had spread throughout the western United States. Even

more serious at the time was the drying up of municipal reservoirs: in affluent Marin County, for example, where water was trucked in so that residents had enough to drink and to maintain health and sanitation standards. Residents of Marin, Santa Barbara, and other counties bent on limiting growth by voting against aqueduct project funding seem undaunted in their opposition despite such emergencies.

The effects of the drought on California's natural vegetation and wildlife were serious and would have been devastating had the drought dragged on into this decade. In its last year (1977), the drought was blamed for pushing commercial timber losses 250 million board feet over normal by making *conifers* (cone-bearing trees such as pines and firs) more susceptible to the ravages of pests and disease and by increasing the incidence of fire. Chaparral and other fireprone plant communities became all

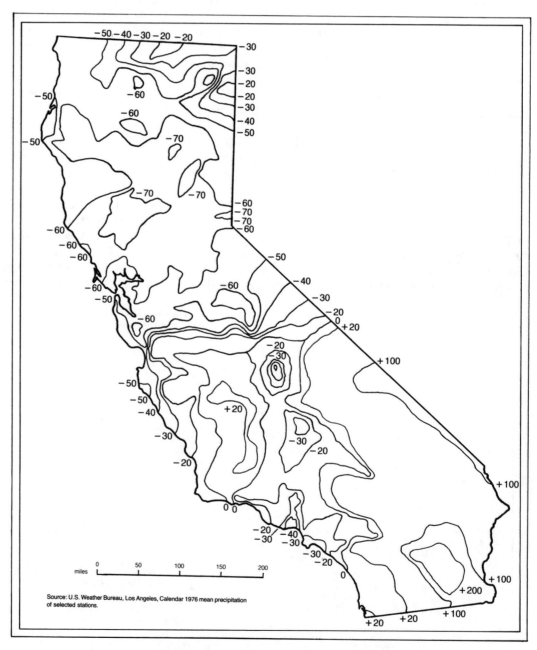

Figure 5.3 Precipitation deviations from normal in California in 1976. The map shows percentages of precipitation during 1976 versus normal amounts. Below-normal rates are indicated with a minus sign; above-normal rates with a plus sign. Notice that above-normal precipitation occurred only in the southeastern part of the state. (Robert Huson)

the more menacing to suburbia, not only in and of themselves but for an increasing chance that there might not be enough water to control a fire.

Among the hardest-hit wildlife were salmon and steelhead trout, who on their return migration from the sea found their ancestral stream waters too low and/or too warm to spawn successfully. Landlocked fish perished in countless numbers as lakes and streams disappeared, especially at elevations below 6,000 ft where diversion projects and evaporation took their toll of existing water. Burros, mustangs, antelope, bighorn sheep, deer, and elk saw their browse vegetation vanish for lack of rain. Also faced with starvation were coyotes, foxes, hawks, and other predators who found their prey (rodents, for example) in declining supply. Because wetland habitats were disappearing for lack of rain and/or diversion of drainage for irrigation, migratory waterfowl became hard pressed to maintain their flyways across California. The dearth of water also promoted insect and disease infestation among most wildlife.

GROUNDWATER AND DROUGHT: THE CASE OF THE OWENS VALLEY

California has a significant groundwater potential in its soils, subsoils, and certain rock formations, and it is this resource, properly developed and managed, that can stave off environmental and economic disaster in time of prolonged drought. The economically and physically usable storage capacity of the state's groundwater basins totals over 140 MAF, several times the available active storage of all the surface reservoirs under planned development in the state. During the drought *artesian* and *subartesian wells,* as demonstrated in Figure 5.4, brought much of this naturally stored groundwater to the surface for use on the farm and in the city. The sandstone and other *permeable* (porous) rock strata that form the *aquifers* (Fig. 5.2) holding most of this capacity were extensively *recharged* by two years (1978 and 1979) of record precipitation following the drought. Although *land subsidence, saltwater intrusion* (Fig. 5.2), and increased pumping costs often accompany groundwater utilization, they can be minimized if groundwater reserves are saved for dry years. Moreover, stored groundwater does not evaporate away like reservoir water does.

As with surface streamflow, most of the groundwater resources in California are remote from major population centers. The earliest major regional project aimed at rectifying the geographical inequities of water supply and demand in the state involved diversion of the eastern Sierra–Owens Valley drainage to the City of Los Angeles via the 233-mile Los Angeles Aqueduct. Since before the aqueduct began operating in 1913 until the present, the Owens Valley Project of the Los Angeles Department of Water and Power (DWP) has been the subject of bitter controversy (the dispute is viewed in historical perspective in the next section of this chapter). It is noteworthy that San Francisco actively sought far-off Sierran water resources before Los Angeles did, but political controversy over its Hetch Hetchy dam and 186-mile aqueduct projects delayed completion until some 15 years after the Los Angeles Aqueduct opened (the San Francisco

water controversy is also discussed later in the chapter).

As seen in Figures 5.5 through 5.8, this diversion project, which enables Los Angeles to grow and satiates the thirst of most of the city's 3 million residents, now extends another 105 miles farther north to the Mono Basin and includes two aqueducts. Most of the water entering the 338-mile aqueduct system comes from surface streams, but the drought of the last decade and the decline in Colorado River Aqueduct (Fig. 5.5) allotments in this decade make utilization of the 38-MAF storage capacity of the Owens Valley Groundwater Basin very tempting to the DWP.

The actual amount of groundwater available in the basin literally depends on the weather. The Owens Valley proper averages only 6 inches precipitation annually because of its rain shadow location; the orographically prolific eastern Sierras, however, usually force several times this much precipitation from the heavens, except in dry years. The falling rain and melting snow move down the eastern slopes either by surface stream or by seeping into aquifers or underground water tables mapped in Figure 5.8. The mountain runoff percolates into both the upper aquifer or *water table* and the lower or *confined aquifer,* with layers of nearly *impermeable* (nonporous) silt or clay separating the two zones.

Other sources of water supply to the aquifers include seepage from irrigation canals and ditches and groundwater flow from underground basins in Round Valley, Chalfant Valley, and the volcanic tableland between those two small valleys (Fig. 5.8). In wet years the DWP also contributes to recharging the aquifers by *spreading* excess water via percolation in channels near Big Pine and Laws and on the alluvial fans of the western side of the valley.

Although diversion of surface runoff in the Owens Valley dates back to prehistoric times when Pauite Indians irrigated some of their Round Valley lands, groundwater pumping did not commence until early in the twentieth century. Los Angeles drilled its first wells in 1908 to provide water for dredges used in constructing the aqueduct. The first drought-induced well drilling took place in the early 1920s; by 1931, pumping wells provided a then-record 142,630 AF of groundwater to be sent down the aqueduct to Los Angeles. The excessive 1931 pumping, however, slowed pumped well production to a scant 140 AF in 1932.

Throughout the rest of the 1930s, 1940s, and 1950s, pumped groundwater production was practically nil and flowing wells averaged only about 10,000 AF annually. Then in 1960, about two years into a minor drought, pumped production revived anew with 40,460 AF bound for Los Angeles. Except for 1961 (111,880 AF), pumping during the rest of the sixties averaged only about 11,000 AF each year. But spurred largely by the worst drought in decades, pumped production increased on the average nearly tenfold each year, up to and including the last year (1977) of the dry period.

It is noteworthy that the pumped output in 1977 of 142,790 AF was about 30 percent of the proposed average export of 482,000 AF per year in the two existing aqueducts. With nearly 500 wells and test holes (more than 90 of them pump-equipped) on 307,000 acres of city-owned land in the Owens Valley, the proportion of

A   B

Figure 5.4 Owens Valley groundwater pumps and free-flowing wells are supplied with water by water-bearing rock formations (aquifers) that consist of alluvial deposits, lake bed sediments, and/or fractured volcanic flows, the latter typically yielding 10 to 20 cubic feet per second (cfs) or 3 to 4 times the yield of an alluvial aquifer. Water coming to the surface under its own hydrostatic pressure through a well is artesian (A); if it has to be pumped to the surface, it is subartesian (B). An artesian or capped pressure well usually taps deep, confined aquifers where relatively high pressure levels exist. (Crane Miller)

groundwater flowing down the aqueduct system to Los Angeles could be substantially increased. In fact, the DWP has proposed in its June 1979 *Final Environmental Impact Report (EIR) on Increased Pumping of the Owens Valley Groundwater Basin* that pumping be increased to 112,000 AF in an average year and to 227,000 AF in a maximum year.[3] The former figure is about equal to the annual rate of the 1970s; the latter is nearly 50 percent of the projected total average annual export of surface water and groundwater from the valley.

The environmental impact of the proposed increase in groundwater pumping is much less a game of numbers, but much more a source of controversy, than the pumping itself. In its 1978 *Draft EIR,* the Department of Water and Power claimed that the water table would not lower sufficiently to cause any significant change in existing plant or animal life and thus the ecology of the Owens Valley would remain much the same as it is today. "Quite the contrary," responded environmentalists, Inyo County, and even some state government agencies, who foresaw water tables dwindling below the rooting system of most plants once increased pumping was permanently implemented. This action, they stated, would doom animal life as well as the vegetation it depends upon. The Owens Valley would become nothing more than a barren desert filled with shifting sand and a dusty atmosphere polluted

by blowing alkali. The few existing natural *springs* would disappear with increased pumping, leaving behind no natural oases around which some semblance of wildlife might otherwise survive. Many of these concerns were published in their original form, as received by the Department of Water and Power, in the second volume of its 1979 *Final Environmental Impact Report.*

As the following summary of environmental impacts and mitigations from the *Final EIR* demonstrates, the Department of Water and Power responded in an objective manner to the severe criticism of its original draft. At the same time, though, the DWP states its own case:

> *Geohydrology.* Lowered water tables and reduced pressure in confined aquifers will occur in the vicinity of well fields. This is expected to cause springs to dry up within the zone of influence of pumping wells.
>
> *Flora.* There will be an impact on flora in the high groundwater areas within the pumping influence zone of wells. Of the total influence area, vegetation changes are expected to occur on 69,000 acres of . . . Valley floor . . . land. This is 43 percent of the Valley floor or 11.5 percent of the broader expanse between the bases of mountains. Changes will be most evident in those portions of the alkali grasslands and the alkali scrublands, which will no longer be able to draw from the groundwater basin. Vegetation losses will also occur near springs and flowing wells which run dry. Diversions of surface water into spring habitats will maintain a wet habitat and thereby partially mitigate that impact.
>
> *Fauna.* . . . Species will be reduced in numbers and modify their range of habitat in response to vegetation changes; however, none are expected to be threatened with extinction. Tule elk are not expected to be impacted except that the Independence herd may modify its range. Domestic livestock will be removed from Los Angeles land if competition with tule elk develops.
>
> *Air Quality.* . . . Impact on air quality in the Owens Valley cannot be estimated with reasonable accuracy. Reduced vegetative cover resulting from the project is

[3] A maximum year refers to a dry year, one in which pumping would peak. Of the 112,000 AF pumped in an average year, 55,000 AF would be exported to Los Angeles and 57,000 AF would remain for in-valley use. The overall Los Angeles water supply picture presently looks like this:

Los Angeles Aqueduct		78%
Owens Valley	61%	
Mono Basin	17%	
Los Angeles area wells		17%
Colorado River and California Aqueducts		5%
		100%

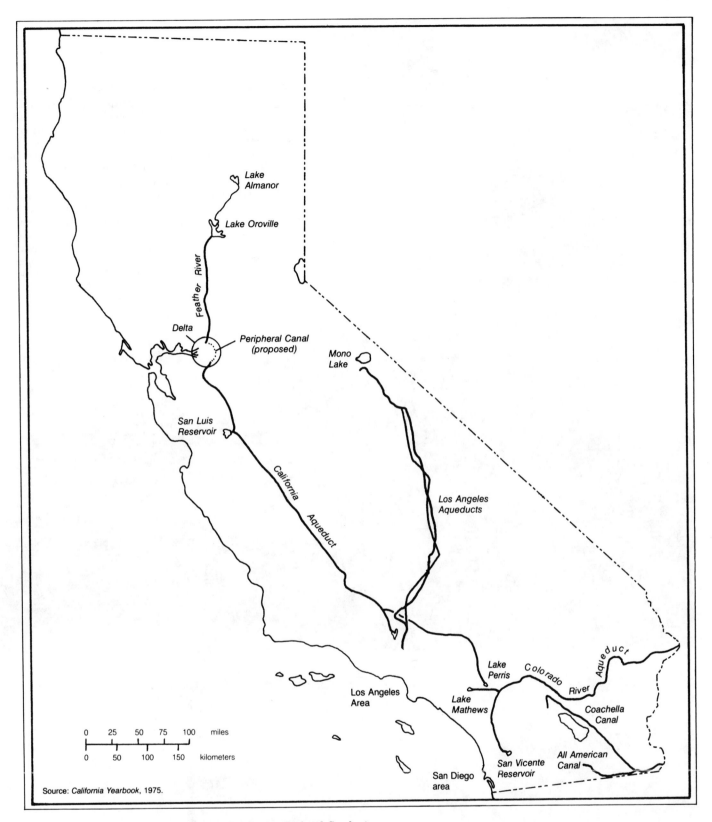

Figure 5.5 Aqueducts serving Southern California. (Richard Crooker)

expected to cause some increase in particulate concentrations during duststorms which occur 5 to 10 times per year, and there could also be some increase in suspended particulate during lower wind conditions. The Federal Environmental Protection Agency has recognized that the toxic fraction of fugitive dust in areas without the impact of manmade pollutants is small. Consequently, the EPA has excluded rural areas from its priorities for control, electing to focus instead on urban areas and industrial sources.

The proposed project will have a beneficial effect on air quality in the South Coast Air Basin in the amount of 0.8 tons/day fewer pollutants because hydroelectric energy generated by the project will reduce energy generation necessary in fossil-fueled plants in Los Angeles. Furthermore, the project reduces water needs from the State Water Project and consequently reduces its energy requirements from fossil-fueled plants. This benefit is equivalent to the reduction in pollution resulting from the burning of 306,000 barrels of fuel oil annually.

A

Figure 5.6 Mono Basin is a 1,000 sq mi basin of interior drainage located at the edge of the northeastern escarpment of the Sierra Nevada and seen here encompassing Mono Lake in the upper center of the satellite image (A). Basin drainage is into 60 sq mi Mono Lake (6,400 ft elevation) to the south, formed during the late Pleistocene period. Volcanic activity beneath the lake formed Paoha ("the longest") and Negit islands about 2,000 years ago and continues to the present as evidenced by minor steam eruptions early in this century. With Los Angeles diverting water from creeks feeding the lake since 1941, lake level will continue to drop until about the year 2070, when water supply from streams, numerous springs, and precipitation will equal evaporation, and the lake will stabilize at about 38 sq mi in size. As water level lowers, more of the unusual-looking, calcareous formations, emanating from springs and known as *tufa towers,* appear (B, C). (A: NASA; B, C: Crane Miller)

B

C

Figure 5.7 Los Angeles Aqueduct in the Owens Valley near Lone Pine. The original 233-mile aqueduct, beginning just south of Tinemaha Reservoir (Fig. 5.8) at the Owens River intake and terminating in the northern San Fernando Valley at Los Angeles Reservoir (formerly Van Norman reservoirs, which were damaged in the February 9, 1971 earthquake; see Chapter 2), was completed in 1913. In 1940, a 105-mile extension of the aqueduct system to Lee Vining Creek in the Mono Basin was completed, increasing the system's length to 338 miles. In June 1970, a second aqueduct from Haiwee Reservoir (Fig. 5.8) south to Los Angeles was put into operation, one of its purposes being to increase the delivery capacity of the system in order to handle increased groundwater extraction in the Owens Valley. In the controversy over increased groundwater pumping in the Owens Valley, Los Angeles contends that since the California Environmental Quality Act (CEQA), which requires assessment of environmental effects of such projects, was not adopted until November 1970, the question of the city's preparing an environmental impact report on the second aqueduct did not arise until after that aqueduct was in operation. The second aqueduct increases water delivery capabilities from the eastern Sierra and Owens Valley to Los Angeles by nearly 50 percent. (Crane Miller)

Energy. The proposed project will consume a small amount of energy for pumping from wells. However, the pumped water that is exported will generate energy in the Los Angeles Aqueduct hydroelectric power plants as it flows to Los Angeles. This generation combined with the savings of energy which would be required by the State Water Project if that source were used instead of the proposed project, results in a net energy benefit of 184 million kilowatt-hours per year.[4]

To clarify the DWP's "savings of energy" claim, it should be noted that *gravity flow* down the aqueducts from a 4,000-ft elevation in the Owens Valley to near sea level in the San Fernando Valley precludes energy use for pumping anywhere in the aqueduct system. One other benefit of the DWP's presence in the Owens Valley is their prohibition of commercial signs and billboards along U.S. 6 and 395.

Legally, the groundwater controversy will ultimately be settled in the courts. In 1976, an earlier DWP environmental impact report was challenged by Inyo County and later rejected by the state court of appeals. The 1978 *Draft EIR* and the *Final EIR* expanded on the earlier version, but the latter, which called for additional pumping of up to 120,000 AF per year, was rejected by the Third District State Appeals Court on September 30, 1981. In the split decision of its three-judge panel, the

court essentially stated that Los Angeles must broaden the scope of its EIR by considering the impacts of surface stream diversion as well as groundwater pumping. In December 1981, the state supreme court refused to review the lower court's ruling, which means the city will have to develop a third EIR.

Adding to Los Angeles's woes, the Fourth District Court of Appeals in San Bernardino rejected the city's attempt to remove an Inyo County groundwater management measure from the November 1980 ballot. On November 4, 1980, county voters overwhelmingly approved (3–1) the groundwater extraction ordinance, which essentially gives Inyo County regulatory authority over water the City of Los Angeles legally owns by requiring permits for pumping and exporting water. Although Los Angeles has taken legal action against the ordinance, a three-year truce was proposed in April 1981 that would suspend the lawsuits and guarantee water deliveries to that city; otherwise, the issue will probably be settled by the state supreme court. In the meantime, the continued growth of the nation's second largest city and the environmental viability of the state's deepest valley remain at stake.

IMPACTS OF STREAM DIVERSION ON MONO BASIN

Environmentally, the broader controversy involving both stream and groundwater diversion by the DWP may never be resolved. Decades ago, Owens Lake was sent

[4]Los Angeles Department of Water and Power, *Final Environmental Impact Report on Increased Pumping of the Owens Valley Groundwater Basin,* June 1979, pp. B1–3.

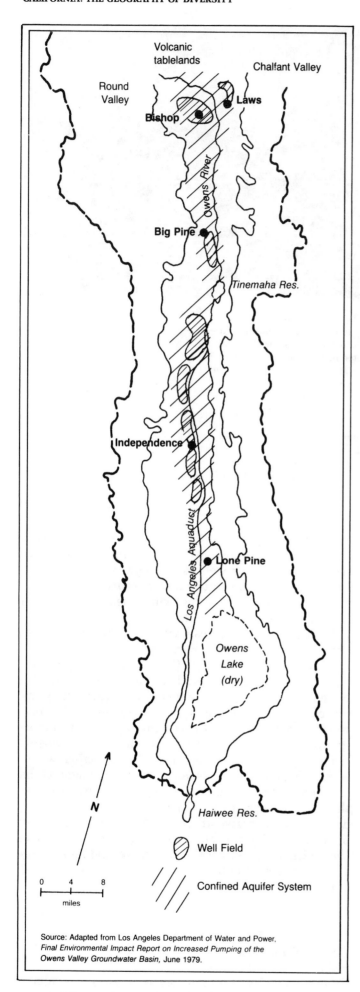

Round Valley

Volcanic tablelands

Chalfant Valley

Laws

Bishop

Owens River

Big Pine

Tinemaha Res.

Independence

Los Angeles Aquaduct

Lone Pine

Owens Lake (dry)

N

Haiwee Res.

Well Field

Confined Aquifer System

0 4 8

miles

Source: Adapted from Los Angeles Department of Water and Power, *Final Environmental Impact Report on Increased Pumping of the Owens Valley Groundwater Basin,* June 1979.

Figure 5.8 Owens Valley groundwater basin well fields and confined aquifer system. (Marc Blodgett)

down the drain, as it were, to Los Angeles; since 1941, the same thing has been happening to Mono Lake (Fig. 5.6).

Will Mono Basin one day resemble the alkali dust bowl that is now Owens Lake playa (Fig. 5.9)? Although the lake area is projected to shrink to 38 sq mi (down from its present area of 60 sq mi) in 100 years, will some future drought necessitate reducing even that area? The environmental impacts of increased water diversion in the Owens Valley and Mono Basin notwithstanding, another drought will leave no choice in the matter if it comes to posing a threat to the well-being of millions of Los Angeles residents.

But Los Angeles's continued diversions (100,000 AF per year) of streams feeding Mono Lake pose a grim if not deadly fate for certain basin wildlife. Specifically, it is the California gulls (*Larus californicus*) of Mono Lake (95 percent of the California population and 20 to 25 percent of the species population reside here) and the brine shrimp (*Artemia monica*) they feed on who are losing their lives and their breeding habitats. As the water level lowers by from 1 to 2 ft per year, the gulls are increasingly brought into double jeopardy: (1) land bridges form that connect their island nesting sites to the mainland, allowing coyotes (*Canis latrans*) and other terrestrial predators easy access, and (2) salinity increases to fatal levels for newly hatching brine shrimp, the gull chicks' prime source of food, and brine flies, another major food source for basin bird life.

The first problem has been combatted by blasting the land bridges apart and erecting chainlink fences across them, but the gulls have nevertheless continued their evacuation of the connected islands. The second problem has proven far more perplexing and may result in the abandonment of the Mono Basin as a rookery for the gulls and as a resting and feeding place for several species of migratory birds. The *Report of the Interagency Task Force on Mono Lake,* of which Task Force the Los Angeles Department of Water and Power is a member, notes that: "Experimental evidence indicates that populations of brine shrimp and flies are likely to decline with increasing salinities. It is unlikely that any of Mono Lake's major bird species, including the gulls, grebes, and phalaropes, will persist at the lake if populations of invertebrates disappear."[5] The distance of suitable alternative habitats for the birds only compounds the problem: The nearest viable environments are Abert Lake, 300 miles north in Oregon; the Salton Sea, 350 miles to the south; the Great Salt Lake, 400 miles to the east in Utah; and San Francisco Bay, 14,000 ft up and over the Sierra Nevada crest, then 175 miles to the west.

Matters worsened in early summer of 1981, when an abnormal percentage of gull chicks perished, the normal survival rate being about 50 percent. However, in a briefing document issued in May 1982 entitled "Los Angeles's Mono Basin Water Supply," the Department of Water and Power stated that

[5]U.S. Forest Service, U.S. Bureau of Land Management, U.S. Fish and Wildlife Service, California Department of Water Resources, California Department of Fish and Game, Mono County, and the Los Angeles Department of Water and Power, *Report of the Interagency Task Force on Mono Lake,* December 1979, p. 20.

The exact causes are not known; however, salinity is not considered the cause as the lake level and conditions were approximately the same as in 1980. Research conducted by the City at ponds adjacent to Mono Lake under experimental conditions has shown that the brine shrimp can thrive in a salinity of approximately 15 percent salt. This salinity content will not be reached in Mono Lake for at least another 30 years. Other research also shows the brine shrimp can tolerate higher salinity. To date, there is no evidence that the brine shrimp could not adapt to an ultimate estimated salinity of 21 percent in Mono Lake, which will be reached very gradually over a period of 80 to 100 years. Although the brine shrimp populations for May and June 1981 were somewhat below the estimated average in previous years during the same period, the populations for July, August, and September 1981 were much higher compared to previous years during the same period. Latest research performed in summer 1981 by Dr. Joseph Jehl Jr., of Hubbs-Seaworld Research Institute, has determined that the migratory birds have visited the lake in their usual large numbers and have found abundant supplies of brine shrimp and brine flies on which to feed.

If one detects an unusual degree of contradiction between the Task Force report and the briefing document, one is reminded that controversy, especially over water, often breeds contradiction.

Environmentalists opposed to diversion of freshwater from Mono Lake's tributary streams are quick to remind DWP of the recommendation made by the interagency task force it belongs to that water export from Mono Basin be reduced by: (1) statewide water conservation, (2) water conservation in the City of Los Angeles only, (3) statewide reuse of reclaimed waste water, (4) reuse of reclaimed waste water in the City of Los Angeles only, and (5) purchase of replacement water from the State Water Project through the Metropolitan Water District.[6] Through media announcements, mailing of watersaver kits to residents, and water reclamation plant development, Los Angeles and other California cities are now actively engaged in implementing these recommendations. But so far only the tip of the iceberg, in terms of what can be done to conserve and reclaim the state's precious water resources, has breached the surface.

Remember, as we next examine water law and the history of Los Angeles's quest for water, that the city's other sources of water supply—the California Aqueduct, the Colorado River Aqueduct, and local groundwater and surface streams—are in some cases shared with communities inside and outside California and thus could become unavailable, as happened when the California Aqueduct was shut off in 1977. When precipitation returned to normal the following winter, the California Aqueduct was turned back on and once again some of

A

B

Figure 5.9 The Owens dry lake (A) was not so dry before Los Angeles began diverting water from the Owens River and its tributaries. In fact, two lake streamers operated in the 1870s carrying silver and lead mined at Cerro Gordo (see Chapter 3) from east to southwest across the shallow lake. It is estimated that nearly 100 billion gallons of water evaporated from the lake annually. Now, though, the only thing leaving the lake via the atmosphere is salty dust, which is observed here (B) being blown eastward by winter storm winds. As Mono Lake recedes, it too is becoming an alkali dust bowl, posing increased visibility and air pollution problems downwind in the Great Basin. (Crane Miller)

Northern California's water began flowing to Southern California. One wonders, though, even if a longer shutdown occurs, if it will really impose a lasting, or even short-term, limit to growth on Southern California. Voter rejection (Proposition 9, June 1982) of the California Aqueduct's proposed feeder aqueduct, the Peripheral Canal (Fig. 5.5), will have considerable bearing on the problem and will be discussed later in the chapter. In the meantime, the City of Los Angeles's decades-old ownership of property in, and legal rights to, the waters of the Owens Valley and Mono Basin are likely to perpetuate that city's continued growth.

THE WESTERN (CALIFORNIAN) REVOLUTION IN WATER LAW

Water is a necessity for humankind. It provides life, crops, recreation, health, and protection. Control and distribution of water has thus become a major modern concern. In areas where water is in short supply, equitable uses are critical and basic to society's existence. California is one such area. As would be expected, laws dealing with water in California have reflected changing

[6]Ibid., fig. 10, p. 28. Of the 19 preliminary alternative solutions suggested by the Task Force, Plan P was selected as the recommended solution. Plan P, among its several recommendations, includes this: "The City's export from Mono Basin would be immediately reduced from an average of 100,000 AF/year to 15,000 AF/year. During extreme drought conditions, consideration will be given to permitting the City to divert more than the 15,000 AF/year from Mono Basin as planned under this proposed plan" (pp. 45–46). In a letter appended to the report (Appendix A), the DWP expressed strong opposition to the Task Force recommendations.

economics, environment, technology, and social conditions. Since water has changed much of the face of California, making habitation, farming, and recreation possible in many places, legal control of this resource represents a significant area of legislation and litigation. It is therefore important to understand the fundamental legal doctrines which underlie much of the debate.

Common Law Riparian Rights

The concept of *riparian rights* is the most common water doctrine in the United States. Simply stated, the riparian doctrine gives certain rights in the flow of water to the owner of land next to the water flow. These water rights are considered to be a part of the ownership interest of the land and a form of real property right. The extent of this right to use water has been debated for years, with two approaches emerging from the discussion. The "reasonable use" theory limits use only to the extent that such use does not negatively affect other users. Thus, the premise is that all riparian users have equally protected rights vis-a-vis each other. The alternate theory, which might be called that of "domestic use," is that the riparian owner may take water for domestic purposes only (family, livestock, gardening) and that other uses may be infringements of other riparian owners' rights.

The ultimate thrust of the riparian doctrine is that (1) the water user must own land bordering the water flow and (2) the water user must limit use to those purposes deemed to be either natural or reasonable. Certain preferred uses, such as domestic or livestock over commercial or industrial, are recognized in riparian law. The doctrine of riparian rights has both advantages and disadvantages: Generally, diversion of water is not permitted under the doctrine, and this limits the use of water by nonriparian land holders. This may be a critical problem where there are few free-flowing streams. Because of the limitations of riparian doctrine, therefore, another major water allocation system was developed.

The Doctrine of Prior Appropriation
(The Colorado Doctrine)

In the absence of abundant free-running water, the doctrine of riparian rights does not seem to be very useful or appropriate. In the dry Western states, consequently, the doctrine met severe challenges. Due to extensive federal ownership of vast tracts of this land, early residents could not claim water use rights as arising from ownership of land they did not legally possess. A practical solution to the problem of water rights evolved that created superior rights for those who first put the water to beneficial uses. This came to be known as the *doctrine of prior appropriation* and permitted the first person to appropriate water from a stream to continue using that amount of water against all subsequent users, as long as that original use was continuous. Appropriation rights, however, can be lost by failure to continue using the water acquired in this fashion.

In essence, this doctrine established a first come, first served legal process for water in the arid West. Miners and settlers were able to regulate legal control of water in accordance with this rule and establish some order

and predictability in the process. It should be noted that the doctrine did not overturn riparian rules or take precedence over the rights of the federal government, which still owned the land, but only served to settle disputes between competing individuals.

Later federal legislation attempted to clear up the question of riparian versus appropriation rights. Both the states and the federal government desired to respect the developing theory of appropriation while still preserving some measure of respect for the riparian doctrine insofar as it might apply to any particular future case. In its purest application (the Colorado Doctrine), however, prior appropriation separated water rights entirely from land rights and put the control of water in the hands of the state as a public trust. This often meant, in practice, that each Western state could establish its own set of rules governing appropriation of water, thus undercutting riparian doctrine almost totally.

Most Western states eventually developed a permit system whereby water users would apply for certain uses to the state and, upon compliance with permit requirements, would receive permission from the state to appropriate water for beneficial purposes. This placed significant power in the hands of the state agency, as well as heavy responsibility for monitoring competing uses and determining overall best interests of the public at large. Competing uses to be considered included personal, household, livestock, agricultural, recreation, fishing, and many others. Finally, the doctrine created a new approach to water use that tried to establish preferential uses of water and protect as many landowners as possible. The new system was better suited to the Western states but needed more refinement to meet the specific needs of each state.

The California Doctrine:
A Marriage of Convenience

Water distribution in California created a unique problem that called for a blending of ideas from both riparian and appropriation theories. The greatest difficulty was not the total absence or shortage of water, but rather its geographically imbalanced distribution. There is an abundance of water in the state as a whole, but most of it is located in the north where there is less need for it. The distribution of water is further imbalanced by its seasonal occurrence. Given this imbalance of location and occurrence, the state attempted from the outset to provide an orderly and consolidated water allocation plan that would serve the needs of all its residents equally.

To accomplish the goal of fair water use, the state of California has created a modified doctrine utilizing aspects of both the recognized approaches. Through various court cases, and eventually by constitutional enactment, a series of rules on water use has evolved.

First, the state declared that it would recognize and honor the water rights acquired under the prior appropriation process. This protected those water users who had established time priority.

Second, the state acknowledged that riparian rights did exist. The California courts noted that the original riparian rights had belonged to the original owner of the land, the U.S. government who took title from Mexico, and that upon transfer to private parties these riparian rights were also transferred.

Third, riparian rights acquired by a recent transfer would not be absolute. They would be subject to those prior appropriation rights that existed at the time of transfer and would be further limited by a proviso that the riparian right would extend only to such amounts of water as were reasonably required for beneficial use of the land. This could prevent a riparian owner from selling water above the amount needed for the riparian land alone.

Fourth, the water resources of the state were declared to be so vital as to require such water to be used for the general welfare and for the public interest. This meant that water use would be subject to specific state control and regulation (although riparian and appropriation owners' rights were to be respected).

Fifth, all water above the amount needed for limited riparian and appropriation uses would be considered "excess water" subject to state control. This control would be exercised by a state water rights board.

Sixth, all uses of water that came about as a result of appropriation would be deemed to be "public uses" and thus subject to state control. In practice, this meant that the bulk of water available in the state was subject to governmental control. Once this fact was established by definition, it remained only for the state to determine priorities of use and provide a permit system for distribution.

The philosophical position of the state is reflected in the California Water Code, which places the highest priority on domestic use, followed by irrigation. Further, applications by a municipality for use of water by its residents is given priority over most other competing uses. Beyond the priorities thus outlined, it is left to the judgment of the Water Board to determine allocations in such a way as to serve the broad public interest. All uses are handled by a permit application process, and the Board acts on a case-by-case basis. Finally, the Board is enjoined to give constant attention to state water plans for coordinated water use (see the discussions of the California Water Project and Central Valley Project later in this chapter).

The efforts of the state of California to develop a comprehensive approach to the use of water were not quickly or easily accomplished. The California Doctrine reflected an uneasy compromise of various rights and arrived at a position that would benefit the most people to the least detriment of any individual. Obviously, some individuals and localities were necessarily subordinated to the general welfare, a circumstance that created bitter and long-standing controversies—the conflict between Los Angeles and the Owens Valley being a case in point.

A CITY'S SEARCH FOR WATER: LOS ANGELES AND THE OWENS VALLEY WAR

One of the enduring controversies in California as well as a source of constant regional tension was the appropriation by Los Angeles of the waters of the Owens Valley. Located in an arid part of the south, with an ever-expanding population, the city has required a dependable and extensive supply of water from outside its boundaries. Without water, Los Angeles would revert to its basic semidesert beginnings. The existence of a reliable source of water, however, has permitted the city and region to sustain a growing industrial, agricultural, and residential base. The development of such a water source by Los Angeles is, in large measure, a microcosm of the traditional conflict of urban south versus rural north—or more directly, the battle between city and country.

Mulholland's Dream

As early as the turn of the century, many residents of Los Angeles began to realize the city's critical need for a reliable source of water. With a near drought in 1904 and the Los Angeles River and a few local wells unable to meet the demand, the city was ready to consider new methods of acquiring the needed water. Population growth figures for the area were astonishing, and long-term planning was critically important.

Based upon a scheme developed by Fred Eaton, a former mayor and engineer for the city, it was proposed that the waters of the Owens River, 250 miles away, be brought to Los Angeles by means of a $25 million aqueduct. After passage of a bond issue by city voters, City Engineer William Mulholland undertook the amazing project in 1908. Pushing a pipe-and-flume, tunnel-and-trench system across the desert, he completed the job in five years. A remarkable feat of engineering even by today's standards (Fig. 5.7), this system brought reliable water service to the city as well as generating vast amounts of hydroelectric power along the route of the aqueduct.

Applying the theory of "the greatest good for the greatest number," the project did divert water from the Owens Valley and prevented a full-scale reclamation program from being completed there. Through a combination of agreements, legal theories, and cooperative actions, the city had succeeded in acquiring rights to this water. Acquisition of excess water that normally would have gone into Owens Lake was accomplished by the process of appropriation. Further, the city purchased riparian land in the valley to control these claims along the river's course. The federal government assisted by closing the remaining land in the valley to homesteading and by granting right-of-way on federal lands for the aqueduct. For several years after completion of the aqueduct, the city set about purchasing most of the riparian land of the Owens Valley, eventually gaining control of in excess of 90 percent of it.

During this period, and throughout the late 1920s, the city faced strong opposition from organized groups in the valley who contested the loss of control of the region and wished to preserve the Valley for its residents. The city claimed that these opponents only wished to force the city to pay unfair prices for the land. Charges and countercharges flew back and forth and finally erupted in open violence.

Dynamite, Vigilantes, and the Owens Valley War

The sources of discontent over the project were many and varied. The most violent criticism accused Los Angeles of "raping" the valley for the benefit of a few un- scrupulous and greedy land speculators who wished to develop the San Fernando Valley with the water brought from the Owens River. The ranchers, businessmen, and farmers of the Owens Valley who had seen the possibility of reclaiming the land and prospering from its resultant fertility were understandably angry and antagonistic to the interlopers who they felt were ruining their valley. Residents who were forced out or bought out under threat of eviction had lost their homes, even if the prices paid were fair—a fact not always conceded. Conserva- tionists and naturalists who saw destruction of the val- ley with the removal of the water expressed their dissatisfaction and ire, but as charges flew back and forth, the ultimate fate of the valley's water was already sealed. Various groups tried to hold out against the land purchases by Los Angeles but soon found themselves overwhelmed. Frustration eventually turned to violence, with dynamiting of the aqueduct occurring at least nine times, along with other forms of violence. These dan- gerous confrontations between armed ranchers and armed guards on the aqueduct only served to heighten bad feelings already at a fever pitch due to misunder- standings, mutual stubbornness, and inept personal relations.

Ultimately the city triumphed, and some long-range benefits both to Los Angeles and to the Owens Valley were achieved. The emotionalism engendered by the con- flict tended to obscure much of the true nature of the project and its role in the development of the state. Clearly, there were examples of greed, dishonesty, and self-serving financial manipulations on both sides. The city needed water, but its political manipulations were often callous and heavy-handed. The Owens Valley res- idents wanted to preserve their homes, but if they could not, they frequently wanted to bleed the city for every cent they could get above a fair and reasonable market value. Bitterness resulted on both sides, leaving a res- idue of ill-feeling in the Owens Valley that has continued down to the present. In perspective, although the dispute was extended, public, and acrimonious, it was only one small episode in the overall drama of water distribution in the state.

BUSINESSMEN VERSUS NATURALISTS: THE SAN FRANCISCO WATER CONTROVERSY

The battles over water in California are not primarily north versus south controversies. Rather, they are a re- flection of urban pressures brought to bear against rural lifestyles. This can be seen even more clearly in the case of the San Francisco Bay water controversy.

As with Los Angeles, the growth of San Francisco brought about an increased demand for water. By the late 1800s, the system of private water companies was unable to keep up with the burgeoning demand. Thus, Bay Area civic leaders began to cast about for a source of reliable and adequate water supplies. As a means of solving the water shortage, San Francisco proposed the then-novel expedient of transporting water from another region of the state by means of an aqueduct. The early 1900s saw the city attempt to purchase water rights

along the Tuolomne River in the Yosemite Park area. Specifically, the city proposed to dam the Hetch Hetchy Gorge and from there build an aqueduct approximately 175 miles to San Francisco. The proposal was met with howls of dismay from naturalists and others, and the battle lines were drawn.

For ten years the controversy raged between those who wanted to preserve and protect the natural beauty of the gorge and those who advocated the critical need for water in the populous Bay Area. The issues were further complicated by the presence of various parties who saw a loss for the private water and power com- panies if the project were allowed to go forward. In en- vironmental circles, John Muir, the Sierra Club, and other nationally known figures attempted to thwart the project. After wavering from one side to the other, how- ever, the U.S. Department of the Interior finally granted approval in 1913. The project was completed in 1931, demonstrating the precedence of urban population needs over rural and environmental issues.

Clearly, this was not an easily resolved problem, and the final solution left a bitter taste in the mouths of many people. It did, however, provide a viable water source for San Francisco. The pattern was also followed by the East Bay cities, which collectively purchased water rights along the Mokelumne River and built the 95-mile East Bay Aqueduct to service their populations.

Thus, the transfer of water from one region to another is not unique to Los Angeles, San Francisco, or the East Bay. Water transfer from rural to urban locales merely reflects the realities of a constantly growing population in the state and related population clustering. One dis- tinction, however, is that the needs of the south became increasingly more evident with the tremendous popula- tion rise in that region of California.

MORE WATER FOR SOUTHERN CALIFORNIA FROM SOMEWHERE ELSE

Just as imported water has enabled Los Angeles to grow to become the second largest city in the nation, so has it helped provide the basis for Southern California as a whole to develop into the most populated and most pros- perous part of the state: The ten-county region's total population stands at about 13.5 million, or nearly 60 percent of the California total, and annual personal in- come regularly surpasses $100 billion. Since the water that flows down the Los Angeles Aqueduct is intended for the exclusive use of the city (and even at that may be inadequate in dry years), neighboring cities have had to search elsewhere to assure their own continued growth. In 1928, the California legislature created the Metropolitan Water District (MWD) of Southern Cali- fornia, which was charged with constructing the 242- mile Colorado River Aqueduct (Fig. 5.5) and using it to deliver water from "the River" to Los Angeles and other southern California communities. In 1941, the first water from the Rocky Mountain states, via the Colorado River and Aqueduct, flowed into a reservoir in Pasadena.

Southland growth and development again boomed fol- lowing World War II, and by 1960 the legislature and the voters had approved what has become the most ambitious water redistribution project in the history of the world: the State Water Project (SWP). By the mid-1970s, the SWP began delivering water from Oroville Dam and Reservoir (Fig. 5.5) 600 miles southward to Perris Dam and Reservoir (Fig. 5.5) via a 200-mile stretch of the Feather and Sacramento rivers and the 400-mile California Aqueduct (Fig. 5.10). The last major link in the SWP, the Peripheral Canal (Fig. 5.5), was to be constructed, had voters approved it in the June 1982 election, during this decade. Fully completed, the delivery capability of the State Water Project would exceed 4 MAF a year, which is many times that of either the Los Angeles Department of Water and Power or the Metropolitan Water District systems.

Although DWP, MWD, and SWP all perform the same basic function of delivering water to Southern California from remote surplus source areas, some differences among the three systems are worthy of mention. The gravity flow of the Los Angeles Aqueduct precludes the need for pumping anywhere along the DWP line. In contrast, water must be lifted 1,617 ft by five pumping plants along the Colorado River Aqueduct and even higher on the California Aqueduct—for example, some 2,000 ft by the Edmonston Pumping Plant to surmount the Tehachapi Mountains. Each acre-foot of water delivered requires 2,000 kilowatt hours (kWh) of electricity for the MWD aqueduct and 3,170 kWh for the SWP aqueduct, and the cost of this energy is rising rapidly.

The Department of Water and Power system enjoys another advantage: Its water is of higher quality, with a salt and other dissolved solids content nearly one fourth that of Colorado River water. State Water Project water, which is nearly equal to DWP water in quality, is often blended with Metropolitan Water District water to prevent the latter from corroding pipes and increasing the salinity of groundwater. SWP serves a much more extensive area than either DWP or MWD. As seen in Figure 5.6, distributary aqueducts from the California Aqueduct serve the San Francisco and southern Coast Ranges regions as well as Southern California. Also, the Feather River Project unit (specifically Oroville Dam) helps control flooding that once ravaged Yuba City and Marysville and provides hydropower to nearby communities.

Neither the Metropolitan Water District nor the State Water Project has been any more successful in escaping controversy than has the Los Angeles Department of Water and Power. The main source of dispute over the Colorado River's waters has been the fact that they are shared by seven states and two nations (the United States and Mexico), most of which are water-short areas. Still another California-based agency, the Imperial Valley Irrigation District, uses the Colorado's waters, diverting them into the valley for irrigation via the All-American Canal (Fig. 5.5). In the 1920s, the Colorado Compact and treaties with Mexico apportioned the river's waters among the several users. But Arizona and California continued to squabble over the Colorado until a 1963 court decision called for MWD to lose half of its existing allotment of river water starting in 1985. The Central Arizona Project, scheduled to begin operations by the middle of this decade, will take what MWD is giving up.

MWD could suffer still further allotment cuts if: (1) possible litigation over the rights of Navajo Indian reservations to the Colorado's waters are resolved in the Navajos' favor and (2) all agencies who have legal rights to use of the waters of the Colorado suddenly exercise them. The latter event is not likely to transpire, but the overcommitment of river water rights should never have

Figure 5.10 California Aqueduct and pumping station in the western San Joaquin Valley. Presently, water from the Sacramento Delta is pumped into the aqueduct at Tracy in San Joaquin County. If and when the Peripheral Canal is completed, it will carry water around the eastern periphery of the Delta into the aqueduct. Opponents of the canal say that reduced flow of freshwater through natural delta channels will increase salinity and cause the demise of irrigated agriculture, commercial fishing, and avian fauna populations. Proponents claim that the canal will do a better job of repelling seawater while at the same time delivering more fresh water to the California Aqueduct. (Crane Miller)

happened in the first place. At times, the Colorado River's bankruptcy has amounted to some 3 MAF more than normally flows in the river in a year.

Like the Los Angeles Department of Water and Power, the State Water Project has to contend only with opposition within the state. But, as the DWP well knows, this opposition can be formidable. Despite sporadic opposition, the development of the state project progressed steadily through the 1960s and 1970s except for two setbacks: the halted development of perhaps the most important link in its system, the Peripheral Canal, and the Wild Rivers Act, which thwarted diversion of northwestern rivers. Without the Peripheral Canal circumventing the Sacramento Delta to carry Sacramento–Feather River water directly into the California Aqueduct and Delta Mendota Canal, Southern California and the San Joaquin Valley are missing out on as much as 1 MAF of additional water a year.

Opponents of the Peripheral Canal contend that if this 1 MAF, or anything like it, is sent southward instead of into the Delta, saltwater intrusion (Fig. 5.2) from the Bay will ruin farming and negatively modify the rest of the environment. Also, they say, the Bay itself will not be as well flushed of saltwater as it is now. The salinity buildup in the San Joaquin Valley, mentioned earlier in this chapter, poses still another problem, for if a proposed $750 million drain is built to carry used irrigation water and its dissolved minerals out of the valley, it will empty into Suisun Bay and impact the Delta, San Pablo Bay, and San Francisco Bay. It is not surprising that opposition to the drain, as well as to the Peripheral Canal, is mounting. Proposition 13 and the accompanying fiscal conservatism of the state legislature also are starting to have a long-term negative impact on financing of both state and joint state-federal water resource projects from special appropriations and/or the state's general fund. Moreover, as witnessed in 1979 by Santa Barbara County voters' rejection of a proposal to import SWP water, the no-growth syndrome among Californians is apparently growing and taking its toll of water resource development proposals. Lastly, although in 1980 both the legislature and the governor approved construction of the 43-mile, $680 million Peripheral Canal, opponents gathered more than enough signatures to have the issue qualify for the June 1982 ballot.

The resounding defeat of Proposition 9 (the "Water Facilities Including a Peripheral Canal" referendum statute) by the voters on June 8, 1982, could be attributed to taxpayers' fear of the facilities' costs as much as to anything else. The *California Ballot Pamphlet* for the primary election listed potential costs (from Senate Bill 200) in excess of $2.29 billion—$680 million for the Peripheral Canal, $139 million for relocation of Contra Costa Canal intake and construction and/or improvement of other Delta and Suisun Marsh facilities, $872 million for Los Vaqueros Reservoir, $493 million for Glenn Reservoir, $112 million for groundwater storage facilities in the San Joaquin Valley and Southern California, and an "unknown" amount for south San Francisco Bay area groundwater storage facilities. Opponents predicted total costs of at least $3.68 billion and as much as $19.2 billion. They also argued that project goals could be achieved by far cheaper means.

Table 5-1
Selected counties' vote counts on Proposition 9, June 1982

Region and County	Yes	No
Northern California		
Alameda	13,680	265,080
Butte	2,552	43,758
Marin	2,437	79,346
San Francisco	7,284	140,574
Santa Clara	29,525	249,616
Southern California		
Imperial	8,404	6,982
Los Angeles	895,716	572,721
Riverside	90,441	60,861
San Diego	306,670	111,013
Ventura	64,014	51,332

Source: *Los Angeles Times*, June 10, 1982, Pt. 1, p. 19.

Perhaps more significant than any other single reason given for the defeat of Proposition 9 was the existence in Northern California of an informed electorate anxious to get out and vote "no" versus a much less concerned electorate in Southern California. Northerners knew well what was at stake for their part of the state; such knowledge seemed to have escaped the minds of many Southern Californians apropos their region. Otherwise, why was Proposition 9 soundly rejected in northern counties and only moderately successful in the south (see Table 5-1)? However the election results are interpreted, the environment of Northern California appears to have won a new lease on life, and Southern California may have imposed upon itself a limit to growth. Whichever side of the environmental and economic issues a Californian may be on, it pays to gain geographic insight into the issues and use that knowledge at the polling place.

CVP: A BOON TO AGRICULTURE

The Central Valley Project (CVP) portrayed in Figure 5.11, differs from California's other major regional water resource projects in two respects: Its primary benefit is to agriculture rather than to municipalities and nonagricultural industry, and it is funded and controlled by the federal government rather than by a city, as in the case of Los Angeles and the Department of Water and Power, or by the state, as with the State Water Project. Actually, CVP originated exclusively as a state-sponsored project with legislature, gubernatorial, and voter approval all given in 1933. But the Depression and the consequent reluctance of the public to buy $170 million in bonds led to the project's takeover by the U.S. Department of the Interior's Bureau of Reclamation in 1935. By 1938, contractors began construction of the project's first unit, Shasta Dam and Lake, as seen in Figure 5.12.

Despite delays caused by shortages of workers during World War II, Shasta, Keswick, and Friant dams, a hydroelectric plant (at Shasta Dam), about 350 miles of main canals, some 200 miles of power transmission lines, and numerous pumping plants, bridges, and tunnels

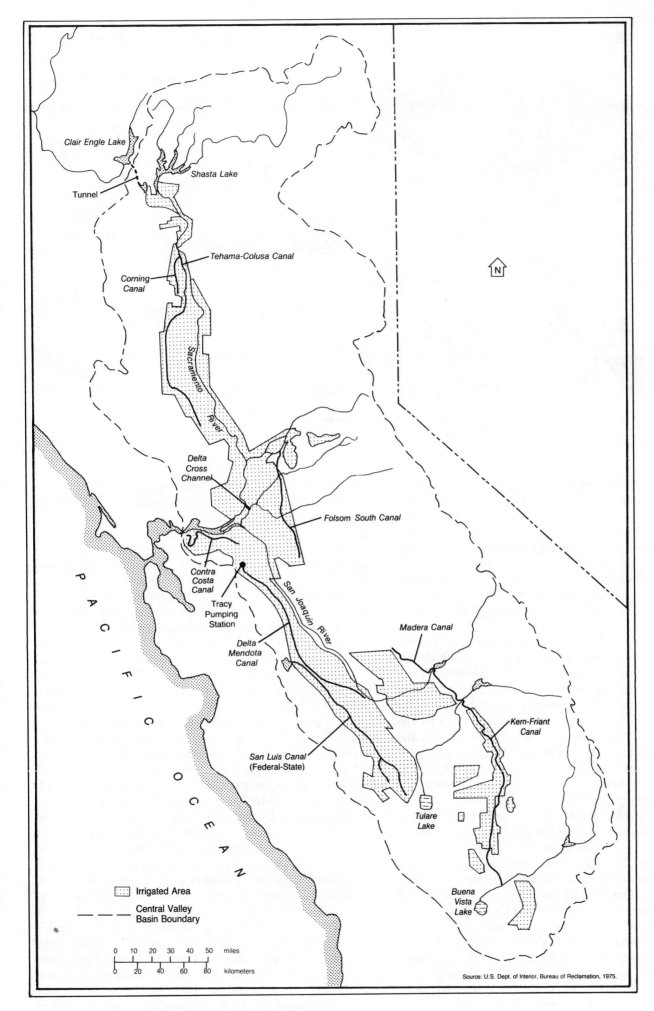

Figure 5.11   Central Valley Project. (Richard Crooker)

Figure 5.12 Shasta Dam and Lake impound the state's largest river, the Sacramento, as part of the federal Central Valley Project. During the 1976–1977 drought, the water level of the lake dropped dozens of feet. (Crane Miller)

were essentially completed by the end of the 1940s. Central Valley Project developments since 1950 include impounding of the Trinity, American, and Stanislaus rivers to meet the Central Valley's growing demand for more irrigation water, municipal water supply, hydropower, flood control, and recreation facilities. A fringe benefit of the CVP system has come about in the form of more water for operation of the Sacramento Ship Channel, completed in 1963, and the earlier-built (1933) Stockton Ship Channel.

The central aim of the CVP, which has been largely achieved with implementation of the projects just outlined, was to improve agriculture in the Central Valley as a whole by supplying water to the relatively arid San Joaquin Valley and by preventing saltwater intrusion in the Delta. Irrigated agriculture got its start in the San Joaquin Valley over a century ago and, with the help of surface stream diversion and groundwater pumping, steadily expanded in area through the early decades of the twentieth century. Blessed with two thirds of the Central Valley's potential farmland but only one third of its natural surface water, however, San Joaquin Valley irrigated agriculture turned evermore to well water to sustain its growth. By the 1930s, overdrafting of groundwater resources, both in dry years and in years of normal runoff, threatened desertification of much of the newly won farmland. The solution lay in diverting some of the Sacramento Valley's two thirds of all Central Valley surface water down to the San Joaquin Valley.

The CVP eventually accomplished this task with its Delta Cross Channel, Tracy Pumping Plant, and Delta-Mendota units carrying Sacramento River water into the heart of the San Joaquin Valley. This diversion freed up more San Joaquin River water for distribution from Friant Dam along the southeastern side of the valley via the Madera and Friant-Kern canals. But these marvels of the CVP notwithstanding, the desert once again threatens to reclaim hundreds of thousands of acres of San Joaquin Valley agricultural land if two problems are not soon resolved: (1) brine buildup, in part caused by the very water that irrigates the land, and (2) the specter of possible revival of the 160-acre limitation on federal irrigation water use, which no doubt would result in farmers keeping their larger holdings by resorting to greater groundwater pumping and thus overdrafting (see Chapter 3 for more on the 160-acre limitation).

Besides transporting Sacramento River water across the Delta, CVP's Delta Cross Channel staves off tidal saltwater intrusion by releasing freshwater and thus helps maintain the agricultural productivity of Delta soils. But will still more valley land, this time in the western Delta, be lost to agriculture if and when an alternative to the Peripheral Canal becomes a reality?

Opponents point out that in low runoff years, much of the Sacramento River's available flow would have been picked up by the Peripheral Canal and lost by the Delta Cross Channel, which in turn would translate into less water available for tidal flushing and more farmland lost to saltwater encroachment in the western Delta. Proponents say the Peripheral Canal was planned to handle the release of water at several points along its course and was to improve water and land quality in the eastern or innermost Delta. But for these CVP and SWP Delta projects to perform their intended ecological tasks in times of drought, another massive input of freshwater will be needed in the system. Will it come from diversion of the Eel River in the far northwest when the moratorium imposed by the Wild Rivers Act on damming of the Eel lapses in the middle of this decade? Or will one of the alternative water resources to be examined next come to the rescue?

WATER CONSERVATION AND REUSE

To most Californians, the drought of the 1970s is a bad but fading memory. For instance, the severity of the drought in 1977 prompted Los Angeles to adopt a water conservation program, but floods in 1978 and continued above-normal precipitation in 1979 have seemed to obscure the fact that this program is based on city ordinances that will be enforced in the event of another drought. The ordinances prohibit certain water uses and call for water use cutbacks in one voluntary and four mandatory phases ranging up to 25 percent. Penalties for not complying with the mandatory conservation phases would include fines, installation of flow restrictors, and even shutoffs. The prospect of such penalties might prompt citizens to avoid them by practicing home water conservation techniques, such as replacing worn faucet washers, installing plastic inserts to reduce shower flow, and placing water-filled plastic bags in toilet tanks to displace flush water.

The costs of administering mandatory water rationing programs could be staggering and make *reclaimed water* projects (Fig. 5.13) appear all the more necessary despite the relatively high cost of the product they produce: For example, the DWP's 1978 *Draft EIR* estimates that reclaimed wastewater costs between $144 and $170 per AF, whereas local groundwater costs only $29 per AF, when available, and Los Angeles Aqueduct water costs $39 per AF, excluding the value of hydropower produced of about $57 per AF. The imported aqueduct water cost with the hydropower benefit subtracted works out to practically $0 per AF, a figure the Department of Water and Power points to with pride in the 1978 *Draft EIR* proposal on the Owens Valley discussed earlier in this chapter. Nevertheless, DWP has joined other agencies charged with water supply and wastewater disposal in Los Angeles and Orange counties in a joint powers agreement to study problems impeding water reclamation.

Figure 5.14 shows a plan describing proposed improvements to Los Angeles's wastewater collection and disposal system submitted by the city's Department of Public Works pursuant to the federal Clean Water Act. It should be observed that the plan suggests only possible groundwater recharge, irrigation, recreational-facility, and industrial uses for reclaimed water. Wastewater quality criteria still need to be developed for groundwater recharge and industrial use, and the California Department of Health expressly prohibits the use of reclaimed water in domestic drinking water systems.

Recharging and recycling groundwater have met with considerable success in the City of Fresno, which like most other San Joaquin Valley cities depends heavily on groundwater to supply municipal and industrial needs. To resolve the problem of a falling water level directly beneath Fresno, the city and the Fresno Irrigation District have entered into agreements wherein the district delivers water from the CVP's Friant-Kern Canal into the "Leaky Acres" recharge basin. In the several years

Figure 5.13 Moulton-Niguel water reclamation plant handles some 300,000 gallons of wastewater per day, with all of its reclaimed output piped to nearby Mission Viejo golf course in southern Orange County. Wastewater comes into such plants from a trunk sewer line and then proceeds through grid chambers to remove suspended solids (A), *aeration* to help purify the water by airing it out (B), settling basins to settle out sludge and thereby produce clear *effluent,* and chlorination to render potentially *potable* or drinkable water. (Crane Miller)

since the recharge operation began, the quantity and quality of groundwater beneath Fresno have steadily improved. Another facet of the agreement involves keeping the water table beneath the city's wastewater disposal plant from rising too high by pumping it and recycling the water through crop irrigation. The Irrigation District in return allows the city additional water from the Kings River equivalent to 46 percent of the recycled water it receives. This water is then used either for recharge or crop irrigation east of Fresno.

There are some 200 wastewater reclamation plants in California "conserving" about 200,000 AF of water for reuse each year. Irrigated agriculture is far and away the main user of reclaimed water in California and the industry considers its use a major step toward water conservation. Other water-conserving practices employed by agriculture include drip irrigation, use of antitranspirants to cut down on evapotranspiration from leaves, control of water-wasting weeds in canals, improvements in dry farming methods, coating of reservoir

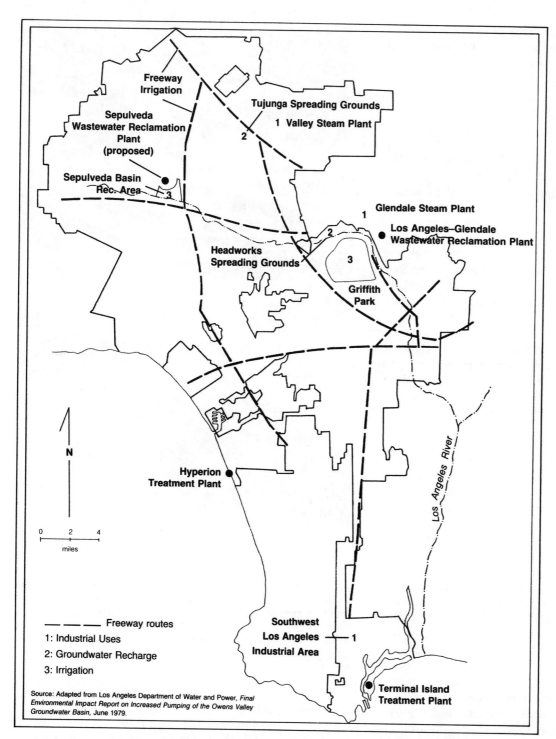

Figure 5.14 Potential uses of reclaimed water within the City of Los Angeles. (Marc Blodgett)

water surfaces with a thin, harmless chemical "film" to reduce evaporation losses, and implementation of special systems to produce greenhouse crops with a minimum of water use.

In summary, water conservation and reclamation practices should continue to gain favor, especially in irrigated agriculture, where some of the cost and quality constraints mentioned earlier are minimal. For instance, reclaimed wastewater that is used to irrigate crops near the plant where it was treated may cost only a few dollars per AF. Nevertheless, the present 200,000 AF of reclaimed water produced each year is a mere drop in the bucket when compared with California agriculture's total annual consumption of some 25 million AF. Moreover, during a drought there is simply less water to reclaim.

Even if the production of reclaimed water increases dramatically—say, 4 or 5 times the present annual rate—reclaimed water will still remain a minor alternative resource.

THE PACIFIC AND THE COLUMBIA: PROLIFIC BUT UNLIKELY WATER SUPPLY ALTERNATIVES

In times of drought especially, many a Californian might cast envious eyes upon the blue waters of the Pacific Ocean and/or Columbia River and be overheard to mutter, "There it is, let's take it"—much as the water seekers of Los Angeles did decades ago when "discovering" the Owens Valley. Nobody denies the seeming infinity of water supply these two sources have to offer, but an unfavorably changing energy picture and mounting environmentalist and regional opposition make the prospects for development of either source appear dimmer with each passing day.

Seawater can be desalted either by evaporation under a transparent cover, using the sun as an energy source, or by evaporation from steaming seawater brought to a boil by heat energy derived from fossil fuel or nuclear sources. The former method is relatively cheap, but it is also slow, cumbersome, and generally inadequate for large-scale use. The latter process, on the other hand, is capable of meeting the demands of large populations but has become prohibitively energy expensive. It takes some 20,000 kWh of electricity to render 1 AF of seawater *potable* (drinkable), whereas one tenth that much energy delivers 1 AF of Colorado River fresh water to Lake Mathews and an actual net gain in electrical energy is realized with each AF of Owens Valley freshwater delivered to the San Fernando Valley.

Steam desalinization plants not only use copious amounts of energy but also are expensive to build and operate. Inflation was a major factor in halting development of two desalting facilities that came closer to realization than most of the others proposed for California. These were: (1) the Bolsa Island Nuclear Desalting Plant, with a freshwater production capability of 150 million gallons a day, which was to be located on a 40-acre artificial island two thirds of a mile off the Orange County coast; and (2) a San Luis Obispo County desalting plant, with a 40-million-gallon daily production capacity, which was to be built adjacent to the existing Diablo Canyon nuclear plant. Antinuclear sentiment, the California Coastal Plan, concern for disposal and/or sale of accumulated salt by-products, and a declining population growth rate were other factors that nullified the proposal. Could it be that desalinization is an idea whose time has come and gone—at least until a cheap and safe source of energy, such as fusion power, is developed?

Any resident of British Columbia, Washington, or Oregon who has traveled in the Owens Valley, seen the movie *Chinatown,* or read *The Water Seekers* would no doubt turn red with rage at the merest suggestion of exporting Columbia River water to California. Yet schemes aimed at accomplishing wider distribution of the Pacific Northwest's vast water resources, such as those suggested by the formation of the North American Water and Power Alliance (NAWAPA), are still bandied about. There is no question that Canada could reap considerable income from the sale of surplus water—not water rights!—to the United States or that Washington and Oregon would derive benefits from a Pacific State federal water transfer project. As it is, Southern California has been receiving hydroelectricity for years from the Columbia River via the Pacific Intertie system.

Still, opposition by northwesterners to exporting water to California appears to be stiffening, and with good reason when Portland's "brownouts" and other rigors of the 1970s drought are recalled. There is also mounting resistance among many states to spending more federal money on California's water problems. In any event, water could well be the next major natural resource to limit California's economic development.

6

ENERGY: THE ASSUMED RESOURCE

Like most of America, California has assumed for many years that the sources of energy are unlimited. Within the last decade, this assumption has undergone serious challenge. As a consumer of half the total resources of the world (with less than one fifteenth of the total population), America has been forced to reexamine its future. Petrochemical energy sources are no longer the monopoly of this country, and the OPEC nations are increasingly flexing their muscles to demonstrate this fact. Alternate sources are needed, and alternate lifestyles may be necessary. The question is, can Americans, and Californians in particular, meet this challenge?

LIFESTYLE CHANGE: CAN CALIFORNIA MAINTAIN ITS MYSTIQUE?

In many respects, California epitomizes the Western world in its attitude toward and use of nature and energy. The commitment of Western civilization to advanced science and technology has permitted great expansions in life standards for humankind. Much of this progress, however, has been accomplished by following a basic social and religious premise: Subdue the earth. Subduing the earth has, in the short term, brought about a lifestyle of unheard-of luxury, nowhere more evident than in California.

Part of the great mystique of California has been use of the land for pleasure. No place is inaccessible; if there is no way to get there, build a road! Freeways and roads have thus become an important feature of the state. Since beaches and shoreline are beautiful, everyone should be able to enjoy their natural beauty, so beaches and shoreline have been "improved" with vast concrete car lots, artificial fishing jetties, and sand groins to prevent subsequent erosion. To this way of thinking, mountains may be majestic evidence of nature's power, but ski lifts, lodges, artificial snow, mountain-forest condos and improved roads make them even better. The vast California deserts that are among the last American

frontiers possess a fragile, balanced ecology, so dirt bikes, off-road and recreational vehicles must be brought in, the better to see this wilderness before it is destroyed. And, of course, in each instance nature is brought to heel for the enjoyment of humans and their ever-present transistorized stereo-television-radio that they bring along to desert, beach, or mountain as inevitably as trash and garbage. Thus, democracy, religion, technology, capitalism, urbanization, and mobility bring new meaning to the concept "natural environment."

Is the Mobile Culture Affordable?

More than any other single artifact, the automobile is the icon of California, a state that has relied heavily upon individualized transportation for most purposes. Although some limited applications of mass transit exist, these are the exceptions; for the most part, the typical pattern is single-passenger transport. Even in the face of reduced gasoline supplies, most Californians have been reluctant to give up the convenience of a personal car. The vast numbers of commuters have shifted approach only to the extent of moving toward smaller, fuel-efficient cars.

Further use of mobile energy resources is required by the nature of recreation in the state. Californians have seldom been deterred by distance in pursuing their entertainment, either as spectators or participants, be it theater, sports, or sightseeing. And it is not only a matter of just the family sedan or wagon, either; the proliferation of recreational vehicles, off-road vehicles, motorcycles, and sports cars has not slackened off perceptibly into the 1980s even though the availability and cost of gas have become important factors.

As a new century approaches, the question of mobility becomes more vital. Clearly, Californians cannot continue in their present pattern. If mobility is to remain a part of the state's identity, forms of transportation must change, since the costs and impracticality of the current mobile culture cannot be borne much longer.

The Poolside Goddess: A Thing of the Past?

The aquatic image is also a part of the California mystique. Southern California in particular is a vast checkerboard tract filled with backyard swimming pools and Jacuzzis. The lifestyle promoted in fashionable magazines, decorators' drawings, newspaper ads, and "house beautiful" publications includes the swimming pool and hot tub as vital elements of the good life. The social and sexual revolution in suburbia focuses upon this symbol, and common wisdom dictates that a home's value jumps with such an addition. No apartment complex or condominium development could survive without the accompanying water sports playground, and the costs have been no object in the past.

Heating water, however, is not an inexpensive proposition. Climbing energy costs have mandated a reexamination of this luxury symbol. The stereotypic golden-tanned poolside goddess relaxing by bubbling, heated water, may soon have to find new sybaritic toys. With both water and energy becoming critical resources in the state, certain priorities must be considered. Swimming may well continue, but in winter months, at least, Californians may have to develop hardier constitutions.

Can Californians Become Energy Spartans?

In the 1970s, the average electrical energy consumption per person per year in America was estimated in the range of 8,000 kilowatt hours—a truly impressive amount. Californians generally held their own in this energy usage and in some respects outstripped it. The needs to which energy was applied ranged over a broad spectrum. Although reduced temporarily during the energy crisis of the early 1970s, this consumption has edged back up, and Californians, like Americans elsewhere, continue to insist on some relatively marginal uses. The extent of these uses can easily be seen during the Christmas season with the prolific and prodigious displays of lights and electrical decorations. Throughout the rest of the year, Californians insist on widespread outdoor lighting of houses, patios, tennis courts, pools, and driveways. Likewise, luxury and convenience appliances remain fast sellers in department and discount stores. Californians seem unable to function without garage door openers, trash compactors, electric toothbrushes and can openers, televisions, and electric knives. Yet in the face of conflicting choices and limited supplies, new energy uses may have to be found in wrists, shoulders, and backs.

The California penchant for air conditioning may undergo a severe test. Although hermetically sealed skyscrapers, schools, enclosed shopping malls, and modern tract houses may not have enough design flexibility to permit natural air circulation, thermostatically controlled indoor climate may soon be an expensive luxury. The assumptions of unlimited energy that have made such design and construction possible in the past can no longer be indulged. Californians must reluctantly face the harsh reality that their energy uses are often wasteful and that the old assumptions do not serve. Petroleum and water, electrical and other forms of energy are valuable assets to the state. Simple belief in unlimited plenty cannot take the place of responsible searches for alternate forms of energy.

ENERGY AND ELECTRICITY: CONSUMPTION AND SUPPLY

Industry, electric utilities, and residential-commercial users each consume from 20 to 25 percent of California's energy supply. The fourth and major energy market category is transportation, which annually requires more than 30 percent of the total energy supply. The latter is considerably above the national average for transportation (about 25 percent) and is attributed to Californians' love affair with the automobile and their aversion to public rapid mass transit. Cars alone in California consume some 20 percent of all the available energy each year. Thus, it is not surprising that California's proportional consumption of petroleum (about 50 percent of the state's total energy supply) is several percentage points above the national average. California's other sources of energy are natural gas (about 35 percent), hydropower (about 10 percent), nuclear power (2 percent), coal (2 percent), and geothermal power (1 percent).

In the realm solely of electrical energy supply and demand, the percentages change noticeably. Transportation all but drops out of the picture, and industry, commerce, and residential users share almost equal thirds of the supply pie. The annual demand for electrical energy has skyrocketed in California over the last quarter century, increasing from 56 billion kWh in 1960 to a projected 250 billion kWh in 1985. By the end of this century, annual consumption of 500 billion kWh of transmitted electricity appears in the offing. As we turn next to a brief examination of each of the sources of electrical energy available from inside and outside California, it is well to bear in mind our earlier discussions of the influence of climate, weather, smog, and water resources on electrical energy supply and demand.

HYDROPOWER

In theory, hydroelectric energy can be generated wherever a controlled water supply can be dropped to a lower elevation. Given California's abundance of high mountain ranges and its orographic precipitation patterns, such hydropower dam sites are plentiful in the state. Locally, rugged topography also facilitates *pumped storage* hydro projects such as seen at Castaic in Figure 6.1. Where water supply is unreliable or relatively small, however, which includes most of the southern third of the state, hydropower development is not practical. And a long drought can all but eliminate hydroelectricity production within the state.

Currently, hydropower meets about 25 percent of California's electrical energy needs, but in another 20 years it is projected to decline to less than 10 percent, droughts or lack of them notwithstanding. The drop of hydro's proportional input is attributed to two factors: (1) the predicted doubling of electricity consumption in the next 15 years, and (2) an already almost fully developed hydropower potential.

California has several major developed hydropower source areas, both inside and outside the state. The Sacramento and its tributaries make up the premier hydro river system in the state, boasting such hydropower fa-

Figure 6.1 Castaic Power Project is operated by the Los Angeles Department of Water and Power in cooperation with the California Department of Water Resources (DWR). The pumped storage facility has an installed capacity of 1,250,000 kilowatts (kW) or 1,250 megawatts (MW), enough power to supply several hundred thousand Los Angeles Basin customers with their electricity needs during daily peak demand periods—*peaking periods* usually occur during afternoon and early evening. Seven *penstocks* (six seen in photo A, with one out of view to the right) both deliver water from Pyramid Reservoir (7.5 miles west via Angeles Tunnel and 1,060 ft higher) to seven reversible generator-pumps (six each producing 200 MW and one yielding 50 MW) and carry it back uphill to Pyramid, which is the *upper forebay*. The reverse pumping is done during normally low power demand periods in the late night and early morning, with power coming from steam electric plants in the Basin and water coming from the *lower, or pumping, forebay* (B). If this were not a pumped storage facility, but rather a standard powerhouse where the water is not recycled, the water seen here would be occupying an *afterbay*. The *surge chamber* or tank seen above the penstocks acts as a giant shock absorber to relieve excess pressure in the tunnel and penstocks during a sudden shutdown. When needed, additional water supply for Pyramid Lake originates from the West Branch of the DWR's California Aqueduct as its waters are being pumped up and over the Tehachapi Mountains. (Crane Miller)

cilities as Oroville Dam and Shasta Dam (Fig. 5.12). The San Joaquin River system is a distant second but claims one of the state's unique hydro diversion projects in Southern California Edison's (SCE) Big Creek Project (Fig. 6.2). The undeveloped rivers of the northwest augment the state's hydropotential, but with the exception of the Eel River after 1985, the Wild Rivers Act protects them from development. Environmentalists, who object to the inundation of wildlife habitat, damage to fisheries,

change in microclimate, displacement of people, and elimination of free-flowing streams caused by dam building, may also put a damper on development of what's left of California's hydropower potential (although they now seem to have their hands full fighting the proponents of coal and nuclear power development, which pose ecological hazards far greater than those of hydropower).

California's two main outside sources of hydropower are power plants along the lower Colorado River and the Pacific Northwest/Southwest Intertie, which imports Columbia River energy. The Bureau of Reclamation's Hoover Dam is the showpiece of Colorado River Basin hydro development: Its power plant has a rated capacity of 1,345 megawatts (MW), which is enough electricity to air condition and light up Las Vegas, Nevada around the clock and still have 513 MW left over to send to Los Angeles, assuming there is plenty of water flowing down the Colorado.

Southern California gets another massive input of interstate hydroelectricity from the Pacific Intertie via direct current (DC) and alternating current (AC) transmission lines. The 845-mile DC line is the longest-distance high-capacity line of its kind in the world, stretching from a converter station near the Dalles and other Federal Columbia River Power System dams to the Sylmar DC-AC converter terminal. DC lines use fewer cables (usually two per circuit), fewer conductors, cheaper towers, and less right of way (*easement*) than AC lines and thus are about 35 percent less costly to build than AC lines. Yet DC lines have the same transmission capacity as AC lines, which in the case of the Pacific Intertie is 1,400 MW. The Southern California utilities sharing the Intertie's output from the Sylmar station are Southern California Edison (50 percent), the Los Angeles Department of Water and Power (40 percent), and the local power agencies for the cities of Burbank, Glendale, and Pasadena (10 percent for all three).

Adding still more hydropower to the southland's hydro pool are the DWP's Los Angeles Aqueduct power plants in Owens Gorge (110 MW, with storage in Crowley Lake) and San Francisquito Canyon (74 MW, including power generated at Los Angeles and Franklin Canyon reservoirs in the Santa Monica Mountains). Indeed, Los Angeles and neighboring communities are well off hydroelectrically despite the region's lack of a dependable water supply.

The central purpose of intertie systems is to ensure a supply of electricity during emergencies and during time of routine power plant maintenance. In essence, the Pacific Intertie is insurance for Los Angeles against the type of blackouts that have occurred in other major cities such as New York. But an intertie is reciprocal as well. For instance, when a severe blizzard in the winter of 1968 caused hydroelectric outages in the Pacific Northwest, SCE sent power generated at local steam electric plants to Oregon and Washington via Pacific Intertie AC lines, thus averting what could have been a major disaster. The intertie system also links Northern California's Pacific Gas and Electric Company (PG&E) with both SCE and the Federal Columbia River power projects.

Actually, Pacific Intertie is international in scope by virtue of its use of some of the so-called *Canadian entitlement power:* Three dams built along the upper Co-

Figure 6.2 Big Creek Project in the southwestern Sierra Nevada was developed by Southern California Edison (SCE) early in the twentieth century to provide up to 700 MW of hydropower to the Los Angeles Basin. Project reservoirs and their elevations include Florence Lake (7,328 ft), Huntington Lake (6,950 ft) (seen here), and Shaver Lake (5,370 ft). The waters of the South Fork of the San Joaquin River are diverted at Florence Lake and from Mono Creek at Lake Edison into the Ward Tunnel, which carries them 13 miles west to Huntington Lake. Tunnels, penstocks, power houses, and dams downstream from Huntington Lake combine to provide the hydroelectric output. Recreation is also a significant reservoir use. (Crane Miller)

lumbia River in British Columbia provide "stored capacity" of some 2,800 MW, which by international treaty and subsequent agreements can be used by U.S. utilities until such time as Canadian utilities need it. The DWP, for example, has contracted to purchase a substantial proportion of Canadian entitlement power for transmission to Los Angeles over Pacific Intertie DC lines.

The ultimate in intertie exchange developments will be a *national grid* connecting all major utilities from coast to coast. With such a nationwide system, a *peak power demand* at 6 p.m. in New York, for example, could be met with surplus power from the Pacific Northwest or California, where it would be only 3 p.m. and peak demands would not be occurring. Three hours later, *peaking power* supply could be shifted, with New York augmenting the West Coast's electrical energy demands. Ownership, control, and dissimilar power markets in the four time zones are the biggest obstacles to development of a national grid. In the meantime, though, Pacific Intertie already affords California participation in a *regional grid* system that goes a long way towards preventing blackouts of the sort that have plagued the East Coast.

OIL AND NATURAL GAS

Since the late nineteenth century, petroleum and (later) natural gas have been California's most valuable mineral products, and for a few decades in this century California led all states in production. But in the 1960s, the mounting energy demands of an expanding population and an increasingly automated society forced California into importing these hydrocarbons. Today, California ranks third behind Texas and Louisiana in petroleum

production and much farther down the list in natural gas production.

In-state and imported oil and natural gas presently provide about 60 percent of California's electrical energy through their use as the fossil fuels that fire steam electric plants (Fig. 6.3). The significance of fossil fuel power is exemplified by Los Angeles, whose Department of Water and Power can generate more than 3,300 MW from its steam electric plants versus about one third that amount from its hydroelectric sources. By the end of the twentieth century, though, oil is projected to supply only about 10 percent of the state's power and natural gas is predicted to drop out of the picture altogether.

California's own natural gas supply is all but exhausted, as demonstrated by the fact that Southern California Gas (SCG), the state's largest gas company, was importing 96 percent of all its gas in 1980 from two out-of-state suppliers: El Paso Natural Gas Company (Texas Permian Basin) and Transwestern Pipeline Company (New Mexico's San Juan Basin). This projected loss, as discussed previously in this chapter, could have a devastating effect on both the economy and the environment unless liquefied natural gas (LNG) or some other clean-burning form of energy comes to the rescue.

In-state petroleum reserves are dwindling, too, causing oil companies to mount pressure on the government to open up the U.S. Navy's Elk Hills field in the San Joaquin Valley and to allow an increase in offshore drilling leases (Fig. 6.4). Offshore oil reserves may surpass all those on dry land in California, but their exploitation may never be fully realized because of constraints evoked by memories of the devastating Santa Barbara Channel oil spill of 1969 and by the passing into law of the California Coastal Plan. Although 1.3 million acres offshore from Humboldt, Mendocino, Sonoma, Marin, San Mateo, Santa Cruz, San Luis Obispo, and Santa

Figure 6.3 Moss Landing Plant, near San Jose, and other oil-fired steam electric plants along the California coast and inland rivers meet most of the state's electricity demands. Steam electric plants, whether fossil fueled or nuclear powered, consume much water for cooling purposes, which explains the preference for waterside location. (Pacific Gas and Electric Company)

Barbara counties are under study by the federal government for its proposed oil and gas leasing program, environmentalists are certain to fight tooth and nail to prevent oil rigs from invading this as yet untouched and spectacularly scenic coastline. Meanwhile, environmentalists have already won an important victory in the government's decision to delete from proposed oil lease sale all offshore tracts from Dana Point in Orange County southward along the San Diego County coastline.

While the contribution of natural gas to creating electrical energy has been predicted to decline to near zero before the end of the century, supplemental supplies via pipeline from Mexico and Canada, by ship as liquefied natural gas from Alaska and Indonesia, and as coal gas from a once-proposed New Mexico coal gasification plant may forestall the exit of natural gas from steam electric plant use and also maintain adequate supplies to meet winter space heating needs. Because of the inability to gain a site lease from the Navajo Indians and uncertainty over federal loan guarantees, plans for building the nation's first coal gasification plant were abandoned early in 1979 by Pacific Lighting Corporation. Thus, the LNG supplement appears to hold the most promise, for it will about double the amount of both the already contracted Canadian supplement and that of a coal gasification plant, if plans for building the latter are ever revived and then implemented.

Location of an LNG terminal poses some thorny problems. Wherever LNG is unloaded from tankers, it must be reconverted to gas, the unloading of the low temperature liquid and its reconversion requiring the utmost care to keep explosions from occurring. State law expressly prohibits such a facility operating anywhere near populated areas. Thus, with the public safety in mind, the California Public Utilities Commission (PUC) has long favored siting the state's first LNG terminal at Cojo Bay near Point Conception, which is centrally located with regard to San Francisco, Los Angeles, and San Diego, but some 40 miles away from the closest city of any appreciable size—Santa Barbara.

The Point Conception site also presents problems, however, including some of the roughest seas found anywhere along the California coast, the usual seismic hazards, Indian claims to the land, and the federal government's coolness towards LNG as a desirable energy source. To prevent Point Conception's becoming a graveyard for tankers, a half-billion dollar breakwater would have to be built. Another extra cost in developing the terminal would be incurred in building structures that could withstand a 7.5 Richter scale earthquake. Indian claims, which were expressed by an encampment at the site of up to 50 Indians from May 1978 until March 1979, are not likely to be resolved until the Indians at least are granted some kind of permanent access for religious purposes. And, in any case, the federal government would rather see greater development of domestic reserves of natural gas, even though it has given California the go-ahead to import LNG from Indonesia. In the final analysis, each of these problems seems capable of solution. If and when they are solved and the joint PG&E-SCG Point Conception terminal is developed, it will satisfy about 10 percent of California's natural gas wants.

Whether or not liquefied natural gas ever comes to California, the import of overseas crude oil will no doubt continue to increase both in amount and in environmental impact. Until the mid-1970s, most tankers were small enough to be unloaded inside California's refinery ports. But now a growing number of the vessels are supertankers too large to enter the state's ports. This means that the large tankers must lie outside and have their petroleum carried into port by smaller ships in a process known as *lightering*. The negative impact on the environment comes in the form of fumes escaping into the atmosphere when the oil is being transferred from the larger to the smaller vessel.

The problem has become especially acute off San Diego, where on some days these emissions account for more than 10 percent of all local hydrocarbon pollution. The state Air Resources Board (ARB) has regulations which local air quality control districts can use to control the problem. The question arises, however, as to whether or not California has the right to regulate air pollution from sources outside its territorial boundaries. Nevertheless, if lightering operations can be moved considerably farther offshore than the present average of 60 miles, it is possible that winds will carry the pollutants away from the coast and/or dissipate them before they reach coastal cities.

If what has been said so far seems frustrating as regards the best efforts of some Californians to establish more fossil fuel terminals, consider for a moment the Sohio controversy. In the mid-1970s, Sohio (Standard Oil of Ohio, which is partly owned by British Petroleum) proposed construction of a $1 billion terminal in Long Beach (Fig. 6.5) to transfer Alaskan crude oil to an unused gas pipeline and pump it on its way to Midland, Texas and from there to refineries in the Midwest. The purpose of the project was not to supply California with more oil but rather to save about a dollar a barrel (1 barrel or bbl = 42 gallons) in extra shipping costs incurred in shipping Alaskan oil through the Panama Canal and increase Alaskan production. The President of the United States, the governor of California, and the voters of Long Beach all approved the proposed terminal and the principal air pollution issues had essentially been worked out with some tradeoffs.[1]

In March 1979, however, Sohio suddenly canceled the proposed project; apparently it could not countenance any further delays in gaining final regulatory approval

Figure 6.4 "Texas towers" in Santa Barbara Channel, although unsightly, pump oil from California's prolific offshore reserves. On January 28, 1969, a well drilled from one platform blew out, leading to an oil spill that spread along 20 miles of seashore and 40 miles out to sea. Beaches were befouled and birds by the thousands died. GOO (Get Oil Out) and other groups opposed to offshore drilling were quick to organize and warn of the potential for another such disaster. (Standard Oil Co. of California)

from local and state agencies. As it was, Sohio had already spent $50 million and filed more than 700 permits and applications in trying to get the project underway. There also existed uncertainty over threatened citizen suits and the possibility that Sohio might not gain access to the pipeline it planned to use.

Whatever the reasons for abandoning the project, it is clear that in matters of energy supply and environmental quality, California is never likely to have its cake and eat it, too. For it now seems that every new energy input proposal must be so airtight that it can survive any number of legal challenges. Such assurance is, of course, impossible. In the meantime, the state and the nation edge ever closer to the brink of energy disaster. On the other hand, perhaps the seemingly infinite number of squabbling public and private personalities and agencies involved in the Sohio terminal controversy will be able to join forces and resolve the problem in a way that will serve as a model for the successful development of future energy projects.

Until the Long Beach terminal is built and put into operation, however, Alaskan oil will continue to reach the eastern United States via the more expensive Panama Canal route and some may even go off to Japan in a swapping arrangement that would bring more foreign oil into East Coast ports; at present, oil companies are prohibited from exporting Alaskan crude. Moreover,

---

[1] Under the Clean Air Act, no new source of pollution is allowed where the air is already dirtier (as in SCAB) than federal regulations allow. As is the case with lightering, unloading of tankers at the terminal would involve release of hydrocarbon fumes, but Sohio agreed to suppress other sources of smog as a tradeoff. There also exists the chance of an in-harbor oil spill, but this hazard is present at oil tanker terminals everywhere. The Los Angeles Basin is a major refinery center, although it will not refine the Sohio project oil.

Figure 6.5 Los Angeles–Long Beach harbor coal-loading facilities exported an estimated 6 million tons of coal in 1981 and are to be expanded to handle tenfold that amount by the end of the decade. In Northern California, coal port facilities are proposed for Redwood City, Sacramento, and Stockton. One million tons of coal were shipped in 1981 from existing facilities in Stockton. Japanese, South Korean, and other Far Eastern steam electric plant operators are converting from oil to coal and consequently provide an ever-increasing demand for American coal. The coal is strip-mined in Colorado, Utah, and other Rocky Mountain states and then shipped by unit train to Los Angeles–Long Beach and Stockton. (Crane Miller)

with the terminal Alaskan daily production could be increased from the present 1.2 million bbl to 1.6 million bbl. Clearly, building the terminal is in the national interest.

COAL

California is not a coal state, in terms either of minable reserves or imports. But several nearby Western states lay claim to what may be collectively the world's richest reserves of "strippable" coal—coal that is accessible to surface or *strip mining* as opposed to tunnel or *shaft mining*. California steelmakers and utilities presently use a tiny portion of this coal, the former being the only major importer.

At present there are no coal-fired steam electric plants in the state, although DWP and SCE now receive up to 2,000 MW of coal power from such plants in Arizona, New Mexico, and Nevada. And if all goes as planned by the end of the decade, DWP hopes to be meeting almost half of Los Angeles's electrical needs with imported coal power. Southern California Edison is said to be considering siting a coal power plant somewhere in Southern California and is already going ahead with plans to develop a demonstration coal gasification facility jointly with Texaco at its Daggett electric generating station in the Mojave Desert. In Northern California, Pacific Gas and Electric is considering in-state coal-fired power plants in several locations, including Montezuma, near Solano; South Yuba, near Yuba City; Butte, near Oroville; and Willows, between Red Bluff and Sacramento.

Coal, whether it is burned inside or outside California, poses monumental economic, environmental, and social headaches for the entire Far West. Some remedies are being developed, however. Coal may be regionally plentiful and therefore a relatively cheap form of energy raw

material, but it is dirty, bulky, and thus costly to transport, even by *unit train* carrying the single product on a regular schedule from strip mine to market.

One answer to the hauling problem is the mixing of pulverized coal with water into a *slurry*, which is then pumped through a pipeline to its ultimate destination. For instance, a coal slurry pipeline now operates between the Black Mesa coal mine in northeastern Arizona and the jointly operated (by the Department of Water and Power, Southern California Edison, and four other agencies) Mohave Power Plant in Nevada south of Las Vegas.

Slurry may provide a solution to another, more serious problem—that of air pollution from coal burning, which was touched on in Chapter 4. For as the Germans demonstrated during World War II, product slurry can be distilled into a liquid fuel that is rid of much of the sulfur inherent in solid coal and thus may not necessitate the use of *scrubbers* to clean up the exhausted fumes and smoke following its burning. At present, though, it looks like we are a few years away from a *coal liquefaction* process that will render coal liquids competitive with solid coal or oil in price.

Another type of coal-caused air pollution that is not as readily capable of solution is that caused by coal dust kicked up at strip mining sites. Between more strip mines with their coal dust and more power plants with their coal fumes, the Great Basin, once one of the clearest regions in the country, may one day become nearly unbreathable.

As for the socioeconomic benefits and costs of increased coal exploitation in the Far West, they range from more jobs and income for some residents to the disruption of native Indian lifestyles and the social disorganization of fly-by-night towns following strip mines from site to site. It seems inevitable that the cowboy and the Indian are destined to be replaced by the strip miner and the coal power plant operator. And what will happen to the magnificent Western landscape that has drawn so many tourists and retirees? The strip mining people say they can make it look like new again when they are finished with a site. Ranchers and environmentalists say it will never be the same.

Perhaps the *coup de grace* in the whole matter of coal for California comes when other Western states are spoken of as energy colonies of California. The death of the giant Kaiparowits coal power project proposal in southern Utah in 1976 was undoubtedly a signal from nearby states that California had better look in its own backyard for coal-fired steam electric plant sites. To outsiders, California's 1,200 miles of coastline seemed ideal for such sites, especially since steam electric plants need copious amounts of water for cooling purposes and the prospect of future droughts acts as a limiting factor to the development of interior Great Basin sites. To most Californians, though, there were already more oil-fired steam electric plants along the coast than was desirable. Furthermore, the state's Air Resources Board looks dimly upon coal power plant development in urban areas, either along the coast or in the interior, and the federal Clean Air Act would seem to preclude such development in any event. It may be that California will have to await the perfection of liquefied and/or gasified coal, which can be burned in already existing oil- or gas-fired steam plant boilers, before coal will supply appreciably more than the present 10 percent of the state's electrical energy needs.

GEOTHERMAL POWER

Mention of geothermal energy development does not trigger the same negative feedback that oil and coal do. Maybe this is because most Californians are unfamiliar with its environmental impacts. Or perhaps the apparent lack of furor can be traced to the fact that only a paltry 2 percent of California's electrical energy demands are presently satisfied by geothermal power. Yet California is the sole national producer of commercial geothermal power and holds the greatest potential for its future development.

Pacific Gas and Electric's Geysers facility in Northern California's Sonoma County is the only geothermal power plant in the contiguous United States, except for relatively small pilot facilities in the Salton Trough. Presently, it has an electrical generating capacity of 500 MW, but the Geysers' estimated potential capacity is 2,000 MW, a power output that is sufficient to serve one half the present needs of the nearby San Francisco metropolitan area. The nation's second commercial geothermal power plant, being developed jointly by Chevron Resources Company and Southern California Edison near Heber in the Imperial Valley, is scheduled to be *on line* (transmitting electricity to customers) in 1983. Its generating capacity of 50 MW will meet the electrical needs of a community of some 30,000 homes. Where the third and succeeding geothermal power plants will be located is uncertain, but the Salton Trough and other geothermal fields throughout California are all possibilities.

As with projections on the future use of coal in California, there is considerable variance as regards geothermal energy. In a 1976 Federal Reserve Bank energy study, the Rand Corporation predicted geothermal, solar, and *fuel cell* (similar to a battery) energy sources will supply 15.1 percent of the state's electric energy by the year 2000, whereas the Lawrence Berkeley Laboratory foresaw only 8.9 percent and the utilities projected a scant 5.1 percent. Advancements in geothermal recovery technology, as discussed in this section, will eventually tell the story.

In undergoing radioactive decay, magma and semi-molten rocks deep within the earth release heat energy which convects toward the surface. Where this heat concentrates in rocks near the surface and mixes either with naturally occurring groundwater or artificially injected water from the surface, it constitutes a geothermal field that can be tapped as *steam, hot water,* or *hot rocks,* as shown in Figure 6.6.

Hot water or *flashed steam* systems are the most common found in California, throughout the Salton Trough, for example, from the Imperial Valley southward to Cerro Prieto in Baja California. Unfortunately, flashed steam systems are much more costly and difficult to develop than dry steam systems because the hot water usually contains dissolved minerals that corrode pipes and other equipment. The brine buildup problem has slowed development of the Salton Sea Geothermal Field to a snail's pace, and potential negative environmental impacts, such as noxious hydrogen sulfide odors, hot wastewater and brine disposal, and the atmospheric effects of cooling towers, portend still more delays.

On the positive side, geothermal power plants have a distinct advantage over fossil fuel and nuclear power plants in that almost all the activities involved in producing geothermal power take place at or adjacent to the plants. For example, a geothermal power plant's raw

Figure 6.6 Geothermal electricity generation at the Geysers, 70 miles northeast of San Francisco. (Pacific Gas and Electric Company)

material—steam or hot water—is extracted from the earth right at the plant site, whereas oil, coal, or uranium are often mined hundreds or even thousands of miles away from where they will eventually be used to generate power. These fuels are not only costly and often risky to transport (tanker oil spills, for example), but in some cases they must be refined and stored before use. It is well to remember that hydro, solar, and wind power plants offer on-site advantages similar to those of geothermal power plants.

NUCLEAR POWER

The films *Chinatown* and *The China Syndrome* are similar not only in title but also in the fact that they add fuel to the fires of controversy over the development of certain resources: the former focusing on a big city's water schemes, the latter coming down hard on the nuclear power industry. *Chinatown* was released decades after Los Angeles had firmly established its water storage and distribution system and thus the movie was not likely to cause the undoing of anything. *The China Syndrome,* on the other hand, came out essentially before nuclear power plant proliferation was underway and at a time (March 1979) when the nuclear industry was already taking its lumps with five nuclear power plant closings in Maine, New York, Pennsylvania, and Virginia; antinuclear protests in New Hampshire; a cooling system malfunction causing dangerous radioactive steam leakage at the Three Mile Island nuclear power plant in Pennsylvania; and the discovery of possibly hazardous levels of radioactivity from old buried radium mine tailings in Denver, Colorado.

In the same month, however, the nuclear industry got some good news, too: A U.S. District Court judge in San Diego voided a 1976 California law requiring the state Energy Commission to determine that provision for nuclear waste disposal exists before the construction of a nuclear plant. In essence, the ruling confirmed federal rather than state control over such matters and lifted what had effectively been a moratorium on nuclear plant development in California.

All told, the foregoing events seemed symptomatic of the many troubles of the nation's most suspect energy source, *nuclear fission,* whereby heat energy is released by the chain reaction splitting of uranium (U-235) atoms, which leads eventually to the generation of electricity. At the root of these troubles are vital public concerns such as (1) the disposal of nuclear power plant radioactive wastes, (2) the location of nuclear plants in earthquake-prone regions, and (3) the possibility, albeit remote, of a meltdown of the reactor in a nuclear power plant. A near meltdown is effectively dramatized in *The China Syndrome,* and for a few days in March 1979 there was the outside chance that the Three Mile Island accident might lead to a meltdown.

The suggestion that nuclear power's time may have come and gone in California bears credence when both the present and future status of nuclear power plants is pondered. As pointed out in Figure 6.7, nuclear power plants at two different sites presently supply between 3 and 6 percent of the state's electricity and only about

A

B

Figure 6.7 The San Onofre nuclear power facility, jointly operated by Southern California Edison and San Diego Gas and Electric, is located near the Orange–San Diego county line. Reactor 1 (to the left in the aerial photo, A) produces up to 436 MW of power; but once reactors 2 and 3 (in photo B) are on line, production will increase by 2,200 MW. Rancho Seco, near Sacramento, is the state's only other on-line nuclear power facility, Humboldt in northwestern California having discontinued use of nuclear fuel several years ago. Pacific Gas and Electric Company's controversial Diablo Canyon nuclear plant, which is located on the central coast near San Luis Obispo and was completed in 1979 at a cost of $2.3 billion, had its license to load nuclear fuel and commence low-power testing suspended by the federal Nuclear Regulatory Commission in November 1981 so that the plant's earthquake protection features could be verified. PG&E contemplates compliance and relicensing in 1982. (A: David Vechik; B: Crane Miller)

2 percent of all its energy demands. When the second and third San Onofre reactors finally come on line, nuclear energy's input will jump slightly. In the meantime, however, rising capital construction costs actually involved in completing San Onofre pose one more threat to atomic power expansion in general. On the other hand, the comparatively low cost of nuclear fuel bodes well for the nuclear power industry from the standpoint of energy economics.

Aside from environmental concerns and given that Californians have long assumed a cheap and abundant supply of electrical energy, economics may ultimately dictate the extent of our commitment to nuclear power. Will too rapid a lifestyle change resulting from the rising price and limited amount of foreign oil push us into more atomic power development? The Federal Reserve study mentioned earlier seems to indicate so. The Rand Corporation predicts that 59.1 percent of California's electricity will come from nuclear plants in the year 2000, and the utilities forecast 50.1 percent. Only the Lawrence Berkeley Laboratory, with a projection of 30.6 percent, is somewhat less optimistic about nuclear power's future. But all these predictions were made back in 1976 before the nuclear power industry fell victim to what has become of late a rash of unfortunate circumstances.

Nuclear innovations, including development of *breeder reactors* and *fusion power,* could one day prove a boon to the industry. Different types of breeder reactors, any one of which "breeds" enough fuel to replenish itself and drive another reactor over a number of years without the assistance of uranium enrichment facilities, are presently in operation at several locations in Europe and the Soviet Union. The specter of breeder reactors overproducing plutonium and thus fostering the runaway buildup of atomic weaponry has caused many government leaders in this country to take a dim view of breeder reactor development. So far, no commercial breeder reactor power plants are operating in the United States, although a demonstration plant along the Clinch River in Tennessee was proposed by the Westinghouse Company and a demonstration core has been installed at a nuclear power plant in Shippingport, Pennsylvania as part of the Naval Reactors Program.

By comparison, nuclear fusion technology is far behind that of breeder reactors. Fusion is the opposite of fission in that atoms combine rather than split to produce energy. But for fusion to be useful, it must yield more energy than is invested in heating it. Temperatures of about 100,000,000°C must be reached for fusion to occur, and so far this has been impossible to attain. Laser fusion may provide an answer, but this research, too, is only in its infant stages.

SOLAR ENERGY

Solar energy derives ultimately from the nuclear fusion process as it takes place deep within our sun. The sun's nuclear energy rises to the surface and is emitted there in the form of energy known variously as *solar radiation, electromagnetic radiation,* or *shortwave radiation.* Solar energy travels out into space at a constant speed of 186,000 miles (300,000 km) per second. The earth, an average of 93 million miles (150 million km) or about 8 minutes and 20 seconds away, intercepts only a tiny fraction of the sun's total energy output. The intercepted energy or *solar insolation* then changes form as it penetrates deeper into the earth's atmosphere, losing much of its dangerous shortwave component long before reaching the troposphere: X rays are absorbed at 50 to 60 miles altitude and ultraviolet rays are mostly screened out in the ozone layer at 10 to 30 miles above the earth, although the latter process may have been weakened by the rampant use of fluorocarbon aerosols here on earth. Once the incoming solar radiation reaches and passes

through the troposphere, it loses much of its energy to scattering, reflection, and absorption caused by the presence of water vapor, dust, chemical molecules, and clouds. Finally, the approximately 50 percent of remaining solar radiation is first absorbed by the ground and water surfaces of the earth and then reradiated as *ground radiation* or *longwave radiation* (principally *infrared* energy) that heats and maintains the air we breathe.

This transformation to longwave radiation and its retention by any barrier to escape, be it a cloud layer in the sky or the well-insulated walls and roof of a house, as illustrated in Figure 6.8, provides us with our most basic use of solar energy—*solar heating.* Southern Californians started amplifying this *greenhouse effect* in 1909 with the building and installation of *solar collectors* to heat water. But by the late 1920s, natural gas was economically outcompeting the sun, resulting in some 15,000 solar collectors in the greater Los Angeles area falling into disuse. Now, though, solar energy use appears on the threshhold of an unprecedented renaissance as natural gas grows scarcer, oil becomes more expensive, coal pollutes more of the environment, and nuclear fuels seem more dangerous than ever before.

Other signs of a solar revival are seen in the granting of a federal tax credit for those homeowners who install solar equipment; the involvement of General Electric, Reynolds Metals, Exxon, General Motors, Jet Propulsion Laboratory (JPL), and other large corporations in solar research and development; federal, state, and city government promotion of solar development; and possible utility company offerings of low interest loans on approved solar and other energy conservation devices. For solar energy's new life to last and prosper, however, inadequate financial incentives from government and private money lenders and lack of consumer confidence in the solar industry will have to be overcome.

Figure 6.9 illustrates the fortunate position California occupies in relation to the rest of the nation as regards the development of solar power plants: It is one of only four states that has an appreciable amount of undeveloped land lying inside of the 500-langley maximum solar radiation *isoline* (line along which a given value is equal). (A langley is a unit of illumination used to measure temperature equal to 1 gram calorie per square centimeter of irradiated surface.) The Great Basin, Mojave Desert, and Colorado Desert portions of California have ample area for space-consuming arrays of solar collectors and concentrators (mirror-lens systems) that would provide the heat energy necessary to run the turbine generators of each *solar thermal electric* power plant developed—two or more such plants may be in operation in the region on a demonstration basis before the end of this decade.

In October 1980, the site of the nation's first solar electric plant, Solar One, was dedicated near Daggett in the Mojave Desert. Solar One, a joint venture of the Los Angeles Department of Water and Power, Southern California Edison, the U.S. Department of Energy, and the California Energy Commission, will generate 10 MW from 1,818 heliostats (mirrors) reflecting the sun's rays onto a collecting "power tower" containing a steam boiler. Steam will then drive a turbine and generator.

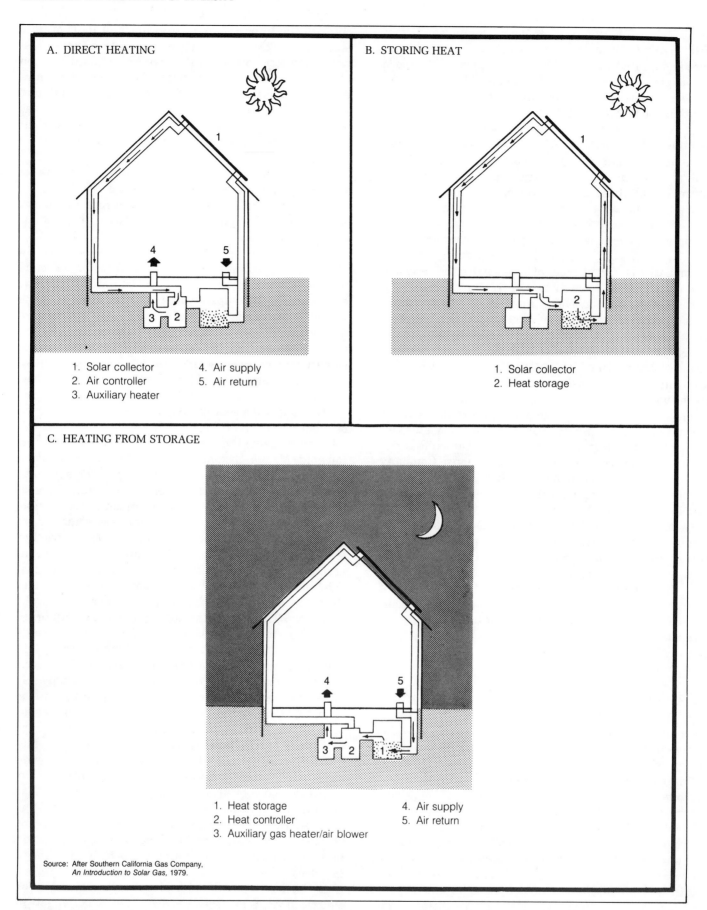

Figure 6.8 Home solar heating system. (A) Air is circulated through a collector, absorbing heat from the sun as it passes through. The heated air is either ducted directly into the house for instantaneous use or (B) stored for several days. The storage system shown here (C) is a large bin of small rocks that absorb heat from the hot air passing through them. When cooler outside temperatures prevail, a blower circulates the warm air from the storage bin throughout the house. Because of uncertainties of weather and practical limits of storage capacity, the sun cannot supply total heating requirements. A conventional gas heating system is therefore required for the times when there is not enough solar energy to heat the home. (Richard Crooker)

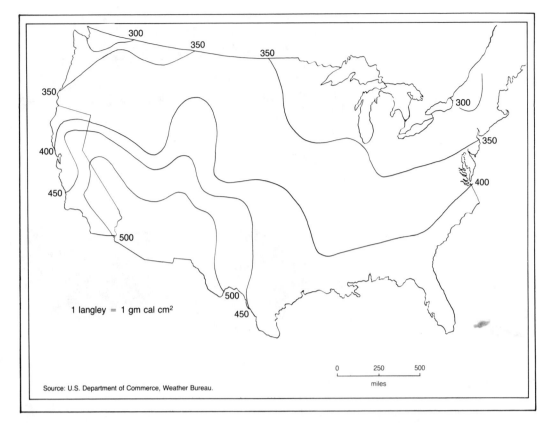

1 langley = 1 gm cal cm²

0   250   500
miles

Source: U.S. Department of Commerce, Weather Bureau.

Figure 6.9   Mean daily solar radiation (in langleys) in the United States annually. (Karen Geissler)

The negative environmental impacts of large areas of desert covered by unsightly solar collector farms (130 acres at Solar One) and possible microclimatic thermal imbalances seem mild in comparison with the impacts posed by fossil fuel and nuclear power plants. Development of *photovoltaics* or *solar cells,* which convert solar energy directly into electricity and which have already proven reliable in supplying on-board power in all manner of satellites, is expected to progress to the point in the next several years of rendering solar cells economically competitive with conventional electrical energy sources. Now, though, electricity from photovoltaics costs 30 to 100 times more than from conventional power plants. But solar electric plants energized by photovoltaics would consume relatively little desert land by eliminating the need for solar collectors. A third desert solar energy innovation, now being tested by the oil-short Israelis, is the *solar pond.* Plans are already underway to develop solar pond power plants by DWP at Owens Lake and by SCE at the Salton Sea.

Given the intermittency of solar energy—that is, there is none of it at night and greatly reduced amounts on cloudy days—the storage problem is perhaps the biggest single drawback faced by the solar industry. For space and water heating, as shown in Figure 6.8, heat can be stored in well-insulated water tanks or rock beds. For commercial solar electric plants, the storage problem is much more difficult, although some solutions may lie in utilizing electrochemical storage (storage batteries and fuel cells), pumped storage, and production of hydrogen for solar electricity (the hydrogen would then be burned as a fuel when needed).

If solar cells accompanied by any one of these storage facilities could be adapted to individual structure use, such as a single-family house, that building's occupants could receive enough solar energy to meet all their heating and electrical needs around the clock and be free of any energy input from utilities or other outside sources. For example, taking into account such geographical variables as location, average cloud cover, and hours of darkness, a square foot of area anywhere in the United States receives on the average the equivalent of 17 watts of electrical energy per hour from the sun. Using this 17-watt amount and applying only a 10 percent efficiency factor to the use of solar cells, a 20 × 30 ft panel of solar cells could produce about 25 kWh of electricity per day in one year's time. This is sufficient output to satisfy the electricity needs of a single-family household of four. For larger numbers of people and/or bigger buildings, photovoltaic panel size would simply be increased. Another technique, involving either home solar cells or windmills, would tie homes into a reciprocal system whereby surplus electricity generated at homes during the day or during high wind periods would be transmitted to nearby power plants. At night or during windless periods, power plants would return electricity to the homes.

WIND POWER

Harnessing *wind energy* to generate power, *bioconversion* of agricultural and municipal wastes into fuel, and generating electricity from *ocean thermal* differences (temperature change from ocean depths to surface) represent still more ways in which we can utilize solar energy. Again, as stressed earlier, California's sunny climate, mountainous topography, and location next to the Pacific Ocean place it in an enviable position in North America for utilizing all forms of solar energy.

Given California's unique atmosphere-land-water relationships, the development of wind power appears to hold the most promise among the more unconventional forms of solar energy. The high, continuous ridges of the Sierra Nevada, lying almost perpendicular to the prevailing westerlies from the Pacific, provide the windiest, albeit perhaps the most hazardous, wind power sites in the state. Environmentalists are not likely to be enamored of the prospect of windmills along the John Muir or Pacific Crest trails, but it is such high-altitude locales that offer the strongest and most constant winds in the state. Desert mountain passes—in eastern San Gorgonio Pass, for example, where SCE is testing a 3-MW, triple-bladed, 200-ft wind turbine electric generator—are also strong candidates for selection as windmill sites. Figure 6.10 demonstrates a wind power and storage test facility recently installed in the Mojave Desert at Soda Lake.

Utilization of wind power dates back many centuries but, as with other types of solar energy, lost favor with the advent of fossil fuel use. Now, with oil rapidly becoming economically unattractive, windmills may stage a mild comeback. Today's technology permits only up to a maximum of about 5 MW of power from the largest wind turbine, which means thousands would have to be installed in California before wind power could be considered any more than an experimental curiosity. Doubling or tripling their capacity might begin to make wind power seem like a viable energy alternative. But the intermittency of wind and the consequent storage problem make major utilization of wind energy and other forms of solar power seem a distant prospect.

ENERGY CONSERVATION AND ENVIRONMENT

Conservation is one of the best ideas yet suggested in grappling with the energy crisis. It has had trouble, however, getting much past the hypothetical stage. The 55-mile per hour speed limit, better gas mileage from more compact cars, utility company consumer conservation and education programs, buildings designed to be energy efficient, and the like have had some effect, but energy consumption continues to increase at an alarming rate. If the present pace does not abate, unleaded gasoline may cost $3 or $4 a gallon and electricity use will double in the nation by the end of the century. Even now, Americans use twice as much energy per capita as citizens of the most developed countries in Western Europe.

Californians are a bit better off than residents of most other states as regards the cost of energy, although the $200 and $300 per month electrical bills many Northern Californians received in 1982 would seem to belie this claim. The state's mild winters largely preclude the use of heating oil, the outlandish bills for which have driven many an Easterner to California. In summer, Los Angelenos and San Franciscans utilize air conditioners, but considerably less than Chicagoans or New Yorkers do. And when there are oppressive heat waves and smog attacks, most California urbanites have the option of quick escape to the beaches or mountains. But getting there, or even back and forth from work, is usually accomplished with a motor vehicle, often occupied by only one or two people. More and better rapid transit systems are what California needs if the state is going to begin

Figure 6.10 Windpower at Soda Lake near Zzyzx (A) meets some of the electricity needs of the California State University Desert Studies Center, a gasoline-motor-driven generator supplying the bulk of electrical output to the facility. Storage batteries (B) provide power when the wind dies down. (Crane Miller)

to put a dent in both the nation's highest gasoline consumption and its worst smog conditions.

The premise that conservation is the best energy source appears to be gaining support. In a study recently completed by Harvard University faculty,[2] it was concluded that $200 billion spent in conservation would save more than $200 billion put into exploration for new fossil fuel reserves. And Americans would not have to become energy spartans to the point of sacrificing lifestyle and economic growth and prosperity. The study also supports commitment to the expanded use of all forms of solar energy. Even hydropower's future appears brighter as higher-capacity turbines are developed for both existing and new hydroelectric dams. It is conceivable that solar power and hydropower, coupled with adequate conservation measures, could supply a quarter of the nation's total energy needs by the year 2000. But

[2]Roger Stobaugh and Daniel Yergin (eds.), *Energy Futures* (New York: Random House, 1979).

that isn't even 20 years away, and right now hydropower provides a meager 5 percent of energy in the United States and solar power practically none at all. Clearly, the nation must move quickly if it is to begin the serious replacement of fossil and nuclear fuels with conservation programs and solar power development as the energy bases of the twenty-first century.

The most important benefit to be reaped from energy conservation is giving the environment we depend on a longer lease on life. For the more energy is conserved, the less the pressure on the environment—be it emissions from automobiles and fossil fuel power plants; dust from strip mines; *thermal pollution* of the ocean, lakes, and streams by warm water discharged from steam electric plants; or radiation above normal background levels wherever a nuclear accident has occurred.

As we shift focus from the atmospheric to the biotic component of the California *ecosystem* in Chapter 7, it would be well to remember that energy is the basis for everything that functions in any environment, be it human or natural. When energy is plentiful, nonpolluting, and readily distributed throughout an ecosystem, whether by power line or food chain, that environment will prosper. When energy becomes scarce, polluting, and unevenly distributed, however, the environment in question will deteriorate. At first glance, the latter scenario un-

fortunately seems to fit California more closely than the former. But when California's most abundant energy source—the sun—is brought to mind, it is not difficult to perceive the state's human population and natural resources on the brink of a new prosperity.

At the risk of casting a dark shadow on solar energy's vast potential, we should caution against overenthusiasm regarding development of solar energy technology, at least in the short term. For instance, the home solar electricity system mentioned earlier in this chapter is years, if not decades, away from being anywhere near cost competitive with conventional utility company electricity, and this is to say nothing of the economic and environmental costs of producing solar cell systems. Even today's relatively sophisticated solar heating and cooling systems are in some cases priced so prohibitively high that there is no real reason to convert from conventional systems. Both tax writeoffs and amortizing the cost of solar space and water heating over the long term help make these options attractive, but such systems can be very expensive to maintain. Beyond heating rooms and pools with sunlight or cooling them with wind, solar energy is really not free. Nevertheless, we can remain confident that solar energy is slowly but surely becoming a viable alternative. In the meantime, patience is a virtue and energy conservation a must.

7

FROM REDWOODS
TO SAGEBRUSH

California's majestic landforms, innumerable climates, more than 1000-mile ocean front, and great latitudinal range provide an unrivaled rendezvous for plant and animal life. This complex of natural influences has produced a native California flora that is unique and yet at the same time mirrors almost any other part of North America, from the Arctic to the tropics or between the coasts.

Stately redwood groves are all but exclusively Californian and at the same time represent southward invasions of the coniferous rainforests of the maritime Pacific Northwest. Ancient bristlecone pines are perched high atop several mountain ranges west of the Rockies, but it is in the alpine tundra of California's White Mountains where they are most numerous and were first discovered to be the oldest of living plants. Douglas fir and yellow pine forests by the millions of acres underscore California's high ranking among lumber-producing regions in the West. Oak woodland–grassland pervades the Sierran foothills and Coast Ranges and in the green of spring resembles the deciduous woodlands of the East. Chaparral—a fireprone shrubland characteristic of Mediterranean climates—belongs almost exclusively to Southern California, albeit many a hillside resident would sooner give it away. Sage-covered high deserts and cactus-dotted low deserts give eastern California the appearance of the arid Southwest. And native fan palms in oases scattered about the Salton Trough and southern Great Basin add a final tropical touch to California's natural landscape.

Given such diversity of plants and remembering that wildlife variety, population, and distribution are regulated by the availability of food and shelter within natural communities, it can be assumed that California's fauna is no less diverse than its flora. Whether one ponders reptiles and rodents eking out an existence in the water-short desert, seabirds and sea mammals prospering from a bountiful ocean, remnant herds of antelope and elk browsing on Great Basin vegetation, bears and coyotes rummaging through Forest Service garbage cans, or salmon and steelhead trying to swim past hordes

of Labor Day fishermen upriver to their ancestral homes, California's wealth of wildlife is everywhere to be found. Most of these and a multitude of other animals can be seen in their natural habitats even by the typical car-bound Californian, if he or she is but willing to get away from the city.

Human interaction with California's flora and fauna began perhaps 50,000 or more years ago; but only in the last 200 years, with the advent of European settlement, has human modification of natural communities taken place. In some cases, whole native landscapes have been altered beyond recognition, as witnessed in the speedy victory of agriculture over the once-pervasive bunch-grasses of the Great Central Valley or the cutting away of most of the virgin stands of coastal redwood. In other instances, individual species have either been eliminated altogether from the California scene, as in the case of the ill-fated grizzly bear, or come dangerously close to local extinction, as have the condor, sea otter, tule elk, and other fauna too numerous to mention. Yet countless species of exotic plants and animals, ranging from Australia's eucalyptus trees to Europe's wild hogs, have been introduced and prospered as successfully in the California wilds as they would have in their ancestral homelands. With a human population of 24 million so recently attained, a quickened pace of ecological change in California is inevitable.

What these modifications forebode for the future of the biotic elements of our environment is uncertain. Knowledge of California's contemporary biogeography, however, is a step toward intelligent participation in the conservation of the state's rich biotic resources.

PRINCIPAL BIOMES

Biomes or *ecosystems,* those biogeographical units that contain both particular physical environments (landforms, waterbodies, climates, and soils) and the energy-producing plants and energy-consuming animals found there, are generally classified at several different areal levels.[1] The sun is the ultimate source of biome energy and our solar system could be considered the largest ecosystem of which we have any appreciable knowledge. The hierarchy of ecosystem sizes ranges from the earth down through the continents and regional biotic communities to units as small as a local stream or a pond.

California's diverse physical geography has made for literally dozens of different biotic communities named for characteristic plant assemblages that appear dominant, such as the pine-oak woodland of the western Sierran foothills or the coastal sage association bordering the seashore of Southern and central California. Since it is the main aim of this chapter to present a condensed biogeography of California rather than a complete naturalist's guide to the state, we shall systematically examine only some of the more representative biotic communities in each of the broadly based *principal biomes*—those biomes consisting of California's coniferous forests, woodlands, grasslands and marshlands, desert shrublands, chaparral and coastal shrublands, and littoral tidal shoreline.

Coniferous Forests

California's coniferous forests, generally described as areas nearly or completely covered by needle-leaved, cone-bearing trees, occupy nearly one fifth of its 158,693 square miles. The natural distribution of this 17 million acres of commercially accessible redwoods, firs, pines, and other evergreen softwoods is determined largely by climate and topography, as a comparison of Figures 2.1, 4.1, and 7.1 demonstrates. Wherever orographic precipitation is heaviest, which includes the west flanks of the northern Coast Ranges, Klamaths, Cascades, and Sierras, verdant forests of conifers are likely to be the prevailing form of natural vegetation. Despite rain and snowfall mostly in winter and rarely in other seasons, humidity, latitude, nutrient supply, direction of slope exposure (*aspect*), soil moisture, and other local conditions also favor forest growth along the northwest coast and windward mountain slopes.

Adaptation by distinct associations of plants and animals to these localized environmental influences has led to the formation of a myriad of biotic community types throughout California's coniferous forest biome. Most are *climax communities*: They have developed to a point of stability or equilibrium with their environment throughout several stages of *ecological succession*. Succession may take hundreds of years, as when a red fir (*Abies magnifica*) forest slowly establishes itself on a former meadow, or it may occur in a matter of decades, as when lodgepole pines (*Pinus murrayana* or *contorta*) quickly invade a recently burned-over area.

In terms of special adaptation and long succession, and even world renown for that matter, California's redwoods are unique among climax forests. The distinction actually is shared by two spatially separated species of redwoods, both of which are almost exclusively Californian and variations of the single genus *Sequoia*: (1) *Se-*

quoiadendron giganteum (formerly *Sequoia gigantea*), which are commonly known as sequoias or simply the "big trees" and are found only in small groves scattered along the western slope of the Sierra Nevada; and (2) *Sequoia sempervirens*, usually called redwoods, which extend in a coastal-oriented band from several miles above the Oregon border southward through Del Norte, Humboldt, and Mendocino counties and still farther south in isolated coastal mountain groves well into Monterey County. Both species enjoy unparalleled stature— the tallest coastal redwood claiming a world's record of nearly 400 ft and the General Sherman tree in Sequoia National Park measuring 27.5 ft in diameter from a dozen feet above its base. The species are not short on longevity, either; many a big tree and coastal redwood is in excess of 2,000 years old. The majestic General Grant sequoia is an estimated 3,500 years of age, following by only a few hundred years some scraggly-looking bristlecone pines (*Pinus aristata*; see Fig. 7.2) as the oldest of living trees. Indeed, older sequoias and redwoods are often spoken of as living fossils in deference to an ancestry that dates back perhaps a hundred million years when *Sequoia* and similar genera were distributed far beyond the bounds of California as we know it. Then, as now, these trees endured because of long-acquired survival features including fire-resistant fibrous nonresinous bark; moist and decay-resistant wood; lack of lower limbs, a characteristic that deters the spread of fire over a forest floor; abundance of small cones, each filled with hundreds of seeds; ability to seed-root or stump-sprout; and certain flood tolerance capabilities.

For all their environmental adaptations, the coastal redwoods' accommodation with California's wet winter, dry summer precipitation regime is most remarkable. Copious amounts of winter rainfall coupled with mild temperatures contribute to the redwoods' presence along the central and northern coasts, but it is the lingering fog of summer in this region that ensures their success. Year-round high relative humidity and the attendant cool air in California's fog belt help satisfy the trees' water requirements by diminishing moisture loss from leaves and soils caused by evapotranspiration. Were it not for fogs drizzling upwards of 20 inches of moisture upon the forests in a normal rainless summer as seen in Figure 7.3, most of the state's 1.5 million acres of coastal redwoods would simply not exist.

During the Pleistocene, when these cool cloudy summers extended farther south and inland, redwoods populated the mountains and coasts of Southern California. Today, although *endemics* (species originating naturally and exclusively in a given region) that are *relict* in their area (endemic in a different time and climate) such as big-cone spruce (*Psuedotsuga macrocarpa*) and Torrey pine (*Pinus torreyana*) still barely manage a natural existence in the southland, redwoods are likely to be found doing well only in the artificial environments of irrigated ornamental plots and experimental forests.

Few, if any, North American trees command the deep respect and high value accorded the redwood. In the Sierras, its groves are named after generals; in the northwest, after churchly architectural forms. Among environmental activists, "Save the redwoods!" is a commonly heard cry. And in retail lumber yards, the price

---

[1]Biomes are classified by the dominant vegetation found within them, whereas ecosystems are likely to be determined by climate and soil conditions within their boundaries. Both can be thought of as systems.

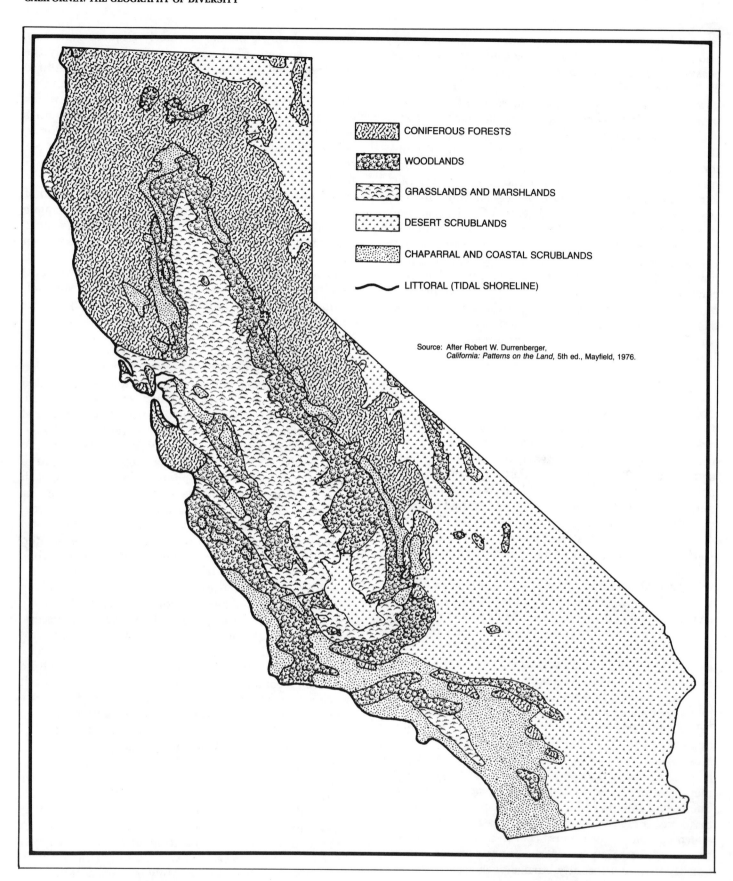

CONIFEROUS FORESTS

WOODLANDS

GRASSLANDS AND MARSHLANDS

DESERT SCRUBLANDS

CHAPARRAL AND COASTAL SCRUBLANDS

LITTORAL (TIDAL SHORELINE)

Source: After Robert W. Durrenberger,
California: Patterns on the Land, 5th ed., Mayfield, 1976.

Figure 7.1 Principal biomes. (Richard Crooker)

of redwood, like oil or any other rapidly disappearing resource, is skyrocketing. Coastal redwood is a durable wood, highly prized by architects, builders, and other users. The increasing demand for the wood over the last century or so has seen to the cutting of more than 90 percent of the original old growth redwood stands. Today demand persists as the resource shrinks: California has less than 30 billion board feet (1 BF = a 12″ × 12″ × 1″ board) of commercially recoverable redwood saw timber in reserve, but with an average annual cut rate of 1 billion BF presently doubling the average yearly replenishment rate of new or second growth redwood, the resource may run out more rapidly than anyone realizes.

As seen in Figure 7.4, the 58,000-acre Redwood National Park, adjacent expansions of the park, Muir Woods National Monument, and state parks serve to save some of what is left of the virgin stands from the chain saw and even some of the ravages of nature. Some foresters contend, however, that further major expansion of protected areas for coastal redwood will eventually weaken the forest's ability to stave off fire, floods, disease, and other natural disasters. This seems a reasonable argument as far as it goes, but the fact remains that the national park and other existing preserves are really so meager, spatially so disjunct, and recreationally under such pressure as to represent anything but a viable natural ecosystem. Redwood National Park boundaries and jurisdiction, for instance, do not extend inland far enough to directly influence logging activities in upstream portions of the Eel River, Smith River, and other

Figure 7.3 Redwood rainforest in fog in Armstrong Redwoods State Reserve in northwestern Sonoma County. The Parson Jones redwood is 310 ft high and nearly 1,500 years old. A moist environment, lack of lower limbs, and thick bark help preclude the spread of fire through a redwood forest; if burned down, however, the forest will regenerate itself as seeds flourish in barren soil and sprouts issue forth from stumps and roots. (Crane Miller)

major regional watersheds where greatly accelerated erosion eventually affects drainages all the way to the sea.

The related problem of cutting more timber than is being replaced occurs not only on private lands bordering the national park but throughout the state in privately owned forests that make up almost half of the entire 17 million acre commercial timberland resource. And, albeit some companies are striving for sustained yields through tree farming and other sound forestry practices, the fact persists that the bulk of redwood forest remains in private hands and the species continues to lose ground because of it. What's more, the public's national forests (Fig. 7.4) are subject to *multiple use* management, which includes lumbering as well as grazing, mining, recreation, and utility and transportation line easements. About 1 million acres of wilderness areas in national forests are exempted from these uses (except for some recreational uses), but most of the wilderness land is far inland of the coastal redwood range.

Fortunately for conservationist, logger, and tourist alike, redwoods do not stand alone in northwestern California. Intermingling with redwoods near the coast and

Figure 7.2 Bristlecone pines in the White Mountains east of Owens Valley are the world's longest-living plants, with some individuals dated at more than 4,600 years of age. Their longevity owes to a seeming paradox of harsh environmental conditions including the presence of thin, alkaline soils weathered from chalky dolomite outcrops; highly reflective, heat-avoiding soils and rock outcrops; a mean elevation of the groves of 11,500 ft above sea level; meager annual precipitation of 15 inches, almost all of it falling as snow; and unobstructed gale-force westerlies whose wind chill factor reduces already cold temperatures even more. The bristlecones have adjusted to these timberline hardships by growing slowly; having a minimal amount of live foliage, which reduces moisture loss through respiration; having dense, decay-resistant wood; and clustering on shady slopes, where snow stays on the ground longer. Limber pines resemble bristlecone pines and are often found nearby, but the former prefer residual soils derived from granite rather than from dolomite. (Crane Miller)

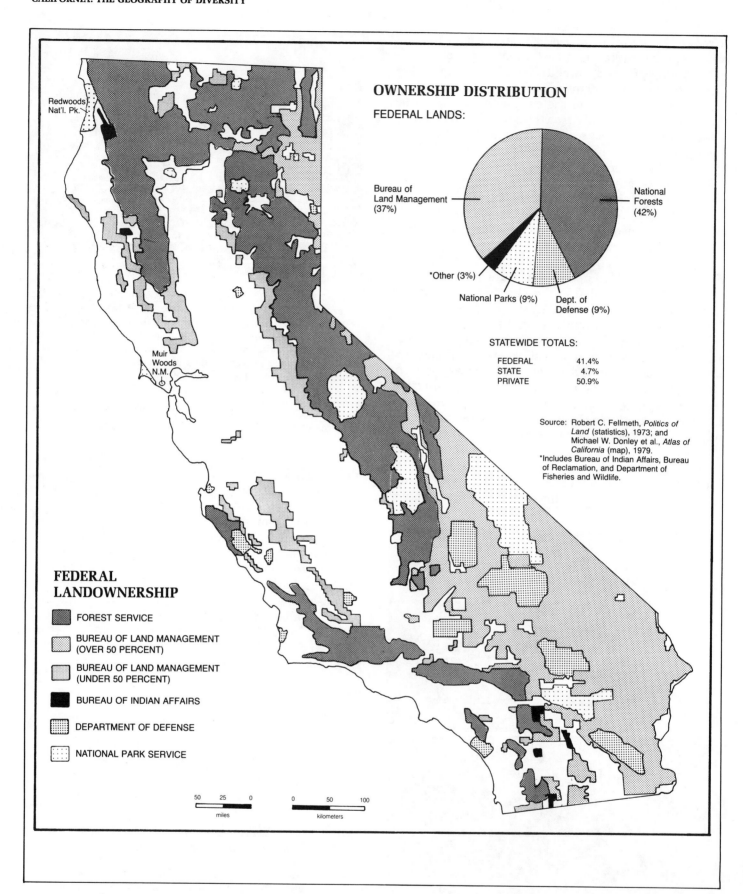

Figure 7.4 Federal land ownership and distribution. (Richard Crooker)

Figure 7.5 Mixed coniferous forests in the Coast Ranges of Northern California contain redwood, Douglas fir, tanoak, madrone, and treelike ferns on shady slopes; live oaks and California buckeye on drier, sunny slopes; and red alder, Oregon ash, and wild azalea along streams. (California Department of Parks and Recreation, photo by Suzanne Reed)

forming nearly pure stands inland on the windward slopes of the Klamaths, Coast Ranges (Fig. 7.5), Cascades, and northern Sierras, Douglas fir forests constitute the most prolific raw material source for the state's wood products industry, with some 90 billion BF of the species in reserve on 2.5 million acres and annual cut and replacement rates of well over 2 billion BF and slightly under 1 billion BF, respectively. Because the main stands of *Pseudotsuga menziesii*—not a true fir as its "false hemlock" scientific name implies—lie in the physically less accessible interior mountains of the northwest part of the state, they were not exploited by the timber industry as early nor as readily as were coastal redwoods. But a postwar construction boom, modern roadbuilding equipment, and fleets of hauling trucks thrust Douglas fir from obscurity into prominence almost overnight. The flexible, knotfree wood soon became the chief raw material for everything from plywood to rough carpentry.

In recent years, Douglas fir has been the wood most responsible for the following effects: (1) that California places a close third after Oregon and Washington among the nation's leading lumber producers, (2) that the forest products industry as a whole (but mostly lumber products) has captured about 5 percent of the California economy, (3) that some 100,000 Californians are employed in various forest products industries, and (4) that the main source of income for the northwest's economy derives from timber. As regards the latter and the sawtimber and milling industries in particular, a fluctuating demand for new housing and automation have contributed to chronic high unemployment in the northwest. Conservationist pressures to exclude more forests from cutting have aggravated the situation, especially as far as jobless loggers are concerned. But, high interest rates have saved more trees and depressed more economies recently than have environmentalists' actions.

If jobs and a whole industry are to be saved, sustained yield must soon be achieved in the northwest's Douglas fir forests. But there is a loser in such an undertaking, and it is the already beleaguered coastal redwood. Douglas fir grows faster than redwood and other second growth conifers, progressing from seedling to sawtimber size in 30 to 60 years. Also, Douglas fir prospers in both rainforest and drier alpine climates. Nevertheless, the removal rate of the species still more than doubles the growth rate, and extensive cutting of remaining virgin stands continues for the most part to sustain the timber industry. To narrow the disparity between the two rates and save something of the old growth Douglas fir forests at the same time, timber firms generally do not reseed cut redwood areas with redwood but rather with quicker-maturing Douglas fir. Both species are subject to *clearcutting,* which can leave a hillside barren except for stumps. And in reseeding a logged-over area, both are alike in requiring the drenching sunlight of a clear cut. Unlike redwoods, however, Douglas firs do not defend well against fire, flood, and pest, nor can they grow back from stumps. A paradox it may seem, but the redwood's natural competitive advantage has furthered its undoing. As foresters correctly point out, redwoods can regenerate on their own, whereas Douglas firs need help. And since Douglas firs can be harvested more often, they get that help. It would appear that if sustained yield is one day to be realized by Douglas fir, it will continue to be at the expense of coastal redwood.

Ascending the mighty Sierra Nevada anywhere along its 400-mile western front, one cannot help but be struck by the immensity and variety of coniferous forests. Here, indeed, are forests that rival those of the northwest by almost any measure. The first to be encountered in an eastbound ascent of the Sierra are the oak-pine woodlands, but as foothills give way to longer and steeper mountain slopes, California's greatest gathering of conifers soon prevails. Averaging from 2,500 to 7,500 ft in altitude range, this is the Sierran yellow pine belt, wherein tall stands of *Pinus ponderosa* and sugar pine (*Pinus lambertiana*) reach for the sky on sunny slopes and ridges, while mixed forests of Douglas fir, white fir (*Abies concolor*), and aromatic incense cedar (*Libocedrus decurrens*) take cover on shaded mountainsides beneath groves of giant sequoia. All these species provide sawtimber of varying grades; together they comprise a several million acre forest resource, the largest single area of its kind in California. Yellow pine alone (mostly from the Sierras, but elsewhere as well, as noted in Fig. 7.6) is second to Douglas fir in volume of lumber produced statewide.

Above the yellow pine belt on up to 9,500 ft, the lodgepole pine–red fir belt prevails. Besides its namesake species, this second long wall of conifers contains the ponderosa lookalike Jeffrey pine (*Pinus jefferyi*) and the bluish green mountain hemlock (*Tsuga mertensiana*). The four species add still more to the Sierran timber resource.

From 9,500 ft to timberline, forests thin out into scattered groupings of trees nestled on granite flats or clinging to precipitous ridges. Commonly seen in the thin environment of this high alpine belt are spectacularly deformed Sierra juniper (*Juniperus occidentalis*), bulky-looking limber pine (*Pinus flexilis*), wind-blasted foxtail pine (*Pinus balfouriana*), and dwarflike whitebark pine (*Pinus albicaulis*). Of no commercial worth, these loftiest of California's conifers nevertheless add the final living touch to the priceless solitude of the High Sierra.

The role of orographic precipitation in accounting for the vertical zonation of different climax communities is brought into noticeably sharp focus in the Sierra Nevada. In this relationship, profiled in Figure 7.7, average annual precipitation attains its maximum in the upper yellow pine and lower lodgepole pine–red fir belts of the central Sierra. As expected, these wettest forests are also the richest forests. Not only do they contain the many conifers previously described, but also small groves of aspen (*Populus tremuloides;* see Fig. 7.8) and other broadleaf deciduous trees and shrubs, wildflowers and other flowering plants, flowerless and seedless ferns, and all manner of lichens and mosses.

Limited largely to winter and occurring at elevations above 5,000 ft, precipitation over these forests falls mostly as snow. Hundreds of inches of snow accumulate during the cold season, forming both a protective blanket of insulation for vegetation against windchill and a slow-melting reservoir of water to see plants and animals through the long summer's drought. The cold, snowy winter combined with a warm, dry growing season (three to seven months, depending on altitude and latitude) also favors predominance of evergreen over deciduous trees. For the former keep their needle-shaped leaves the year around with no need to expend energy producing new foliage every spring.

In essence, California's Mediterranean climate, as discussed in Chapter 4, has largely precluded the natural

Figure 7.6 Yellow pine forests, here seen at about 5,000 ft elevation along California 20 in Nevada County, dominate the western slopes of the Sierra. The Southern Cascades of northeastern California and the San Gabriels and San Bernardinos in Southern California also contain commercially exploited ponderosa pine forests. *Selective cutting* of mature or rotation-age trees is practiced in these forests rather than clear-cutting, the latter not being essential for the growth of seedling yellow pines. The cleared areas seen in the background are scars left along the South Yuba River by the Alpha and Omega gold mining operations of decades ago. (Crane Miller)

existence of large deciduous forests anywhere in the mountainous regions of the state. Myriads of microclimates, such as in the shade of a large tree or on a sun-drenched south-facing slope, have further fostered a broad variety of native and endemic species of evergreen conifers throughout California's forests.

In terms of photosynthetic plants and the food chains they energize, as briefly defined in Chapter 5, California's coniferous forests provide the best of worlds for wildlife. One such world and its food chain, pictured in Figure 7.9, is found at a forest's edge in a Sierra stream where plentiful sunlight activates green chlorophyll in algae, which is fed upon by insect larvae and water snails. These small aquatic animals are then eaten by endemic rainbow trout (*Salmo gairdnerii;* see Fig. 7.10) who in turn are sometimes taken by nonendemic *Homo sapiens.* (Fishermen often use the term "native" to refer to a trout that was born in a stream rather than in a hatchery.)

Another such producing and consuming ecosystem lies deeper within a forest on the western slopes of the Sierra. Here chipmunks (*Eutamias* spp.) and squirrels (*Citellus* spp.) scurry about harvesting pinecone seeds while at

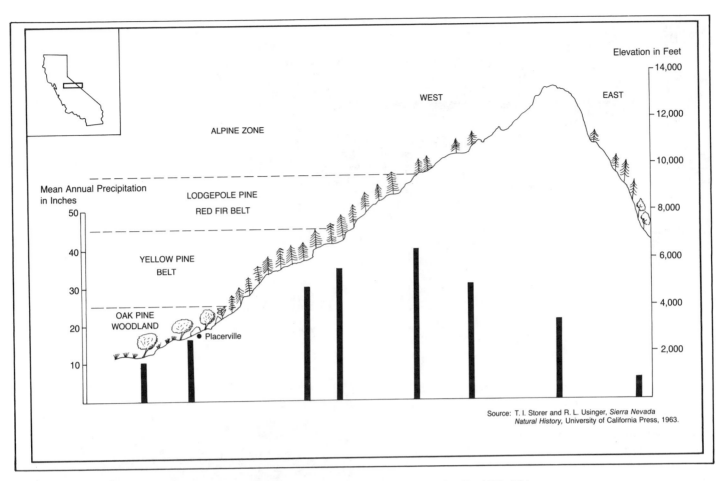

Figure 7.7 Vertical zonation of precipitation and vegetation in the central Sierra Nevada. (David Vechik)

Figure 7.8 Aspen and similar deciduous trees in the Sierras prefer the higher and more northerly reaches of the ranges, as seen here along lower Leevining Creek near the eastern entrance (Tioga Pass) to Yosemite National Park. (Crane Miller)

Figure 7.9 Sierra stream profile provides an aquariumlike view of aquatic fauna along a diversion of Taylor Creek, which flows into south Lake Tahoe. (Crane Miller)

the same time keeping a wary eye out for predators such as gray fox (*Urocyon cinereoargenteus*) and mountain coyote (*Canis latrans*), who rarely deviate from their carnivorous instincts, or black bear (*Ursus americanus;* see Fig. 7.11) and raccoon (*Procyon lotor*), who as omnivores will eat just about anything they can get their claws on.

Figure 7.12 shows still another forest food chain, but this time in the hypothetical construct of an *ecological pyramid* representing avian as well as aquatic and terrestrial fauna involved in the transfer of energy through a biotic community. Of course, these are only three examples of countless intricately different food chains that make California's coniferous forests a self-regulating system. They should, however, suffice to emphasize that every ecosystem has certain components that are vital to its success as a climax community. Should one of these components fail or be forced to fail, as with the loss of a predator species, the ecosystem as a whole may eventually fail.

Humans as hunters and fishers often represent the ultimate consumer or *apex species* (Fig. 7.12) in an ecological pyramid. Indians fulfilled this role for millennia as they sought fish and game in California's forests, lakes, and streams. Because their numbers were small and they took only what was required for food, clothing, and shelter, the Indians' overall impact on native wildlife populations was not destructive. But European and American settlement, especially after the Gold Rush when loggers, miners, and ranchers began exploiting the forest regions of the California northwest and the Sierras, brought sinister new dimensions to hunting. Hunting solely as a subsistence activity soon gave way to hunting for sport and to rid the landscape of unwanted animals. Weaponry changed as well, from snare and bow and arrow to chemical poison, rifle, and shotgun. No animal, however small or large, could long escape the new hunter bent on its eradication. And escape they did not, as witnessed in the extinction by the mid-1920s of the California grizzly bear (*Ursus arctos* or *horriblis*)

Figure 7.10 Rainbow trout is the dominant endemic or native trout of all cool streams in the western Sierra. It has been successfully transplanted as far away as Western Europe and New Zealand as well as elsewhere in California. About 23 million rainbow and other trout are raised in 14 state Department of Fish and Game hatcheries each year, to say nothing of the millions more bred in California's lakes and streams. A cousin of the rainbow, the steelhead trout, and its traveling companion, the Pacific or Chinook salmon, are *anadromous* species; that is, they are born in freshwater streams, migrate to sea when 4 to 18 months old, remain in the salty Pacific for two to five years, and then return to their ancestral streams to spawn and die. With the building of dams on most western Sierra streams, their return was forever blocked. Consequently, steelhead and salmon have largely abandoned the Sierra for still wild northwestern streams. (Crane Miller)

and the near extinction of other such forest and woodland predators as the weasellike marten (*Martes americana*), the bearlike wolverine (*Gulo luscus*), the red fox (*Vulpes fulva*), the mountain lion (*Felis concolor*), and the bald eagle (*Haliaetus leucocephalus*).

Populations of these predators must have seemed infinitely large to hunters at first; but, as is the case with any food chain excluding man, the quantity of apex consumers (Fig. 7.12) is always relatively small. The reduction of small predator populations by overhunting brought on a subsequent rise in the already larger numbers of their prey. Forest and woodland communities from the Sierras to the Klamaths were thrown out of ecological balance as herbivore populations boomed, local vegetation was overbrowsed, and animals invaded foreign territory seeking food. Drought and disease checked some population explosions, but ironically it was humans with their guns and poisons that stepped into the void created by the predator's forced absence. Today, for instance, it is hunters more than natural predators that control mule deer (*Odocoileus hemionus;* see Fig. 7.13) populations and it is animal exterminators by some other name that poison ground squirrels (*Citellus* spp.) in order to save a golf course from having more than 18 holes.

More subtle, but potentially more disruptive to ecosystem balance than either felling trees or killing animals, is the recent wave of recreational and residential development sweeping large regions that lie within California's forests, notably in the Sierra Nevada. The land rush that has replaced the Gold Rush in the Mother Lode and the building boom at Mammoth are areally expanding their environmental impact with every day that passes. How long, for instance, will it be before the built-up eastern arm of metropolitan Sacramento engulfs Placerville or 100,000 skiers crowd the slopes at Mammoth and June on a typical winter weekend?

Nowhere in the Sierra, though, has human overpopulation and overdevelopment posed a greater threat to a strictly coniferous forest–alpine lake ecosystem than at Lake Tahoe. One of the clearest bodies of freshwater found on earth, the lake itself is in danger of being turned pea soup green from excessive algae buildup caused by bulldozed forest organic material (soil and vegetation, basically) that drains into the lake basin. The air above the lake is likely to become polluted more regularly as the numbers of motor vehicles increase and the prospects for a mass transit system decrease. The forest around the lake seems destined to lose more ground, not simply from being cleared away from the path of oncoming buildings and roads, but from more perplexing depredations, such as housing and commercial developments. Much of the forest will be left intact to furnish evergreen amenity and to camouflage structures, but it will—or already has—become the habitat mostly of man and domesticated animals rather than of native wildlife.

These and other modifications of the Tahoe ecosystem appear inevitable in view of the fact that winter populations alone—and Tahoe is a place for all seasons—now push 150,000. Thousands of new housing units are projected to be built before the end of the decade, as are still more motels, luxury hotels and casinos, and the bistate Tahoe Regional Planning Agency is apparently unable, for whatever reason, to thwart runaway development. Regional planning with no teeth will obviously not save Tahoe. But the suggestion that a national recreation area be established may do the trick. After all, the U.S. Forest Service owns three fifths of the land in the Tahoe basin; what better control could there be over development than outright ownership of most of the land? A step toward greater federal ownership was taken by Congress late in 1980 when it approved a $30-million proposal for purchase of more Tahoe area land, the rev-

Figure 7.11 Black bears, the largest mammals in the Sierra (occasionally weighing in excess of 300 pounds), are most common in the yellow pine and lodgepole pine belts of the western Sierra. Bears shelter in caves, rock piles, hollow trees, and thickets, but once winter hibernation is past, they frequent campgrounds in search of food and are considered extremely dangerous. (California Department of Fish and Game)

enue to come largely from the sale of federal land elsewhere in Nevada. The legislation should strengthen the bistate planning agency's role in controlling development and will impose a moratorium on most forms of development until a new regional plan is implemented.

Woodlands

If there is any single landscape that best typifies past and present California, it is that of seemingly infinite numbers of oaks and other stately trees randomly scattered over grassy, rolling terrain as far as the eye can see. Of little worth to the lumber industry and thus spared from the axe and the saw, these woodlands appear today much as they did 150 years ago, when a pastoral life reigned over California, and for hundreds of years before that, when oak acorns and pine nuts were staples in a hunting, gathering, and trading economy.

Now, as then, woodlands pervade the foothills of the Cascades and the Sierras, the stream courses of the Central Valley, the central and southern Coast Ranges, and the inner coastal valleys of Southern California. There are places, such as the Los Angeles Basin and the Santa Clara Valley, where native trees have given way to housing tracts and shopping centers. But these days many an oak and even an occasional parkland are left in the midst of an expanding suburbia to serve as living reminders of a once natural landscape.

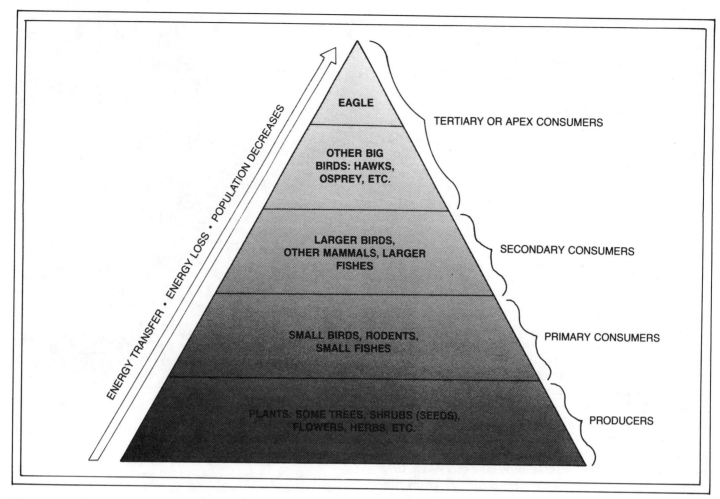

Figure 7.12 Energy pyramid. (Richard Crooker)

The distribution of woodlands, as noted earlier and mapped in Figure 7.1, is based on their ecological role as a transition zone or *ecotone* between the well-watered forests of higher elevations and the drier grasslands and shrublands of lower-lying locales. As expected where such an intermediate environment exists, there is a mixture of conifers down from the forest and broadleaf trees up from the hills and valleys, all adapted to a respectable 10 to 30 inches annual precipitation (almost all of it as winter rain), a long and warm dry season, and a variety of soil conditions and slope exposures.

The genera most often represented in these woodland ecotones are oak (*Quercus*) and pine (*Pinus*), which include several endemic species noted for their special adaptations to California's unique Mediterranean woodland biomes. The deciduous California black oak (*Quercus kelloggii*), for example, mixes with coulter pine (*Pinus coulteri*) from the central Coast Ranges southward into the Peninsular Ranges of San Diego County and with yellow pine in the upper foothills of the Sierra Nevada. In both associations, yearly rainfall is at least 25 inches, winter frosts occur regularly, elevations are above 1,500 ft, and soils vary from rocky to loamy.

The evergreen coast live oak (*Quercus agrifolia*), on the other hand, occasionally consorts with black and other oaks, but almost exclusively in outer coastal shrublands and grasslands and rarely with pines of any sort. Its Sierran cousin, interior live oak (*Quercus wislizenii*), is also evergreen and associates with chaparral, but appears more gregarious in that it is often found with dig-

ger pine (*Pinus sabiniana*) and blue oak (*Quercus douglasii*). The latter two species prefer the fine-grained alluvium of the lower reaches of the foothills and consequently are among the most drought-resistant trees (requiring only 10 to 20 inches of rain a year) in the state.

Last, but most majestic of all woodland trees, is the valley oak (*Quercus lobata;* see Fig. 7.14) sometimes standing more than 125 ft tall and claiming several hundred years' seniority. It is basically a *riparian* species (Fig. 7.15), most often congregating along stream courses that meander through broad, alluvial valleys.

California's woodlands are also the meeting place of wildlife. Most of the forest fauna described earlier frequent the woodlands as well, many of the larger herbivores and carnivores migrating seasonally between the two principal biomes. Mule deer are among the most plentiful of the transients, regularly exiting the yellow pine belt of the Sierras or higher forests of other mountain ranges at the first sign of winter—usually a 6-inch or heavier snowfall in mid-November. As the deer come down into the woodlands to browse on grasses, herbs, and shrubs, they are both met and followed by the ubiquitous coyote and the rare mountain lion. Occasionally, bobcats (*Lynx rufus*) will attack deer bogged down in an unusually heavy, early snow, but squirrels, other small rodents, California quail (*Lophortyx californica*), and other birds are more their cup of tea.

Another woodland predator that rodents, birds, and even lightning-fast black-tailed jackrabbits (*Lepus cal-*

ifornicus) must contend with is the poisonous western rattlesnake (*Crotalus viridis*). Because the rattler's principal adversary is the overfearful human, it has been hunted into near extinction in forest recreation areas and consequently enjoys more peace and freedom in the woodland biome. Predators of all sorts, especially Cooper's hawks (*Accipter cooperi*) and red-tailed hawks (*Buteo jamaicensis*), benefit, when perched high atop oak or pine vantage points, from the openness of woodlands in seeking their prey. Overall, the woodland ecotone appears to offer an unrivaled variety of food chains involving avian and terrestrial fauna.

In the riparian woodlands of the Great Central Valley, the beaver (*Castor canadensis*) is undoubtedly one of the most controversial of native inhabitants. In times past, beaver were quite numerous and seemed in no danger of being eliminated from the local ecosystem by fur hunters. But in recent decades, their industrious dam-building activities have made them the scourge of irrigated agriculture. It seems that beaver chose irrigation ditches for dam sites as often as they would slow-moving streams, at least until these large rodents (weighing up to 50 lbs) were reduced in number and distribution to their present predicament of extreme rarity. Beaver dam a ditch or stream with gnawed-down riparian (streamside) trees, brush, and mud in order to form a pond in which they and their young can avoid predators. Ironically, beaver ponds flooding cropland understandably invite the wrath of farmers and against them our furry friends have no effective stronghold. Beaver have been introduced along streams in the High Sierra, but the shortage of aspens in forests dominated by conifers limits population growth in the new colonies. The inner bark or cambium layer of some poplars (aspens and cottonwoods of the genus *Populus*) and willows (*Salix* spp.) is a staple item in the beaver's diet.

It would appear that if the beaver is to survive in the long run, it will be along foothill streams where its kind of vegetation is available and which lie eastward of ir-

Figure 7.13 Mule deer probably number in the hundreds of thousands, if not over a million, in California. Blessed with a skilled wariness of man, some live in foothill habitats where climate is mild the year around, while others migrate to the higher mountains with the advancing greenery of spring. There are six different varieties of mule deer in California. Large bucks sometimes weigh more than 200 pounds and are obviously sought by hunters, who legally take between 50,000 and 100,000 deer each year. (National Park Service, photo by Richard Frear)

rigated farmland but below the yellow pine belt. Even here, though, the beaver will no doubt have to contend with the pesky little muskrat (*Ondatra zibethica*), introduced a half century ago, which has also turned out to be a destroyer of irrigation systems.

Grasslands and Marshlands: The Central Valley as an Aboriginal Environment

One would be hard pressed to find another landscape anywhere that has changed so dramatically, so rapidly, and on such a grand scale as has the Great Valley. For thousands of years since the last ice age, the valley har-

Figure 7.14 Valley oaks in the eastern Sacramento Valley and *Quercus* species elsewhere in California usually congregate in open woodlands rather than in thickly treed forests. Lack of dense stands and commercial species of oaks and other hardwood trees such as found in the eastern United States has helped spare California oaks from use as raw material in furniture and cooperage (wine vats) manufacturing. Actually, oak trees were far more significant to the aboriginal economy than today's, for their acorns were both staple food and trade items among California Indians. (Crane Miller)

Figure 7.15 Riparian vegetation in broad valley bottoms is generally richer in deciduous broadleaf species and population counts than vegetation associations found away from watercourses. Such streambank plant communities are not only blessed with more available moisture the year around but are subject to cold air drainage and its attendant subfreezing temperatures in winter. Deep, silty soils also contribute to the richness of riparian flora. (Crane Miller)

bored many of California's native peoples, wildlife, grasslands, marshlands, and riparian woodlands. But in barely more than the last 100 years, this natural landscape has essentially disappeared from the face of the earth. What was it like and how did it lose its aboriginal character so quickly?

Before the mid-nineteenth century and the first signs of ranching and farming, the Central Valley was carpeted nearly end to end with perennial bunchgrasses that were golden brown from summer through winter, to be reborn as a sea of green early every spring (if there had been a wet winter). Adding pattern to the landscape, as they do today, were the wandering, tree-lined courses of the Sacramento and San Joaquin rivers, their tributaries, and the great in-valley Delta into which they converged before flowing on toward the Pacific. Far to the south were still more rivers and marshy deltas, but with no exit to the sea. Here, as described in previous chapters, Sierran streams came to rest in tule swamps that stretched over hundreds of thousands of acres of bottomland.

This was a valley literally teeming with wildlife. Chinook salmon (*Oncorhynchus tshawytscha*) ran the streams from the mountains to the sea and back. Beaver and their dams abounded but rarely got in the fishes' way. Warm water fishes, amphibians, and resident and migratory waterfowl populated the tules. Coyotes, grizzly bears, and wildcats stalked herds of deer grazing shrubbery in river woodlands.

Of all the valley's indigenous fauna, however, none was as dependent for sustenance on the grasses of that day as were pronghorn antelope (*Antilocapra americana;* see Fig. 7.16) and tule elk (*Cervus canadensis nannodes*). These animals numbered in the thousands and gave the valley the appearance of one of the great natural rangelands of the world. Today, although a few dozen tule elk survive in a state preserve west of Bakersfield, antelope, elk, and their bunchgrass diet no longer grace the valley landscape. About 6,000 pronghorn remain in northeastern California, mostly in Modoc County. As seen in Figure 7.17, a second controlled herd of tule elk, numbering about 400, occupies the central part of the Owens Valley. Limited hunting of both ungulates (hoofed animals) is permitted, but serious hunters are likely to go elsewhere—to Wyoming, for example, where bigger and better elk and 170,000 pronghorn antelope await them.

The Great Valley's original cultural landscape prospered as well, both in numbers of people and ways of life. Though estimates of aboriginal population vary, the fact that the valley accommodated the largest pre-1769 population of any of California's landform provinces seems substantiated by archaeological settlement sites, data collected by ethnographers from living informants early in this century, and the written accounts of Spanish, Mexican, and American explorers and pioneer settlers. Missionaries' vital records would have further verified the relatively large size of the valley's aboriginal population, but the mission system never penetrated this region. It is important to emphasize that rather than being evenly distributed throughout the valley, Indian subsistence areas and thus population concentrations focused on the lakes and marshes of the southern valley, the central Delta region, and the riparian environments of the rivers and sloughs. These locales, rather than the drier, open grasslands, contained the bulk of biotic resources from which valley Indians derived their relative economic stability.

The southern half of the Great Valley was predominantly Yokuts country, with perhaps as many as 50 tribes of the linguistic stock represented there. Lakeside Yokuts ate fish and waterfowl caught from the shallow lakes of the Buena Vista and Tulare basins and fashioned rafts and huts with tule or bulrush (*Scirpus acutus*) taken from basin swamps. They no doubt evacuated the lowland swamps as the humidity and insects of summer approached and headed for the cooler foothill woodlands some 20 to 40 miles distant. Here they harvested oak acorns on their own and traded for them with other Yokuts tribes. Once leached of its poisonous tannin, the acorn meal provided a staple item in their diet.

Although seasonal variations in the availability of plant foods and the need for animal protein rendered hunting indispensable, Yokuts who preferred it to fishing and gathering almost never found a scarcity of ungulates and smaller game browsing the grasslands or drinking from countless streams and waterholes. In any case, the valley food resource was so varied and the Indian so skilled at utilizing it that drought and other climatic catastrophes may have produced shortages but rarely, if ever, starvation.

Figure 7.16 Pronghorn antelope are not really antelope at all but rather a uniquely North American range animal misnamed by early pioneers. There were upwards of 50 million of these animals in aboriginal North America, California alone perhaps having several hundred thousand. Pronghorn differ from deer in that they are smaller (a buck rarely weighs more than 150 pounds), both sexes have horns, they are faster (able to attain speeds of 60 mph), and they have superior vision, even compared to that of humans. Pronghorn feed on grasses, bitterbrush, sagebrush, and alfalfa (the latter when the farmer isn't watching). Their speed and visual acuity help them to survive their predators, who include bobcats, mountain lions, coyotes, eagles, and humans. (California Department of Fish and Game)

From the Delta region northward through the Sacramento Valley, Yokuts gave way to Maidu, Miwok, and Wintun as the principal languages spoken, but the level of subsistence resources and activities remained every bit as varied as in the south. Both sections of the Great Valley had their riparian woodlands, poorly drained wetlands, and multitude of streams from which Indians drew their sustenance. The middle Sacramento probably did afford a more dependable salmon fishery than the lower San Joaquin, since the former normally receives more runoff and is less likely to run dangerously low in time of drought.

Unfortunately, the Sacramento Valley's wetter environment may have accelerated the spread of an epidemic (possibly malaria) that decimated Indian populations during the 1830s. Some years later, when John Sutter started grain farming on his rancho New Helvetia, most of the native peoples of the Sacramento Valley—perhaps numbering as many as 50,000 a few decades before—were gone. Indian communities here and elsewhere in California were devastated by exotic diseases that accompanied white settlement. Lack of natural immunity among aboriginal peoples often caused a disease to reach epidemic proportions shortly after its introduction.

Just as the coming of the white man was fatal to the aboriginal culture, so it was to the flora and fauna of the Great Central Valley. Some seemingly indestructible oak woodlands survive in riparian habitats and in the foothill margins of the valley, and a few salmon still swim the Sacramento and its tributaries, but the domesticated plants and animals of agriculture have all but swept away any semblance of the aboriginal landscape.

With it went California's only extensive tracts of native prairie grassland as well. A few patches of perennial bunchgrass remain in the valley and on distant hilltops, but they are a pale reflection of the way it was. To Indians, bunchgrasses were important in that they sustained vast herds of game. The rancheros of the mid-1800s looked on the grasses similarly, but as forage for their cattle. In leading the initial assault on the bunchgrasses, the livestock not only overbrowsed and trampled them to death, but in so doing, outcompeted antelope and elk for the tasty perennials.

The next wave of invaders onto the grassland were fescues (*Festuca* spp.) and other annual grasses, first those native to California and then those from as far away as Europe. In a sense, domesticated livestock cleared the way for the annuals by laying more ground bare than already was—bunchgrasses, as their name implies and by nature, do not provide a complete ground cover even when dominant and, once destroyed, cannot revive like a logged-over redwood forest can. The seeds of the annual grasses arrived by every means imaginable: by wind, by wildlife and livestock, and by wagon

Figure 7.17 Tule elk in the Owens Valley range over 150,000 acres of Los Angeles Department of Water and Power land and are managed by the California Department of Fish and Game. Indigenous to the tule swamps of the Central Valley and numbering in the thousands there in aboriginal times, tule elk were introduced to the Owens Valley in 1933. They are larger and slower than pronghorn but share their taste for pasture grasses and thus can compete with ranchers' livestock on multiple-use land. (California Department of Fish and Game)

train. Consequently, annuals quickly took over as the wild grasses of the Central Valley. Even they, however, have long since relinquished the bulk of valley land to crops, fences, irrigation systems, roads, and cities. What has become California's horn of plenty now affords precious few reminders of its flourishing nonagricultural past.

Desert Shrublands

Another name for this ecosystem might be "rain shadow biome," at least insofar as it fits California's biogeography. For prevailing westerly winds and the towering mountain ranges that stand in their way combine to guarantee aridity throughout the lee side of California. Here, mapped as desert shrubland in Figure 7.1, natural vegetation and wildlife have learned to get along with less than 10 inches of atmospheric moisture in most years and with only a trace or no precipitation at all in some years. Compounding the dryness are temperatures that regularly soar above 110° F in summer in the low deserts (at lower elevation, principally in the Colorado and Mojave deserts) and dip below freezing on winter nights in the high deserts of the Great Basin. The desert climate relents a bit in early spring and late fall with pleasantly mild temperatures and in late summer with the occasional thundershower, but through all the seasons desert flora and fauna are prepared to survive the worst of climatic extremes a mid-latitude rain shadow environment has to offer.

The key to survival is making do with what little moisture is or becomes available and it is desert plant-life, because it underpins the food chain, that has made the most significant ecological adaptations. These adaptations are viewed in various ways by different naturalists, but in general they can be envisaged in terms of a desert plant's ability either to gather water with its rooting system, store water in its tissue, or come to life only when, where, and while there is sufficient moisture. In other words, desert plants can be thought of as *water gatherers, water storers,* and *opportunists.* This is an admittedly arbitrary and vastly simplified classification of *xerophytes* (drought-adapted plants) and thus merits the close examination that follows.

Throughout the deserts of California and North America, water-gathering perennial shrubs, like those pictured in Figure 7.18, monotonously dominate the landscape. The most conspicuous feature of this evergreen scrub cover is the amount of open space between individual plants. This openness is attributed to each plant's rooting system extending laterally far beyond the diameter of its visible or above-ground parts so it can absorb soil moisture from as wide an area as possible. The roots spread out horizontally so as to remain close to the surface and thereby maximize the benefit of whatever meager, shallow-penetrating precipitation occurs. In effect, competition for rooting territory keeps water-gathering shrubs apart. The extensive rooting systems of big sagebrush (*Artemisia tridentata*), burroweed (*Franseria* spp.), creosote bush (*Larrea divaricata*), rabbitbrush (*Chrysothamnus nauseosus*), shadscale (*Atriplex confertifolia*), and other desert dominants also reduce soil erosion and protect against uprooting brought on by high winds or flash floods. The latter function is especially significant to all manner of small mammals, reptiles, birds, and insects who seek out the shrubs for shelter and other habitat amenities. The microclimate of shade supplied by a shrub helps ensure the survival of smaller plants as well.

Even humans have sought food and shelter from the water-gathering plants: The Cahuilla Indians of the Salton Trough region, for instance, ate seeds from the Chia sage (*Salvia columbariae*) and beans from the mesquite tree (*Prosopis* spp.). Mesquite with its probing tap roots

Figure 7.18 Great Basin sagebrush and rabbitbrush are mixed with piñon pines in this view of the Owens Valley from the upper edge of the alluvial *piedmont* (coalesced alluvial fans) flanking the eastern Sierra. Porous, granitic soils derive from the adjacent mountains. Such drought-adapted plants are called *xerophytes.* (Crane Miller)

can act as a reliable indicator of groundwater presence usually within 30 ft or less of the desert surface. Joshua trees (*Yucca brevifolia*), when concentrated in their natural alluvial slope habitat, also tell us that groundwater may not be far underfoot.

When things really become grim in the desert, such as during the 32 months of no precipitation that occurred between 1909 and 1912 in the south central Mojave, the water gatherers resort to other means of survival. In this instance creosote bushes lost nearly all of their leaves but did not die; evidently they were able to continue limited photosynthesis in stems or in bark. Leaf loss also reduced transpiration and thereby conserved moisture in the plants. Even when these evergreen desert shrubs have a full complement of foliage, the small size, reflective light color, waxiness, and hairyness of their leaves help keep water loss and heat gain at a minimum. Some of the same mechanisms also see the plants through unusually cold or long winters.

Whatever the season, when the plants die back in a prolonged dry spell, they enter a period of dormancy during which only enough live tissue remains to handle the scant amount of moisture available. Longevity and the slow growth needed to attain it—for example, many a big sagebrush more than 200 years old exists today in the Owens Valley and Inyo Mountains—is yet another reason the evergreen desert shrub is perennial in every sense of the word. These shrubs, bristlecone pines, and many other native California plants literally take life slow and easy, especially during dry times.

Cacti and other water-holding *succulents* comprise the second category of desert plants, the water storers (Fig. 7.19). From the giant saguaro (*Cereus gigantea*), of the Colorado Desert to the smaller, more ubiquitous opuntias (*Opuntia* spp.), the cacti, with their comparatively shallow rooting systems, are notably unique in their ability to soak up surface moisture created by a cloudburst and then store the water in the internal tissue of their stems. A cactus becomes bloated after rain and then shrinks during drought as it uses its own water to survive. The leathery skin and needles of a cactus not only protect the inner reservoir against overheating and consequent water loss but also turn away browsing animals.

Although mountainside thermal belts often accommodate opuntias and the like, lengthy winter frosts largely preclude any extensive distribution of water storers in the high deserts of the Great Basin. Rather, it is the warm, low deserts of the southeast where California's native cactus gardens are to be found. Other tropical genera, such as succulent, swordlike century plants (*Agave* spp.) growing out of rock piles and native fan palms (*Washingtonia filifera*) populating faulted canyon oases, also grace the state's warm deserts.

Finally, we come to the opportunists or *ephemerals*: those desert plants that seem to be here one day and gone the next. Wild buckwheats (*Eriogonum* spp.), sand verbena (*Abronia villosa*), goldfields (*Baeria chyrsostoma*) and other annual wildflowers (Fig. 7.20), so varied as to species they defy identification by many a naturalist, essentially comprise this category. Despite the implication of their classification as annuals, wildflower seeds and bulbs sprout forth only following sufficient

Figure 7.19 The hedgehog cactus, or strawberry cactus, is pictured here in the Anza-Borrego Desert west of the Imperial Valley. Cacti are generally not frost-tolerant; however, low-growing cacti are often found in the high deserts of the Great Basin in mountainside or upper alluvial fan *thermal belts,* where temperatures are a few degrees higher than in basins at lower elevations on cold, still, winter nights. Cold air, being denser or heavier, drains by gravity downslope into basin or valley bottoms and settles there (*cold air ponding*), causing a temperature inversion (see Chapter 4) or warmer temperatures upslope. (California Department of Parks and Recreation)

precipitation, which may not occur for years on end in the desert. For dormant seeds to germinate, precipitation should be spread out intermittently over several weeks or more rather than coming all at once. This explains why the best wildflower displays can be expected to follow a good winter's worth of rain and snow rather than a summer's single tropical downpour, even though the amount of moisture produced in both cases may be roughly equivalent.

Although wildflower seeds generally await their opportunity to come to life in the shelter of large perennial shrubs, they can be inadvertently carried just about anywhere by animals, flash floods, winds, or even humans. Consequently, wildflower crops may be found in such diverse places as alluvial slopes, dry washes, and along the edges of alkali sinks, sand dunes, and highway shoulders. Any of these locations from the Salton Trough north to the Great Basin are good bets for finding the desert in bloom following a normal or wet winter, but the Mojave and the Colorado in April are rarely surpassed. The "desert day" or "wild Easter" lily (*Hesperocallis undulata*), sprouting from a bulb to heights

Figure 7.20 Dune primroses, in the Anza-Borrego Desert, and other desert wildflowers bloom only when normal or above-normal winter precipitation occurs, and even then not always. (California Department of Parks and Recreation)

sometimes exceeding 5 feet, could be said to be the most appropriately named of the ephemerals that herald the blooming of the California deserts in the springtime.

Hiding out from searing solar and earth radiation in summer, avoiding excessive heat loss in winter, and conserving water in every season are challenges that obviously must be met by the fauna as well as the flora of the desert. What is amazing is that the desert literally teems with animal life despite the rigors of aridity.

Both the richness and survival adaptations of the fauna become apparent when studying any one of a number of desert food chains, but perhaps these features are best typified by the members of a seed-rodent-reptile-bird food chain. Many desert rodents, including the bush-nesting harvest mouse (*Reithrodontomys raviventris*) and the rock-dwelling pocket mouse (*Perognanthus* spp.), rely on seeds as the staple of their diet. Pocket mice enjoy an advantage over other seed harvesters in that they are outfitted with a pair of cheek pouches that enable them to carry a relatively large number of seeds home after a single outing. Long-tailed kangaroo rats (*Dipodomys* spp.) also have cheek pouches, but their ability to produce water chemically from plant foliage and seeds is undoubtedly one of the most significant survival capabilities any desert animal claims.

Like kangaroo rats, grasshopper mice (*Onychomys* spp.) dwell underground, but their diet includes insects as well as seeds. Living in burrows by day and harvesting and hunting by night provide many a rodent species escape from the worst of summer heat, although some burrowers, like the round-tailed ground squirrel (*Citellus tereticaudus*) and antelope ground squirrel (*Ammospermophilus leucurus*), are diurnal foragers. Ground squirrels seem nervous enough never to stay in the hot

sun for too long and their light sandy color may minimize heat absorption by maximizing reflection of the sun's rays.

But in spite of desert rodents' quickness afoot, defensive coloration, and other survival adaptations, they are constantly in jeopardy from a whole host of predators. Perhaps most effective in keeping rodent populations from exploding are various species of the venomous rattlesnake (*Crotalus* spp.; see Fig. 7.21). Once their winter hibernation is well behind them, many rattlers hunt both nocturnally, seeking the likes of kangaroo rats and mice, and diurnally, going after ground squirrels, lizards, and small rabbits. Because they are cold-blooded

Figure 7.21 Rattlesnakes are endowed with protective coloring and, along with their elongated shape, are hard to distinguish from shrubbery lying on the ground. The *sidewinder's* diagonal and parallel tracks are unmistakable. Rattlers keep to themselves and have good reason to fear humans more than natural predators, but beware of where you reach or step lest you invite a bite. (California Department of Fish and Game)

animals, rattlers need air temperatures consistently above 70° F before they'll emerge from their homes in burrows or rock crevices on a regular basis. Yet daytime temperatures exceeding 100° F will find them coiled in the shade of shrubs or rocky overhangs and unlikely to expose themselves to direct sunlight where they would lose coordination, lapse into heat prostration and die within a few minutes. Like the desert wildflowers, rattlesnakes like to be out and about during the milder days of spring and this is the time of the year to exercise most caution when walking in the desert.

Other than humans, rattlesnakes fear few predators save the hawk. Hawks, owls, and other large birds of prey, however, more commonly hunt smaller reptiles and mammals. California's largest native lizard, the chuckawalla (*Sauromalus obesus*), is among their favorite prey. It should not be forgotten that besides predatory birds, coyotes, bobcats, and the like are also present in the desert and play important roles as apex species in the food chain.

Petroglyphs (Fig. 7.22) and other archaeological evidence indicate human settlement in California deserts dating back at least 8,000 years. The aboriginal peoples were basically hunters and gatherers and, as would be expected in an arid environment, their populations never approached the densities of those in milder climatic regions. But those Indians who settled along the lower Colorado River and far to the north in the Owens Valley were the only ones known to practice irrigated agriculture in aboriginal California. Their basketry was examplary, too, especially in construction of pitch-covered baskets for carrying precious water from spring or stream to settlement site.

The advent of white settlement in the mid-nineteenth century signaled the beginning of hard times for both native desert peoples and their environment. As noted in Chapter 3, surviving Indian populations have become concentrated on a few widely scattered reservations, rancherías, and in some desert cities and towns, and their lot is generally a poor one. The plants and animals of the California deserts have also lost much ground in the past century, giving way not so much to the spatial expansion of a few small cities as to transient human activity.

The development of dirt roads, paved highways, interstates, power lines, microwave towers, railroads, and fences has been negative enough in itself, but add to this the destruction of desert habitat by off-road vehicles (ORV) and one wonders if much of anything will be left in time. Rabbits being run down by motorcyclists, dune buggies running over desert iguanas (*Dipsosaurus dorsalis*) and tortoises (*Gopherus agassizi*; see Fig. 7.23), and ORVs of all sorts crushing vegetation, accelerating surface erosion, and carving up *desert pavement* (the wind-abraded and polished surface of closely packed, sometimes cemented-together pebbles) and *intaglios* (large figures carved in the sand and gravel landscape by human hands)—all threaten the desert with the prospect of becoming a lifeless dust bowl.

If the Mojave and Colorado deserts are to remain a viable recreational and wilderness resource to millions of nearby urbanites not bent on their destruction, support must mount for maximizing the number of roadless

Figure 7.22 Petroglyphs engraved here in dolomite centuries ago by predecessors of the present-day Paiute Indians in the Inyo Mountains depict mountain or bighorn sheep (*Ovis canadensis*), humans, and other figures. Quite skillful at negotiating the steepest of terrain, bighorn once roamed the mountains of California from the Pacific to the Great Basin and from the Klamath Mountains down to the Peninsular Ranges. But hunters, ranchers, livestock, and feral burros (Fig. 7.26) have greatly reduced their numbers. Today, bighorn are legally protected from being hunted and their populations have been revived by animals imported from as far away as the Canadian Rockies. Bighorn are found at higher elevations than mule deer and are most likely to be seen along rugged mountain crests such as in the California Bighorn Sheep Zoological Area just east of Kings Canyon–Sequoia National Parks. (Crane Miller)

areas (each normally to be in excess of 5,000 acres) under the California Desert Plan as it is completed in 1980 and updated thereafter. The U. S. Bureau of Land Management (BLM), which controls 12.5 million acres of desert land, started the inventory phase of the plan late in the last decade. This California Desert Conservation Area (CDCA), as it is officially designated, will hopefully become a bastion for the permanent preservation of California's desert environment. Before we become overly optimistic about the desert's future, however, it would be well to again ponder the environmental impact, especially on bioclimate, of the possible development of coal-fired and solar thermal power plants (see Chapter 6) in the state's deserts. In the meantime, 1.38 million acres of the eastern Mojave has been designated a National Scenic Area to be managed by the Bureau of Land Management.

Chaparral and Coastal Shrublands

In pinpointing the distribution of this principal biome in Figure 7.1, we should note that although it is concentrated in a mixed fashion on the windward and southwest-facing slopes of Southern California's coastal mountain ranges, dense patches of "pure" chaparral are also found under the same conditions of aspect in the Sierran foothills and farther north. By the same token, along the coast north of Monterey, the more open coastal shrubland exists almost exclusive of any chaparral.

Despite differences in the ground cover density of the two plant communities, however, they share many of the same dominant evergreen species, including laruel sumac (*Rhus larina*), different varieties of ceonothus (*Ceonothus* spp.), purple sage (*Salvia leucophylla*), and scrub oak (*Quercus dumosa*). Scrub oak translates into Spanish as *chaparro*, from which the word *chaparral* was derived. Chaparral is of course California's version of Mediterranean vegetation, and in most ways it is the same thick, evergreen scrub that circles the Mediterranean Sea and goes by the name *garigue* or *maquis*, but with different species. Chaparral plants serve as reliable shelter, food sources, and protection from invaders for a great variety of wildlife. Indeed, chaparral animals are not likely ever to see many Sunday picknickers or intrepid hikers in their territory.

Although chaparral may be singularly unattractive for recreation, it serves humankind by preventing excessive storm runoff and therefore functions as watershed vegetation that minimizes slope erosion. At the same time, though, chaparral poses a greater hazard to Californians than any other biome: It is a *fire climax* community. Put another way, chaparral should burn every so often or it will degenerate. There are a number of climatic and botanical explanations for this hot-tempered behavior, and they are identified in Figure 7.24.

Painful familiarity with chaparral's propensity to burn has, it seems, done little to prevent home builders from developing the Santa Monica Mountains, Verdugo Hills, San Gabriel Mountains, and other chaparral locales overlooking the Los Angeles Basin. Perhaps the tangible and intangible rewards gained from a view site in Bel Air or a secluded sanctuary in Mandeville Canyon cancel out memories of the devastating chaparral fires of 1961 and 1978. A new home in either location, and many are being built, costs hundreds of thousands of dollars. Meanwhile, the controversy over whether or not to develop such a fireprone environment rages on.

The Littoral

Life along more than 1,000 miles of California shoreline goes and comes twice a day with the ebb and flow of the Pacific's tides. The regular rise and fall of sea level created by the gravitational forces of sun and moon acting on a rotating earth help carve out and build various coastal habitats for myriad tidal communities of plants and animals.

When the tide is high there is little to see, but ebbtide can reveal all kinds of worlds. On broad, sandy beaches, long-billed curlews (*Numenius americanus*) may be seen digging for tiny crustaceans while hordes of flies circle about seaweed (kelp of various genera) that has washed ashore. On the outer reaches of rocky headlands, countless tidepools (Fig. 7.25) appear as aquaria, each filled variously with abalone (*Haliotis* spp.), anemones (*Anthopleura* spp.), barnacles (*Balanus* spp.), hermit crabs (*Pagurus* spp.), mussels (*Mytilus* spp.), starfish (*Pisaster ochraceaus*), sea snails and worms, and tiny fish of all descriptions. On rocky crags safely above pounding surf and incoming tides, ashy petrels (*Oceanodroma homochroa*) and cormorants (*Phalacrocorax* spp.) are sometimes visible in their nests. In the isolation of offshore rocks, glimpses of seals (*Callorhinus* spp.) and southern sea otters (*Enhydralutris* spp.) may be caught. In tidal marshes and lagoons, *halophytic* (salt-tolerant) grasses and other plants contain everything from lowly mud-flat crabs (*Hemigrapsus* spp.) to high-flying kingfishers (*Megaceryle alcyon*). And overhead, California seagulls (*Larus californicus*) crowd the sky in an endless search for prey.

Sadly, much of the natural littoral has disappeared, having succumbed to the understandable desire of millions of Californians to reside there if they can afford it. The Santa Barbara oil spill of 1968 and other unnatural events have compounded destruction of the seashore. Passage of Proposition 20 in 1972 and the enabling acts that followed may save much of what remains unspoiled on the California littoral, yet it sometimes seems futile to strive for what is ecologically sound when the nation's hunger for energy may dictate more seaside oil refineries, ports, and offshore drilling rigs for the state.

There are, however, comeback stories, that of the southern or California sea otter being among the more remarkable. Two centuries ago, there were an estimated 16,000 otters along the coast. By one century ago, they had been hunted to near extinction by American, English, Mexican, Russian, and Aleut and Northwest Indian fur hunters. But in 1937, a small band of the little mammals was seen swimming off Carmel. Since then, their population has increased to some 2,000 and their range has extended to as far south as Point Loma. Pismo Beach clam diggers, Morro Bay abalone fishermen, and the like would just as soon see otters disappear once again, for man and animal in this case compete for a diminishing supply of shellfish. But sea otters, now fully protected, are likely to increase their numbers to more than 3,000 by the end of this century, according to Department of Fish and Game estimates.

Figure 7.23 Desert tortoise populations have declined in part because of the ease with which they are captured by pet seekers. The desert tortoise can, however, survive long droughts better than many another desert animal because it can draw from a water-storing bladder when all other moisture sources (mostly plants) have dried up. Moreover, predators have little success penetrating the "armor-plated" shell of the tortoise. (Crane Miller)

THE SUCCESS OF EXOTICS

Since the Franciscans first brought the Old World grape (*Vitis vinifera*) and domesticated livestock in 1769, plant and animal species by the thousands and from the four corners of the earth have been introduced to California

Figure 7.24 Fire, whether in suburban chaparral scrubland or rural coniferous forest (here in Swall Meadows in the eastern Sierra), is both destructive and beneficial to the habitats involved. In adapting to California's long warm-season droughts, many chaparral species produce volatile oils that, when kindled, bring about the quick destruction of the plants by fire. Deadwood and debris also contribute to the rapid spread of fire. On the other hand, fire clears away the debris and produces ash that provides nutrients to the soils. After being burned beyond recognition, many a chaparral species (scrub oak, chamise, and toyon, for example) will stump-sprout to live another day. In the case of some manzanita and ceonothus species, their seeds germinate only after a burn. (Crane Miller)

Figure 7.25 Tidepools such as these teem with small sea creatures. (Roger M. Rhiner)

with unprecedented success. Much of what the Spanish missionaries and others grew and raised in California for the first time would eventually become the basis of the state's most important industry: agriculture (see Chapter 10). Just as many exotics, though, have found their way into perpetuity in California's nonagricultural environments. And, unlike crops and livestock, they have done so without human help, albeit some wild creatures of today, such as desert burros, mustangs, and other *feral* animals (Fig. 7.26) are descended from domesticated lines. Under whatever conditions they exist, however, introduced plants and animals have prospered in no small way from the state's diversity of climates, landforms, and soils. It seems there is an ecological niche in California for just about every living thing, no matter its origins.

Figure 7.27 shows what many consider to be the most successful plant, at least in terms of surviving on its own, ever introduced into the state: the blue gum or eucalyptus tree (*Eucalyptus* spp.). A native of Australia, where there are some 400 species of the tree, the eucalyptus was probably first brought into California in the 1850s. During that decade, nursery people in San Francisco began advertising the availability of seedling gum trees; before long they were competing with native trees throughout much of the Bay Area. Planting of eucalyptus in Southern California began in the following decade and was probably under the supervision of citriculturist, viticulturist, and former fur trapper William Wolfskill. Cultivation continued through the 1880s as eucalyptus became a familiar part of the Los Angeles Basin landscape. Growers foresaw use of eucalyptus in the manufacture of rail ties and other hardwood items, but softer woods that were easier to work with were preferred.

Figure 7.26 Feral burros in the Saline Valley. Feral horses and burros populate the western United States by the tens of thousands and in such large numbers compete for forage with both domesticated livestock and native animals, such as bighorn sheep. They also destroy natural habitats and get in the way of human activities such as at the China Lake Naval Weapons Test Center. An estimated 8,800 burros and 750 wild horses live in the California Desert Conservation Area (Mojave Desert) alone. Burros and horses were introduced to North America in the 1500s by the Spanish, but it was not until the 1900s, when motorized vehicles replaced them as the dominant mode of cross-country travel and drayage, that they were set free in California's deserts by prospectors. The Wild Horse and Burro Act passed by Congress in 1971 sets strict controls over the manner of reducing the numbers of these once domesticated, now returned to the wild, animals. (California Department of Fish and Game)

Figure 7.27 Eucalyptus windbreaks planted decades ago have served their intended purpose well. (Roger M. Rhiner)

Figure 7.28 Fan palms (*Washingtonia filifera*) are native to the Colorado Desert but have been successfully introduced throughout much of the rest of the state. (Roger M. Rhiner)

Eucalyptus oil was another product thought to have a great sales potential, but it too never caught on.

With a market never really developing for eucalyptus products, plantings of the trees tailed off by the end of the century. Thereafter, about the only cultivation involved occasional use of eucalyptus as an orchard windbreak. Nevertheless, the eucalypts have prospered on their own and today seem as much a part of the California scene as any native tree, especially in cities. In Santa Monica and Santa Barbara, for example, there are at least three dozen different species of eucalyptus lining the streets.

Another successful foreign tree, the tamarisk (two species: *Tamarix gallica* and *Tamarix aphylla*), was introduced to the Mojave and Colorado deserts by ranchers and the Southern Pacific Company early in this century. Tamarisks originated in the arid eastern Mediterranean region of the world and thus managed well on their own in California's deserts. In fact, they have become a nuisance—their seeds readily disperse by both wind and bird to places where they're not wanted. Along with palm trees, however, (Fig. 7.28), they have served their original purpose of providing shade and windbreak protection against blowing sand.

Bearing little resemblance to its barnyard cousin the hog (*Sus* spp.), the California wild boar or pig has become the state's most hunted nonnative big game animal. The domesticated hog was introduced to California by Father Serra and the Franciscans in the eighteenth century, but the wild Old World boar came somewhat later. Today, nearly as many wild hogs (32,000 in 1978) as mule deer (35,000 in 1978) are killed legally by hunters each year. California's other major big game animal, the black bear, looms a distant third in number killed annually (a record 935 in 1967).

Wild hog populations are concentrated in the Coast Ranges from Mendocino through Santa Barbara counties and on Catalina and San Clemente islands. In these locales boar subsist on insects, roots, wild barley, and oak acorns. Oak woodlands, coastal shrub, and chaparral also provide them with shelter and refuge. Although some California wild hogs weigh more than 600 pounds, a 200-pounder is considered a good take and will keep two people in pork dinners for several weeks. When cornered, a wild hog of these proportions is a dangerous animal. On the run from hunters and their dogs in open country, however, a hog is rarely if ever likely to turn and go on the attack.

We have examined only a tiny sample of the many success stories of exotic plants and animals in California. Perhaps we could learn as much about the proliferation of introduced flora and fauna by simply gazing out over the artificial landscape of almost any city. Seen in this light, the most significant success gained from the massive introduction of plants to California is in the improvement of the quality of urban and suburban

Figure 7.29 Union Square. Palm trees and hedgerows in the heart of downtown San Francisco with the St. Francis Hotel in the background. (Roger M. Rhiner)

environments. Many of the most densely developed sections of the state's largest cities are all the more pleasant to work and live in because exotic vegetation prospers so well in California. Water it and it will grow, even in the middle of such urban environments as Union Square in downtown San Francisco (Fig. 7.29).

The density of development in such high-rise urban areas notwithstanding, there is quantitatively and qualitatively more vegetation today than there was before urbanization. Most of the west side of the Los Angeles Basin, for instance, was a sparsely treed grassland in prehistoric times, which was barely two centuries ago (the City of Los Angeles was founded in 1781).

Increases in *biomass* (the actual weight of living matter), significantly augmented by introduced vegetation, have improved the looks of suburbia as well, be it frost-sensitive bougainvillea (*Bougainvillea* spp.), hedgerows replacing coastal sagebrush near the ocean in Southern California, or all-weather oleander (*Nerium oleander*) lining a freeway in Northern California. Since it carries on photosynthesis, exotic flora has also made the state's urban air all the better to breathe.

Faunal introductions, from English sparrows (*Passer domesticus*) filling suburban skies to mosquito fish (*Gambusia affinis*) controlling insects in flood channels, have made city life more attractive as well. Unwelcome exotics, such as lawnseed-eating starlings (*Sturnus* spp.) and dozens of weed species, detract from the picture, but in general, the impact *Homo sapiens* has had on the California landscape in their introduction of thousands of species of plants and animals has been a successful one.

THE HISTORICAL GEOGRAPHY OF CALIFORNIA

Scholars have long debated the issue of how much influence the physical environment has had upon the unique development of cultures throughout the world. One side of the debate, often termed *geographic determinism,* holds that the human race, its creations, and its evolution are essentially conditioned by the natural environment. The other side of the debate denies that nature and geography alone are so omnipotent in the unique development of a culture or people.

Perhaps the most balanced view is to recognize the interrelationships between people and the environment. Certainly, many factors influence the evolution of a particular culture, and geography must be credited as one of these important factors. California provides an excellent example of a situation in which physical environment has played a significant role in the events and cultural makeup of a people.

Geography has constantly acted upon the historical development of California, shaping people and events at each point in its evolution. Aboriginal lifestyle was intimately related to environment; European settlement patterns were conditioned by distance, weather, and nature. The offerings of the land, from fertile soil and climate to gold and other minerals, drew Spanish, Mexicans, and Americans alike. The size of the state, its natural resources, and its generally mild weather have continued to play key roles in the economic, social, and cultural life of the state, especially as manifest in agriculture, transportation, oil, and moviemaking. The same factors that brought early immigrants continue to attract modern-day newcomers to the state. Thus, the continuity of California's development can, in part, be attributed to the realities of climate and geography.

THE ORIGINAL CALIFORNIANS

Evidence of human presence in California is among the oldest reported in the United States. We know that as early as 29,000 to 34,000 years ago, primitive people began a Southern California tradition on Santa Rosa Island by barbecuing a dwarf mammoth. There is some additional evidence of human presence in California as early as 50,000 years ago. Evidence of established societal or tribal existence, however, does not appear until much later.

The aboriginal population of California constituted the first wave of immigration to the state. Generally, anthropologists conclude that this immigration into the area came about as a natural result of nomadic wandering through the Bering Strait, across a land bridge, and onward down the North American continent. By the time of the first Spanish forays into California, the Indian population had grown significantly. Although the estimates vary widely, it is generally agreed that at least 133,000 and perhaps as many as 300,000 Indians populated California at the first Spanish contact. It is widely accepted that California reflected the greatest population density of any *nonagricultural* area in the world and had the greatest population density in North America.

The nature of the California Indians can be described as diverse and varied. In language alone, there were at least 135 dialects in no less than 20 basic linguistic families, ranging from the Penutian to the Hokan to the Shoshonean and Athabascan (see Fig. 8.1). Similarly, dress, habitation, and physical stature all varied widely. The only common element, in fact, has been the way California Indians have been characterized historically. Perhaps the most widely circulated image is that derived from the term gratuitously placed on them by the American Forty-Niners—"Diggers." As the term was used, it implied root grubbers and insect eaters of low intelligence and primitive demeanor. Applied indiscriminately as a label of contempt for all California aboriginals, it was a gross oversimplification.

Although generalizations about such a diverse group are difficult to make, nevertheless certain common traits are in evidence. Certainly, measured against European and American standards of aggression, technology, and materialism, California Indians were less prominent. They were peaceful rather than warlike. They were well adjusted to their environment, living with it rather than destroying it. By modern standards, they lived an uncomplicated, simple life instead of a hectic, competitive,

143

Source: Adapted from A. L. Kroeber, *Handbook of the Indians of California*, Scholarly Press, 1972.

Figure 8.1 Main aboriginal Indian groups in the state. (Richard Crooker)

and grasping existence. Their religious life was generally highly developed, their social life apparently well adjusted.

The aboriginal inhabitants of California were attuned to their environment and reflected many of the characteristics we now associate with the state. Isolated by mountain and desert from the rest of North America, they developed a culture of appreciation and reliance on nature. Largely individualistic, living in villages or rancherías of approximately 130 people, the California Indians used dwellings suited to their surroundings. Plank houses were used in the northwest, bark in the central regions, earth on the coast, and brush in the deserts. Dress was, for the most part, "early suntan" attire, consisting of topless two-piece apron skirts for the women and *au naturel* for the men. In cooler weather, a blanket or cloak of hides would be added. Food was provided by nature in the form of acorns, game, fish, or other natural bounty. Only with the coming of the Spanish friars did organized agricultural production become common.

Singing, dancing, and chanting were familiar pastimes, as were gambling games, athletic contests, and storytelling. Public health and sanitation were accomplished by use of sweathouses and periodic burning of the living structures, and herbal medicines were in common use. The dominant form of religion was *shamanism,* a belief that supernatural spirits work for the benefit or detriment of humankind through the intervention of the priest or shaman.

In retrospect, the California Indian appears much more well adjusted, efficient, harmonious, and admirable than generally depicted in the past. If environment does help form social styles, then it may be said that the society of the Indians accurately reflected their surroundings. The mild California environment demanded no excesses from the people, and the people did not seek unnecessary complications for their lives.

The Spanish, Mexican, and American waves of immigration brought major changes, and their collective and progressive impact on the Indians was destructive. Disease, starvation, and violence caused the native population to suffer a continued and drastic reduction in numbers, with various children's diseases, pulmonary ailments, venereal diseases, and other similar maladies taking a huge toll. Similarly, imposed changes in living patterns disrupted the flow of Indian life, whether it was the forced relocations of tribes into mission dormitories by the Spanish or the forcible ejection of tribes from whole areas by the Americans. Victimized in turn by each incoming group, the Indian was, as the respected California historian W. H. Hutchinson put it, "vital to Spain, useful to Mexico, and an annoyance to the United States." The discovery and colonization of California by Europeans truly spelled the end to the simple Indian culture, which could not hope to resist "civilization."

EUROPEAN EXPLORATION

The discovery, exploration, and eventual settlement of California by the Spanish came about in the aftermath of initial explorations of Mexico by Hernando Cortés and others in the early 1500s. Curious about the nature and extent of this new territory, Cortés, Coronado, Ulloa, and others undertook several voyages and expeditions to the north. It was Juan Rodríguez Cabrillo who first entered what would be called Alta California when he sailed into San Diego Bay and on up the coast in 1542. Prophetically enough, he named the coastal area near Los Angeles and Santa Monica "the Bay of Smokes" for the profusion of Indian campfires in the vicinity. Cabrillo died during the course of the voyage, and when the reports of the expedition were passed on to the Spanish officials, little interest in the region was generated.

Although it was true that Spain almost exclusively provided the initial impetus for exploration, California did have some other European visitors. Britain's salty sea dog Sir Francis Drake first set foot on California's shoreline in 1579. He spent a month on shore establishing England's sovereignty (so he claimed), engaging in trade and communication with the Indians, and repairing his ship, the *Golden Hinde.* Having made his ship seaworthy enough to carry the treasure he had stolen from Spanish towns and galleons in the New World, he set sail for England, undoubtedly filled with tales of his adventures and romances in sunny Nova Albion.

Concerned by Drake's activities, the Spanish interest in the area increased enough to send another expedition up the California coast to seek "harbors in which galleons might take refuge" from sea rovers such as Drake. Thus, between 1584 and 1602 Francisco Gali explored the coast, Sebastián Cermeno sailed along the shoreline noting likely harbors, and Sebastián Vizcaíno made an extended excursion, stopping in San Diego, Catalina, Santa Barbara, and Monterey Bay. These expeditions increased Spain's knowledge of the area, but not her immediate interest. Thus, Alta California remained largely an ignored outpost until the 1760s.

One other notable foreign incursion involved the Russians at a somewhat later date. Fort Ross in present-day Sonoma County was founded by the Russian-American Company in 1812. Although primarily concerned with the fur trade in Alaska, the Company did extend southward for both food and other fur sources (primarily sea otter). With the decline of the sea otter and the fur seal populations, however, Fort Ross became merely an unsuccessful experiment that they were willing to sell to John Sutter in 1841. At that point, the Russians withdrew permanently from California.

MISSION SETTLEMENT PATTERNS

As with many colonizations, the settlement of California was largely inspired by international competition. Spurred on by the colonizing activities of Russia and the presence of English and Dutch privateers along the Pacific coast, the Spanish recognized the need to protect their holdings from foreign rivalry. The most effective way to accomplish this goal was to initiate the tripartite policy of presidio, mission, and pueblo.

Under the energetic leadership of José de Gálvez, the inspector-general of New Spain, expansion was initiated. The first major settlement expedition was to build at least three missions and two presidios (military bases).

Under the leadership of Captain Gaspar de Portolá and Father Junipero Serra, the first presidio and the first mission in Alta California were established in San Diego in 1769. Over the course of the next 50 years, 20 more missions were founded, some accompanied by presidios, some by pueblos, and some by both. Approximately 30 miles apart (one day's travel by horseback), they formed a chain strung from San Diego to Sonoma, connected only by a dusty path known as El Camino Real ("the royal road").

For the first 50 years of Spanish settlement, the missions assumed the key role in California life. Intended by the Spaniards to serve the dual role of bringing Christianity to the Indians and of firmly establishing Spanish hegemony over the area, the missions were remarkable institutions. From the viewpoint of the civil authorities, they were inexpensive extensions of empire, requiring only a couple of padres, a handful of soldiers, and infrequent supplies.

Each mission reflected a certain adaptation to California realities. Structurally, the missions evolved an architecture of red claylike roofs, massive buttresses, and thick walls as proof against brush fires and earthquakes, heat and sun of summer, and cold of winter (Fig. 8.2). Agriculturally, each mission operated on a huge tract of around 100,000 acres located in fertile coastal areas supplied with both ample water and Indian population. The dedicated Franciscan friars intended to bring civilization and progress to the Indians. More often, they brought dependence bordering on slavery, diseases for which the native population had no immunity, and early death for many.

Economically, the missions were probably most successful. The missions developed a crude form of industrial-manufacturing enterprise, where weaving, blacksmithing, cattle raising, farming, tanning, masonry, and carpentry became common. Thus, the Indians learned from the friars how to work and toil long hours for their food and livelihood, whereas before the padres' arrival they had merely lived successfully off the natural bounty of the land.

The Spanish presidios and pueblos played a less vital role in the settlement of California, although they were important in extending secular authority to the frontier. The presidios at San Francisco, Monterey, Santa Barbara, and San Diego served to guard against foreign invasion and Indian uprising. With their limited capabilities, however, it was fortunate they were not put to any severe test. In spite of inducements of land, stock, and implements, the establishment of pueblos was not a major success. The pueblos of San Jose and Los Angeles are the only enduring evidence of the civil townships created by Spanish authority (Fig. 8.3).

THE DECLINE OF THE MISSION AND THE MEXICAN PERIOD

The mission period ended suddenly with the disintegration of the Spanish empire in America in the early 1800s. The geography of the mission colonization effort almost inevitably resulted in its separation from the Spanish empire. All of Spain's American colonies were largely independent of the mother country. Thus, in the early

Figure 8.2 Santa Barbara Mission, a classic jewel in the California chain of missions. (Union Pacific Railroad)

Figure 8.3 Pico House in the old Pueblo de Los Angeles, one of the first hotels in Southern California and a favorite of early California cowboys. (Richard Hyslop)

years of the nineteenth century, Spain's American colonies began seceding en masse. After 10 years of sporadic struggle, the Republic of Mexico was formed in 1821. Always a distant outpost at best, California had been little affected by these independence efforts; Mexico, however, asserted its natural trade and political rights as heir of Spain, and California became an official part of the republic.

During the mission period, the establishment of private ranchos had been successfully opposed by the church authorities, with somewhat less than 35 land grants being made to private persons. With the success of the Mexican revolution, however, the number of private land grants increased dramatically.

The Mexican period brought several turbulent changes to California life. Isolated as it was from Mexico, California did not respond well to governors sent to rule from distant Mexico. The *Californios*[1] had been accustomed to being left alone, and a series of unpopular and incompetent governors only helped formalize a tradition of conspiracy, insurrection, and rebellion. Likewise, the Mexican period brought about major socioeconomic upheavals. Perhaps the single most dramatic event was the secularization of the missions by order of the Mexican government in 1834. The mission lands were divided up, eventually becoming private ranchos, often through cheating the Indians or dishonest machinations by the secular administrators. By whatever process, the period of the great private cattle station replaced that of the mission, and for a brief time, the colorful and romantic rancho characterized California life.

THE ROMANCE OF THE RANCHO

Of all periods, that of the California rancho is the most romanticized. A vision of the stolid, cool, tile-roofed ran-

[1]This was the name given to the non-Indian settlers and rancheros who made their homes in the region of modern-day California.

cho, with *ollas* of water dripping peacefully in languorous breezes flitting through enclosed patios is indeed compelling. The colorfully dressed, devil-may-care *caballero* riding or dancing with reckless abandon also provides a dramatic historical figure. Undoubtedly these images have been overdone, reflecting as they do only a small percentage of the population during a very limited period. Nevertheless, they provide a colorful description of a way of life that held sway for some people. Cattle ranching *was* the predominant economic underpinning of Mexican California. The entire population owed its social and economic existence to this activity, which replaced the mission almost entirely by the 1830s. The secularization of the missions brought about an increase in private rancho grants which increased from 20 in 1821 to over 600 by 1846. This covered most of the appropriate lands up to and including the Sacramento area.

The rancho was a natural outgrowth of several economic and geographic factors in California. Perhaps most important was the fact that the California land and climate were ideally suited to cattle and horses. With little or no attention, the California ranchero could let the herds roam the open range, multiplying in wild profusion. *Vaqueros,* or cowboys, engaged in lively cattle roundups twice a year, once for branding and once for slaughter. The best of the wild horses were culled from the lands to provide the predominant means of work, play, and transportation. Since the average rancho was of a size ranging from 4,500 to over 100,000 acres, there was plenty of range for this form of enterprise.

By relying simply upon beneficial climate, abundant land, and biological reproduction, the ranchero could prosper without artificial or unreasonable efforts. Indeed, with cheap or free land grants and with plentiful Indian and vaquero labor, many of the largest ranchos were affluent to an unusual degree. This has produced the nostalgic image now associated with the period of the rancho. Dashing horses and handsome vaqueros, bright costumes, dances and songs, lively rodeos, fiestas, and señoritas all have come to characterize this period in the minds of many people today. If the reality of life in that period was not always exactly as imagined, nevertheless it has provided a fascinating legendary background for the state.

FOREIGN INCURSIONS: MOUNTAINMEN, SAILORS, PIONEERS, AND HEROES

A long-standing consequence of California's geographic isolation from Spanish and Mexican control was the constant interchange with foreign visitors. Early restrictions on commerce with outside visitors were never well enforced in California, especially since Spain itself could seldom provide the trade items, news, and exchange desired by the Californios. Thus, early American incursions into California took the form of Yankee ships that entered her ports for trade and commerce.

American fur traders and explorers also blazed trails into California in the early 1800s, beginning with Jedediah Smith and followed by others such as James Pattie, William Wolfskill, and John Fremont (Fig. 8.4).

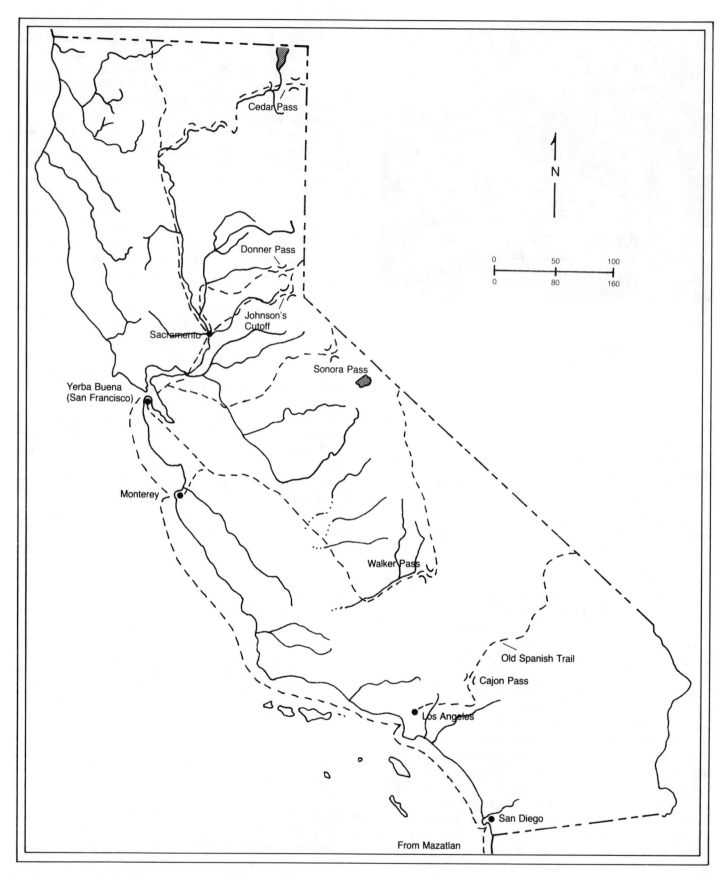

Figure 8.4 Overland and sea routes into California (Richard Crooker)

Although these trappers, mountainmen, and sailors were not welcomed by the government of California, they began a tide of American immigration that would soon lead to a significant shift in demographic and political patterns in the region.

Attracted to the relaxed lifestyle, pleasant weather, business opportunities, and pretty señoritas, American sailors or trappers stayed in California to become residents and influential rancheros themselves. In letters back to the United States and by word of mouth, it soon became known that California was an idyllic and profitable place for settlers. A steadily growing number of Americans began to arrive in the area, and American influence increased far in excess of actual numbers settled in the area. By the early 1840s, American emigrant trains bound for California were a common occurrence, with hundreds of Americans entering the state by various overland trails, the Bidwell and Donner parties being only two of the more famous groups. With growing immigration, the groundwork was laid for the formal political occupation of California by American authority.

There is strong evidence that even prior to the Mexican-American War, the administration of President Polk had its eye set on California and eventual annexation. With the advent of the Mexican-American War the stage was set for annexation of California, and in 1846 American forces seized various points in the area. American desires to annex and the general enthusiasm of the American settlers in California for this move were aided by the general ineffectiveness and indifference of the Californio population to the American takeover. Although there were a few skirmishes in the Los Angeles area, the American occupation was for the most part peaceful and California formally became a part of the United States in 1848 with the signing of the Treaty of Guadalupe Hidalgo. Spurred on by the influence of the new mining population, a constitution was adopted in 1849, and the state of California was admitted to the Union in 1850.

THE GOLD RUSH

If any anomaly of geography or nature helped convert California to a vital part of the United States, it was the presence of a malleable yellow metal in her streams and mountains. The discovery of gold precipitated changes of a monumental nature for the area. Population, travel patterns, socioeconomic shifts, racial balances, and myriad other changes took place. The impact of the event was not lost on America; *Harper's Weekly* observed as early as 1859 that it was "the most significant, if not the most important event of the present century connected with America." This is an observation widely shared by scholars up to the present.

John Sutter did not consciously or directly seek gold. He was interested in the wealth to be gained through another medium, commerce. Convinced that lumber would be a common core of value to any new immigrant, Sutter commissioned James Marshall to survey and construct a sawmill on the American River at modern-day Coloma. In the process of building, Marshall almost casually spotted gold flecks in the tailrace. Slowly at first

and then like lightning, the news spread, bringing would-be miners from all parts of the world. In a year's time, over 10,000 treasure seekers were scattered over the gold country, with hundreds of thousands yet to come.

The peak of gold production was reached by 1852, but the effects of gold on the state endured. By the 1850s, California had become the most populous region in the western United States. Also, gold drew population into the interior of the state and away from the coast, a demographic pattern not previously encountered.

Although the lode deposits were found in a strip running from San Diego to Siskiyou County, a majority of the wealth was located in the Sierra foothills, in a region that became known as the Mother Lode Country (Fig. 8.5). The sense of the times is captured in the names given to the camps and towns. Rough and Ready, Whiskeytown, Angels Camp, Hangtown, Fiddletown, French Gulch, Chinese Camp, Mormon Bar, Drytown, Oroville, Lazy Man's Canyon, Chile Gulch, and Poverty Flat were just a few (Fig. 8.6). These names reflected ethnic influences as well as cultural humor; many of the towns were later to achieve fame through the works of Bret Harte and Mark Twain.

More significantly in the long run, San Francisco, Stockton, Eureka, and Sacramento experienced expansion of agricultural and mercantile activity in response to the needs of the mining regions (Fig. 8.7). The Gold Rush thus helped to awaken California to more than mineral wealth alone. It acted as a magnet to population. It provided a stimulus to service industries such as agriculture, cattle, shipping, and trade. Finally, it drew to California the kind of Yankee aggressiveness needed to develop the state.

The effects on the formerly quiet Spanish outpost were monumental, underscoring the observation of Californio Mariano Vallejo that "the Yankees are a wonderful people. . . . If they emigrated to hell itself, they would somehow manage to change the climate." If the physical climate was not changed in California as a result of gold, certainly the political, economic, and social climates were affected in permanent and dramatic fashion (Fig. 8.8).

THE DECLINE OF THE INDIAN POPULATION

The first years of California as a new part of the United States were turbulent, dramatic, fast-moving, tumultuous, and violent. The sleepy legacy of Spain was forgotten as the state forged ahead into the challenges of a modern world. The American impact on the Indians of California was devastating and permanent. If the Spanish and Mexican periods had fallen with brutal effect upon the California Indian population, the force of the Gold Rush was almost a final chapter. Simple and direct in their lifestyles, the California Indians could not hope to cope with avaricious gold seekers who tore up their lands and societies looking for the elusive metal.

There is no history of savage warfare here, as with the Plains Indians, but the genocidal effects were just as pronounced. Alcohol, measles, bullets, and culture shock all helped bring about the decline of the Indian

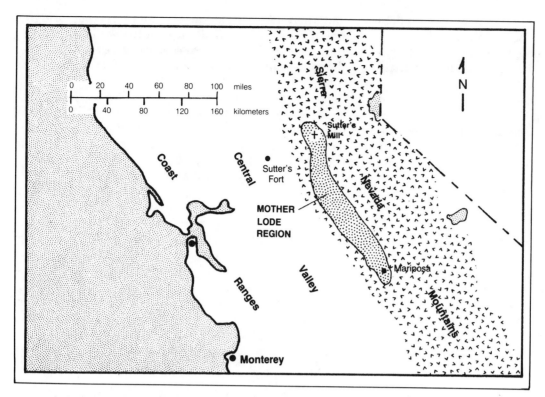

Figure 8.5 Mother Lode region: Gold Country. (Richard Crooker)

Figure 8.6 Downtown Sutter's Creek, a sleepy town with a colorful past. (Richard Hyslop)

population. The few instances of "warfare" were one-sided, brutal events that included wholesale massacre of Indian women and children by the white settlers. Gradually, the natives were killed off or pushed farther into high mountain or stark desert country. This sad chapter in California history is partially captured in Helen Hunt Jackson's *Ramona* and *Century of Dishonor.*

One of the few instances of physical resistance by the Indians was known as the Modoc Wars. Initially, the Modoc tribe had lived in the northeastern part of the state, near Mount Shasta, in a region of timber, lakes, rivers, and lava beds. As more white emigrants passed through the region, the Indians became increasingly hostile. In 1852, an attack and massacre of an emigrant

party occurred. Retaliation by local ranchers and miners was immediate. Thereafter, sporadic battles were waged for the next 12 years. Finally, in 1864, the remaining Modoc Indians were moved to a reservation following a tenuous peace agreement. Placed on the reservation with their traditional enemies the Klamaths, a group of the Modocs under a chief named Captain Jack made their way back to the Lost River area. Talked into returning to the reservation once, the group finally decided to make a stand on the ancestral homelands. When an army force was sent to capture them, the Captain Jack group took to the lava beds and, relying upon their intimate knowledge of the terrain, fought the army to a standstill. Eventually, the shortage of water led to the surrender or capture of Captain Jack and his people in 1873, ending the only notable "Indian war" of California history (Fig. 8.9).

The harsh attitudes of the Americans and the policy of eliminating Indian opposition resulted in a tragic decline of the Indian population. Estimated at around 100,000 in 1850, by 1916 the Indian population had dropped below 20,000. Deprived of land, dignity, spirit, and lifestyle, the California Indian became a victim of the state's "progress." In many respects, the fate of the California Indian is epitomized by the story of Ishi, the last wild Indian in America. Discovered in a corral in Oroville in August 1911, Ishi was the last of a small band of Yahi Indians who had fled from contact with civilization and had lived in the Mount Lassen region. As the last survivor of this small band, Ishi eventually was able to reveal much about the last days of the California Indian to his protector and friend, Alfred Kroeber, an anthropologist at the University of California. Ishi lived and worked with Kroeber until he died of a white man's disease, tuberculosis. His true story is a touching and sad indictment of the treatment of the Indian in California, encapsulating much of the tragedy

Figure 8.7 "Old Sacramento" reflects the past in restored buildings and boardwalks. The area represents the city's desire to recreate some of the atmosphere and spirit of the 1850s when this approximately 28-acre waterfront section was the launching point for many Forty-Niners. (California Office of Tourism)

Figure 8.8 California state capitol. Sacramento was a population center of 12,000 when the state government was finally settled there after being moved between San Jose, Vallejo, and Benicia. This magnificent building was completed in 1874 and has recently been restored to its original appearance. (Sacramento Convention and Visitors Bureau)

of the decline of the native inhabitants of the Golden State.[2]

It should be added that recent legal actions have successfully underscored the fact of the mistreatment of the Indians in California. Beginning in the late 1930s, various court decisions have held that they are entitled to land and money numbering in the millions. Somewhat belatedly, California Indians are receiving part of the bounty of the land that was taken from their ancestors earlier.

RIDING HERD: THE RISE OF THE BEEF INDUSTRY

One benefit of the great Gold Rush on California's society was a diversification of the economic base of the state. With the initial impetus of feeding growing hordes of miners, the cattle industry was able to expand significantly. Although cattle, raised for their hides, had always been a staple of the rancheros in the southern part of the state, the Gold Rush provided a source of eager customers for beef, which by the 1860s numbered more than 3 million head. The decline of the Gold Rush, a serious drought, and high interest rates brought problems to the industry, and other agricultural pursuits assumed equal or greater importance.

Eventually, the economic and geographic realities of ranching in the state caused the evolution of certain forms of cattle production. Large cattle operations became the rule, phasing out the less successful small ranchers. Fenced-in ranges began to replace free-roaming range cattle operations. Cross-breeding and improvement of the meat and dairy aspects of cattle raising became more critical and widespread. Like the state itself, changing conditions led the cattle industry to diversify, broaden, and improve itself. With its appropriate responses to the times, the beef industry has achieved a position in the state as a key agricultural activity. This accommodation has been made possible by the fact that the beef industry has been moved more into the nonirrigable portions of agricultural lands, thus largely avoiding competition with irrigation farming.

In the context of agriculture and land holding, the impact of the Land Act of 1851 was critical. Following California's admission to the Union in 1850, the status of the Spanish and Mexican land grants was placed in doubt. Although the Treaty of Guadalupe Hidalgo had guaranteed protection of the rancheros and land grants, many new American immigrants felt justified in claiming parts of these lands by squatter's rights.

Because of the confusion over imprecise boundaries, historical sources of titles, conflicting claims, and financial difficulties, Congress passed the Land Act of 1851. Over the next several years, the rancheros and other claimants were required to present proof of title to land commissions and courts before their titles would be recognized. This placed a tremendous burden on those rancheros whose proofs of title often required extensive and costly searches of records in Mexican and Spanish

[2]Kroeber's wife Theodora chronicled this story in her book *Ishi in Two Worlds.* Ishi, she wrote, "was the last wild Indian of North America."

Figure 8.9 Lava beds in the Lassen region. This type of terrain was the site of the Modoc Indian Captain Jack's last holdout (see text). (National Park Service, photo by Richard Frear)

archives. The prolonged legal expenses often led to loss of ranchos by debt-ridden Californios.

The whole story of the land title debacle is one in which legality, morality, and honesty were largely absent. The long-term impact was to shift much of the California agricultural and ranch lands from the hands of the legitimate Californio owners to the hands of the recently arrived American squatters and others who benefited greatly by the questionable largesse of the state and federal governments.

TRANSPORTATION AND CALIFORNIA'S EVOLUTION

One of the single most important factors in the development of modern-day California has been the transportation revolution. Just as transportation, or lack of it, was instrumental in the shaping of early California customs, culture, and society, it was to have the same impact in the American period. The creation of new means of transportation brought the state into significant contact with the rest of the nation, thus affecting all aspects of life in the Golden State.

The early Gold Rush activities acted as a tremendous spur to the evolving transportation system. It was quickly evident that mule trains and stagecoaches, ferryboats, and dispatch riders could not meet the growing needs of the state. Although the names of Wells Fargo and Butterfield flash large upon the imagination, they were essentially primitive stop-gaps for the real transportation links that were to come. Indeed, the overland stage operations enjoyed only a brief ascendancy, flourishing during the 1850s and 1860s. Meanwhile, a real transportation revolution loomed on the horizon.

The story of California's development is, to a large degree, a tale of railroad domination. Politically, economically, and geographically, the Central Pacific Railroad Company and its successor, the Southern Pacific,

helped mold the state more than any other single entity. The extent of this influence and the reaction thereto may be encountered in the pages of Frank Norris's *The Octopus,* a book whose title alone is aptly descriptive of the company's pervasive presence on the scene.

Although local lines had begun to develop as early as 1855, the critical event was the connection of these local lines to a transcontinental system. Such a system had been a topic of discussion from the 1850s on, but the intervention of the Civil War and the immensity of the task joined together to delay such an occurrence. However, when the Federal government sweetened the stakes with legislation granting 20 sections (square miles) of public land for every mile of track laid, in addition to loans and other encouragements, the project was begun with effort and drive. The climax of the story is the now-famous meeting of the Central Pacific and the Union Pacific at Promontory Point, Utah on May 10, 1869, sealed with the driving of the golden spike connecting the two lines.

The California involvement focused upon the efforts of the Central Pacific under the leadership of the "Big Four"—Mark Hopkins, Leland Stanford, Collis P. Huntington, and Charles Crocker. These four Sacramento businessmen who controlled the Central Pacific established the Southern Pacific as a holding company to acquire the Central Pacific's assets and develop rail lines within the state (Fig. 8.10). Through their sometimes not-so-scrupulous efforts, the railroad fixed rates and began a rail transport monopoly that extended to every railroad line coming into the Golden State. The exorbitant rates charged by Southern Pacific eventually led to bitterness and occasional violence on the part of farmers and businessmen. Since the railroad also dominated the political scene, however, little real relief occurred until the rise of the reformist Progressive movement in the early 1900s.

The lasting effects of this railroad revolution on the development of California are immense. The whole complexion of population growth and settlement was colored by railroad activity. Uneven transportation and growth patterns largely mirrored railroad desires, expanding where Southern Pacific wanted, or was paid, to go, and bypassing those areas the railroad wished to ignore. Thus, since Southern Pacific had little stake in real estate in the south, development of this part of the state had to wait until competitor lines, such as Santa Fe, were able to break the monopoly and enter the state.

In terms of land ownership alone, Southern Pacific Railroad was (and still is) one of the single largest landowners, with over 10 million acres in the state. Since its business activities, including building of additional lines and land sales, depended upon supplies of people, the railroad also influenced ethnic balances with its recruiting of immigrants from both China and Europe. Its efforts in encouraging immigration resulted in increased labor supplies, customers for business, farmers for the ample land, and tradespeople for the ever-expanding population. On a positive note, it helped tie the state to the rest of the nation and the world through trade and population mobility. On a negative note, it provided a focal point for racial hatred, greed, and questionable business and political dealings. Its excesses led busi-

Figure 8.10 The modern Southern Pacific Railroad system has become a major freight carrier, with efficient and powerful diesel locomotives such as these pulling 90 to 100 car loads. (Southern Pacific Railroad)

nessmen and farmers alike to organize against it and provided reformer writers such as Frank Norris fertile grounds for their works.

The railroad has played a significant role in the evolution of modern California. Without the efforts of Southern Pacific and the Big Four, California would be a different place than it is today. In an era of "robber barons," the Big Four acted as many others around them did and at no time apologized for their methods. They brought progress to the state and placed a lasting imprint on its social, political, economic, and geographic landscape. One need only examine the persistence of the names of these four men to realize how deeply this influence has been felt.

DRY FARMING AND IRRIGATION COLONIES

Agriculture has always been one of the primary economic activities in California. If any one word describes the agricultural pattern of the state, that word is "diverse." With the wide range of climatic and soil conditions throughout California, diversity is almost mandated in crop production. The hundreds of varied crops grown in the state have solidified its reputation as the country's leading agricultural producer.

The nature of California's cultivation of the land has evolved through two stages—dry farming and extensive irrigation. This evolution has brought with it many changes in the economic and human elements of agriculture in the state.

The early period of California established the pattern of dry farming as the dominant agricultural mode. Certainly, the Indian inhabitants of the region engaged in little agricultural innovation, relying primarily upon hunting and gathering rather than organized cultivation. With the arrival of the Spanish, farming assumed greater importance, especially through the efforts of the missions. For the most part, this agricultural development took the form of basic grain, vegetable, and fruit crops that could be grown without extensive irrigation, although the Franciscan friars did introduce some irrigation projects in the southern part of the state. The Mexican period did not further agriculture as a major part of the life of the state, since most emphasis was placed upon livestock.

With the impetus of the Gold Rush and the American presence, organized agriculture assumed a key role. Grain crops became the dominant agrieconomic fact of life in the state, with California reaching second in the nation in wheat production by the early 1870s. The success of these efforts led farmers to more diversification of crops, expansion of orchard cultivation, and experimentation with vineyard activities.

Additional stimulus for California agriculture was provided by both the transportation revolution and the federal government. Railroad development permitted widespread marketing of the expanding volume of crop production, while government policies provided further encouragement and assistance for farm diversification and growth.

The increasing demand for California food crops brought with it a necessity to free agriculture from the whims and caprices of nature. Although dry farming had proved a highly profitable endeavor, irrigation proved to be a more dependable and efficient means of production. Although efforts had been made by the missions to develop irrigation systems, it was left largely for the American period to capitalize upon the potential of large scale irrigation agriculture.

The first irrigation colony of any significance in California developed in the mid-1850s. This was a part of a Mormon settlement in San Bernardino where over 4,000 acres were brought under direct irrigation. Other irrigation colonies followed, including the San Joaquin Valley and Riverside. From this beginning, irrigation techniques spread throughout the state, fostering fruit crops, grapes, and other high-value agricultural products.

The legal foundation for irrigation, the Wright Act of 1887, established the concept of "appropriation and beneficial use" of waters and fostered the growth of recognized irrigation districts. This in turn led to massive efforts to cultivate huge tracts of land such as the Imperial and Coachella Valleys. The eventual success of those efforts underscores the impact of irrigation on California's history, economy, and geography.

With the growth of population and the gradual preemption of agricultural lands for residential purposes, the significance of high-yield irrigation farming has become even more vital. A trend toward consolidation and large-scale production, use of efficient machine labor, and high-density growing will undoubtedly continue, as will efforts toward further irrigation of formerly unusable acreage. Although the manufacturing and industrial character of the state has assumed greater importance, agriculture will continue to play a key role in the life of the state.

THE "BLACK GOLD" RUSH: RISE OF THE PETROLEUM INDUSTRY

When Gaspar de Portolá made his first exploratory march up the coast toward Monterey in 1769, he happened upon a spring with large marshes of pitch and tar. This was the spring of the Alders of San Estevan—now known as La Brea Tar Pits. Although the presence of oil was recognized quite early in California, however, it was not until the late 1800s that any organized effort was expended to recover and use this resource. Certainly, both the Indians and the early Spanish settlers had used the crude tar from oil seeps to caulk canoes, baskets, and the roofs of adobes, but it remained for American entrepreneurs to turn this California resource to significant use and profit.

In its own unique way, the petroleum boom was every bit as romantic and significant as the Gold Rush in California. Based upon a steady, if undramatic, growth, commercial oil production began around the 1860s. Pico Canyon in 1876 is frequently cited as the first *commercial* oil well in California. It was not until the 1890s, however, that the first boom period began. Measured against later production, the state's first "boom" in oil was more of a snap-crackle-pop. Nevertheless, this initial period was similar to its earlier gold counterpart, ranking as a "black gold" rush. Through the late 1800s, various independent oil companies engaged in a variety of activities, mostly in the south. By 1895, the combined output had risen to over 1 million barrels a year. With the further stimulus of the developing automobile, as well as increased rail and manufacturing usages, oil production became even more important.

The second major oil boom began in the 1920s with the discovery of vast fields in Huntington Beach, Signal Hill, Santa Fe Springs, Torrance, and Dominguez (Fig. 8.11). Certain factors urged this development along, including improved drilling technology, increased industrial and heating uses, and growing popularity of the automobile. With the easy availability of petroleum, the automobile became a sort of unofficial state emblem, a position it retains today. The boom of the 1920s was sustained by these developments and further nurtured by the military requirements of the nation. World War II demanded continued production at a high level, and the related demographic changes of the state solidified the key industrial role of industry for the growing population.

The latest chapter in the oil saga is the modern period, dating from approximately the early 1950s. Exploration for new wells has continued on land, with primary emphasis remaining in the southern portion of the state. The Tidelands Act of 1955, however, ushered in a new era of offshore exploration, drilling, and development (Fig. 8.12). With this new emphasis there has also been rising controversy. Environmentalists have pointed to the dangers of oil leakage and spills, such as the Santa Barbara oil spill, and have engaged in a running battle with both the state and the oil companies to prevent development. On their part, the oil companies have increasingly attempted to reduce friction by efforts toward aesthetic masking of offshore sites, public relations campaigns, and safety protections against environmental pollution. Meanwhile, oil production in the state has remained a key part of the economic picture and promises to remain so as long as Californians continue their long-standing love affair with the automobile.

THE ASCENT OF THE WESTERN STARS: THE MAKING OF THE MOVIE CAPITAL

As California began to mature, many businesses and industries were also growing in the state. One of the most widely recognized symbols of the Golden State, the great and glamorous movie industry, emerged at the turn of the century. In many ways, the geography of the region contributed heavily to this development. Several factors made Southern California extremely attractive

Figure 8.11 Oil field in Huntington Beach, located near a golf course in the middle of a densely populated neighborhood of single-family residences. (Standard Oil Co. of California)

to the newly expanding independent moviemakers. The climate was mild and attractive, necessitating far less expense in filming on locations and sets, open space was readily available for use in such sleepy towns as Hollywood, and the Southern California region was about as far away from New York and other major Eastern cities as these producers could get. This last factor was crucial, since many of these enterprising business artists were engaged in running battles with patent holders and the so-called "movie trust" back East. California offered both distance and the Mexican border if legal processes were pressed too hard.

Soon after the filmmakers arrived, the Hollywood area achieved dramatic success, both in terms of economics and publicity. By very early in the 1900s, California had come to be known as movieland, and by 1915, Hollywood was the self-proclaimed "film capital of the world." With the rest of the country ripe for this level of entertainment, the state soon acquired a new major industry. The movies employed a marvelous variety of persons, including actors, carpenters, designers, researchers, writers, and publicists. With the expansion of sophisticated equipment, sound, and color, the industry brought even more attention to the state. To many people, Hollywood came to represent California. To many others, California came to represent America. With a system that rewarded stars such as Mary Pickford and Charlie Chaplin with weekly salaries in excess of $10,000, the glamor of the good life of California became even more appealing.

Through the peak period of the 1930s and 1940s, the movie industry significantly affected the state as well as the rest of the world. Internally, at least three key factors were in evidence. First, the tourist attractions of Hollywood drew millions of people and their money to the state. Second, a major center of industry was created

A

B

Figure 8.12 Offshore oil development is a growing business, with some efforts being made to disguise the oil rigs as islands, as in Long Beach (A). Other wells, such as those off Huntington Beach (B), are far enough off the coast so that camouflage is unnecessary. (Richard Hyslop)

Figure 8.13 Movie studios still abound in Culver City and Hollywood, ranging from traditional giant Metro-Goldwyn-Mayer (MGM) (A) to picturesque Paramount (B) to smaller Chartoff/Winkler Productions (C). (A: Photograph courtesy of Metro-Goldwyn-Mayer Film Co.; B: Greater Los Angeles Visitors and Convention Bureau; C: Richard Hyslop)

in the state, spinning off secondary economic activities such as cosmetics, electronic technology, broadcast enterprises, and clothing. Third, the magic aura of the Golden State was artificially enhanced, drawing a greater population to the West Coast.

Ultimately, the challenge of television reduced the role of Hollywood as prime dispenser of dreams and entertainment for America, and many movie companies disappeared. Although the industry has subsided

substantially from its peak period of the 1930s and 1940s, however, it retains a preeminent role in the life of the state. The majority of films made in America still originate in Southern California. West Los Angeles, Century City, Universal City, Culver City, Studio City, and Burbank have joined Hollywood as movie entertainment cities (Fig. 8.13). Even though television has surpassed movies as the single most important dispenser of popular arts, television itself has become *the* major customer of the movie industry. Further, the lure of Hollywood continues, as evidenced by the throngs of tourists who annually trek to view Hollywood Boulevard's "walk of the stars," Mann's (Grauman's) Chinese Theater, and Buena Park's Movieland Wax Museum.

From the first commercial film produced in California in 1908 (*The Count of Monte Cristo*) to the first "talkie" (*The Jazz Singer*) to the most recent disaster, disco, or dramatic spectacular, the movie industry of the state has molded attitudes, economics, and social styles in an astonishing fashion. Like its host state, the movie industry has built upon a golden legend. In the process, California has added one more romantic attribute to its identity.

WORLD WAR II: ENTER DEFENSE PLANTS, EXIT JAPANESE-AMERICANS

California had enjoyed glamor, success, expansion, romance, excitement, and action during the course of its development. The Gold Rush, oil boom, Hollywood, transportation, and agricultural bonanza had all brought progress and change to the state.

The Great Depression of the 1930s, however, brought a different tone to California, the rest of the nation, and the world. Unemployment in the state rose drastically, while crops rotted in the fields and orchards for lack of markets. At the same time, due to the attraction of climate and its movie-created reputation, thousands of unemployed migrated to California seeking the golden dream. Sadly, the state could not live up to its legend and the economic situation remained bleak, as did the lives of hundreds of thousands of new and old Californians.

The agricultural industry was particularly hard hit. Conditions of life for farm workers were deplorable at best. Steinbeck's *Grapes of Wrath* gave accurate voice to the despair of these workers, underscoring the depth of depression both in spirit and social reality. Although efforts were made to provide relief, it was not until the advent of World War II and America's entry into that conflagration, that California and the nation climbed out of economic depression.

In many ways, World War II had a profound and overwhelming influence on the modern development of the state. The war brought with it a significant shift to urbanized, industrialized lifestyles as well as an increasing racial ambivalence reflected in the roles of Japanese-Americans, Mexican-Americans, and blacks in the life of the state.

Well before the attack on Pearl Harbor, relations with Japan had been seriously strained, a fact reflected in California legislation and popular attitudes. This reaction in California had its roots in a variety of motives, both genuine and contrived. Certainly, patriotism and legitimate concern over security played roles in the hostility and suspicion which was generated toward the Japanese-Americans. Equally important, if less noble, was the historic sense of jealousy, greed, and competition that the successful Japanese businessmen and farmers engendered in the minds of "native" Californians.

With a tradition of hostility toward Orientals and other foreigners, the California response to the Japanese bombing of Pearl Harbor was predictable. Foreigners generally, and Orientals in particular, had been physically driven out of the state before. Here was a natural reason to gather, incarcerate, and reject the Japanese again. (It should be noted that although Hawaii was also under martial law, Japanese-Americans there were not rounded up and quarantined from the rest of the population.) Under pressure from California public opinion and military zeal, President Franklin Roosevelt on February 19, 1942, authorized military control of "enemy aliens" to the War Department. Thereafter, citing military necessity, the head of the Western Defense Command, General John L. De Witt, issued relocation orders resulting in the forced "voluntary" internment of approximately 110,000 Japanese from California, Washington, Oregon, and Arizona, two thirds of whom were native-born Americans.

Treated as untrustworthy, ordered to assembly centers such as Santa Anita, and hence transferred by the military to "relocation centers," the Japanese were sheared in one stroke of their basic civil liberties and were detained by barbed wire and armed guards in barren locations such as the Owens Valley (Fig. 8.14). While they were being forced to live in stark barracks, it was remarkable that the majority retained their sense of patriotism to the United States—a patriotism that saw many of the young men join Nisei units of the U.S. Army and serve with unusual valor and loyalty.

The costs of this removal were immense. Economically, the Japanese suffered losses of at least $365 million by the short-term forced sales of homes, businesses, and land. Psychologically, the humiliation and hatred suffered by these Americans of Japanese descent was a bitter indictment of California racial attitudes. Politically, this suspension of constitutional guarantees was a frightening precedent inspired largely by California hysteria and racial hatred. Finally, the loss to the country and the state was considerable. In a period of intense demand, some of the best businessmen and agriculturalists in the state were removed from the production lines. Viewed in retrospect, this episode in California's history provides a continuing example of where prejudice and racism can lead.

At the same time that Japanese were being removed from the life of the state, massive population movements into the state were occurring. World War II demanded a maximum output from California. Defense plants in the south of the state and shipyards in the north demanded enormous numbers of workers. With the exodus of the Japanese, large numbers of migrant Mexican laborers and blacks from the Southern states moved into the vacated agricultural and industrial jobs. There was also a massive influx of military personnel. California held strategic value as a military area due to its open land, transportation facilities, and convenience as a debarcation point for the Pacific war. Vast training bases drew huge numbers of people to the state, implanting in their minds for later years the images of palm trees and balmy climate. Although most of these people were temporary residents during the war years only, many were haunted by their memories and returned after the war to become permanent citizens of the state.

The impact on the state's economy was tremendous. The aircraft industry, already established in Southern

Figure 8.14 Bleak reminders of Manzanar detention camp are found in the stone guard/entry houses. Snow-covered Sierras in background give testimony to the cold winters in the camp, located between Lone Pine and Independence off U.S. 395 in the Owens Valley. (Richard Hyslop)

California, experienced an unprecedented explosion and became the largest growth industry in the state. By 1941, orders for aircraft made this the key industrial base, with companies such as Northrop, Lockheed, Douglas, North American, and Hughes employing hundreds of thousands of workers. The population impacts on the state were as great as the economic effects. This period saw the beginning of a flow of immigrants from other states that barely slackened after the war was over. Indeed, the lasting industrial profile of Southern California was well fixed during this period. In terms of both population and economics, the war years created massive changes in the state, with a built-in potential for even greater changes to come.

POSTWAR CALIFORNIA: AMERICAN SUBURBIA

The boom in population begun during the war continued surprisingly strong through the postwar years. In fact, the population figures for the state rose by over 1 million in the years immediately following the war, and the total growth exceeded 50 percent in the years between 1940 and 1950. Much of the growth could be attributed to returning servicemen who had seen California during the war and had returned with their families. The attractions of the Golden State were also compelling enough to retain large numbers of workers who had migrated to the state during the war.

It was not surprising that the growth figures exceeded those of most other areas of the country. The desirability of California as a place to live created new settlement patterns for the state, transforming much of the landscape from rural to predominantly urbanized settings.

The necessity for housing this growing population helped develop a somewhat unique California style, the "ranch house" in the uniform tract suburb. The checkerboard tracts of those areas came to typify the population sprawl of California (Fig. 8.15).

In terms of the economic and industrial growth of the state, the postwar years also saw significant growth. The actual reconversion to a peacetime economy had begun in the state before the end of the war. The state government attempted to plan for this future by the creation of economic planning commissions, tax bases, and other activities.

Several factors helped ease this transition and make the shift less traumatic. The population growth itself carried with it the germination of new economic activities. New housing stimulated the construction industry, and if assembly-line production of housing was monotonous, it was nonetheless profitable.

The immediate slack from defense activities was largely taken up by retooling for consumer products such as furniture, clothing, and automobiles. Similarly, the heavy wartime industries had recognized earlier the need for diversified production capability and were already moving into needed peacetime activities. Former war plants now engaged in civilian-oriented steel production, food processing, and other useful manufacturing activities. Construction- and transportation-related industries alone accounted for a large share of this postwar surge.

Except for a very short pause, the defense industry continued to hold a strong position in the economic growth of California. Although World War II had ended, the Cold War provided a continued impetus to military spending and development. The challenges of the new kind of war moved California's defense industries more into areas of science and research. They soon began exploring uses of nuclear energy, missile systems, space exploration, and electronic weaponry. Federal defense contracts supported huge programs in research and development, and "think tanks" such as the Rand Corporation and Jet Propulsion Laboratory were made possible by these grants. By the early 1960s, California's share of federal expenditures for military purposes was around 25 percent of the total for the country. By the late 1960s, at least one third of the state's industrial production was funded by defense and space activities.

The impact of this military-related economic growth had both positive and negative effects. It placed heavy reliance on federal government largesse for continued favorable employment figures. It converted a large proportion of the California work force into white collar jobs. When there was a sharp downturn in government fiscal activity, a concomitant slump occurred in the employment of aerospace and defense-related workers. Thus, unemployment figures climbed during the 1960s before other industrial growth helped pick up this loss.

Significantly, other diversified industries have balanced out uneven employment in the aerospace business. For example, the petroleum industry remained a key employer in the state, as did transportation-related businesses. Agribusiness has also held a strong place in the economy of California. Likewise, the large population has acted as a constant source of demand for consumer goods and services. A fascinating growth of the computer industry, especially in the area of microprocessors, has given rise to the description of the San Jose–Santa Clara Valley area as "Silicon Valley."

California has continued to be successful with people, money, and attitudes. Climate, the promise of economic opportunity, and the California way of life have all contributed to the appeal of the state. In addition to the goods, produce, and entertainment exported to the rest of the world, California has continued to export its image and style to millions of people. In spite of future uncertainties and past mistakes, it is still seen by many as the Paradise of the West.

PATTERNS FOR THE PRESENT AND FUTURE

One might conclude that accidents of history combined with unique geography have molded California's development in a major fashion. This conclusion provides a base for viewing present and future evolution of the state. Many patterns begun in past years are likely to persist, while positive changes may result from the lessons of the past.

On the positive side, California seems destined to assume an even greater influence in the life of the nation. Socially, lifestyles and behavior in the state, from skateboards to fashions, seem to fascinate and set the pattern for the nation. The Golden State has become a weathervane of interests, reflected in massive tourism, recreation activities, and significant retirement-oriented industries.

Politically, the state has assumed a key role in the nation's power structure. California's voting numbers, political leaders, and political trends are watched

Figure 8.15 Tract housing often strings along ridge lines like birds on a wire. Such view lots usually are premium-priced. (Roger M. Rhiner)

Figure 8.16 Urban California. Single-family residences share the turf with multi-family dwellings, commercial and recreational property, parking lots, and a church. (Roger M. Rhiner)

throughout the nation. One classic example is the "tax-payers' revolt" that began in California with Proposition 13 and spread to the rest of the nation. Similarly, the governor of California, regardless of party, now is a perennial force to be reckoned with in presidential politics. Economically, the state is a key indicator of the health of the country, and any economic slump in California is a problem of national import. Continued population growth and migration to California of hard-working, conservative Midwesterners has lent a particular air of prosperity to the state that cannot be ignored.

On the negative side, however, the state has yet to face up to some of its most pressing problems. Steady population growth has also brought ever-increasing urbanization and congestion. The character of California has inevitably shifted to city life, and growth in certain areas such as Orange, San Diego, and Santa Clara counties has frequently outstripped the ability of those localities to serve the needs of the population (Fig. 8.16).

Although industrial and business enterprises dedicated to providing luxury goods and services have assumed a major position in the state's economy, the *basic* needs of many groups are still not being met. Particularly in the more urbanized areas of the south, racial groups are gradually emerging as a new majority. These groups, as well as other Californians, are demanding a better balance of schools, housing, hospitals, and jobs. With their growth in numbers, these minority races will be able to exercise more authority—a position that is unique in California history.

California also must face its own nature and come to grips with a long-standing tendency toward extremism of all sorts. Many people in the state have been striving to understand the extremes of devotion afforded to such organizations as the John Birch Society and the People's Temple. Certainly these groups have lent California a somewhat suspect air in the minds of many. One is led to wonder whether their existence is a symptom or a cause of California's uncertain role in the future.

The certainty for California's move toward the year 2000 is that the problems do exist and must be solved. The effects of growth on the landscape and habitat of the state must soon be planned and controlled. The quality of life in the state must be stabilized in terms of environmental health, economic security, and social equality. Smog, congestion, cement freeways, inner-city decay, ecological waste, water distribution, and costs of government must be dealt with directly and responsibly. Clearly, this provides a major challenge for the people of the state—a challenge that must be met successfully if California is to remain a "golden" rather than a tarnished state.

CONTEMPORARY FOLKWAYS, CULTURAL LANDSCAPES

California has acquired a reputation not only for diversity, but also for unmitigated strangeness. One of the oft-quoted gibes is that if the whole country were tilted up on end, all the loose nuts would end up in California. This theme, echoed with some degree of consistency throughout the state's history, continues to be a favorite of Eastern writers. It is a judgment that both exaggerates and oversimplifies the astonishing variety of geographical and cultural personalities found in the Golden State. Within the confines of California can be found much of the best and worst of all other 49 states combined. Large-scale immigration has contributed to the phenomenon, as has the wide diversity of climate and landform. Thus it may safely be said that California does have something for everyone.

This diversity of culture takes many forms. Clearly, the various regions of the state differ, one from the other. The redwood country of the north is another world than the concrete-covered south. The quiet calm of the Mother Lode towns contrasts distinctly to the fast-paced life of the southern playground beach communities, as San Francisco does to Los Angeles. Diversity is more than regional, however.

The range of entertainment forms in the state is phenomenal. Californians can choose from many forms of theme parks, ersatz historical locations, zoos, wildlife parks, and night spots. The choice of restaurant styles and formats adds yet another dimension to the leisure-time activities of the state's residents. Apartments for swinging singles vie with retirement communities for space and attention, while artistic cemeteries offer marriage and burial in the same chapels. Ethnic populations vary from locale to locale, district to district, county to county. In all, the state provides an anthropologist's heaven for the study of varied cultures, peoples, lifestyles, and behaviors.

CULTURAL GEOGRAPHIC ODDITIES

The correlation between geography and culture cannot be ignored or dismissed. Although geography by itself does not fix the cultural personality of a region or people, its impact on lifestyles, economic patterns, and social characteristics is nonetheless readily apparent. California provides an interesting study of varying cultural identities that can be traced in significant part to the shifts of geographic, climatic, and demographic conditions from one part of the state to another. Although the generalizations that follow necessarily pass over individual divergences, it may still be agreed that some common identity does exist. This collective personality or culture of a region does provide some fascinating insights into the motivations of people and how they interact with the environment in which they live.

Logging Paul Bunyan–Style: Redwood Country, Northern Forests, and Plains

One of the first associations that comes to mind in connection with Northern California is giant redwoods. Certainly, the redwood forests of the north are dramatic, unique, and picturesque. The role of lumber in the state, however, does extend beyond that one imposing species. California's timber production ranks among the highest in the country, with fir, pine, and redwood constituting the major forest regions of the state. Compared with most of the rest of California, the northwest portion of the state is a green and wooded world of its own (Fig. 9.1).

Another rural element of the north is the preponderance of livestock, with ranching playing a key role in the lives of many citizens. The open ranges of the northeast, in particular, foster a way of life that is close to the land and reliant on its bounty. Clearly, the prime element and predominant theme in the northern portion of the state is nature (Fig. 9.2).

Given the closeness of the people to nature and the land, it is not surprising that controversy has arisen over the question of proper use of the land and resources. The bitterest controversy has centered upon the expansion of national and state parks. Environmentalists argue the need to preserve and protect the priceless forest land, while logging and local economic interests advocate jobs, economic growth, and the protection of the forest industry.

Figure 9.1 Redwoods stretch upward toward the sun in northwest California. (National Park Service, photo by Richard Frear)

There is merit to the argument of each side. Few visitors to the extensive federal or state-owned parks, forests, campgrounds, or recreation areas would question the value, beauty, or utility of these areas. Yet with lumber providing the bulk of employment in regions such as Eureka, and with the demand for forest products constantly bolstering the state's economy, the forest industry's position must be equally respected. An uneasy balance will, undoubtedly, continue to exist for some time. Ultimately, the people of the north will be the critical decision makers, with their opinions and behavior determining the balance among competing uses.

Since there is a higher percentage of native-born residents in this region, a strong sense of local identity prevails. The population base is relatively low, and rugged individualism is still a cherished concept. With an economy based primarily upon agriculture, tourism, recreation, dairy farming, ranching, lumber, and commercial fishing, the spirit of the people reflects nature and individual responses to it. There are few cities of any size, Eureka being the largest north of Sacramento. This demographic factor has contributed to the conservative, self-reliant attitude of the people, which in turn has occasionally taken the form of opposition and hostility to development in many parts of the north. There has been genuine reluctance to see expansion or improvement of the state highway system. At the same time, there has been a related desire to protect and promote local control over undeveloped regions.

This is not to say that the north is bereft of any desire to improve, advance, or mature. The presence of Humboldt State University in Arcata has assured the region of a concentrated and respectable effort to promote growth in such areas as forestry, fisheries, and ocean-

Figure 9.2 Northeast California is rural and less green than the northwest, with such volcanic areas as the Lassen region setting a tone of wilderness. (National Park Service, photo by Richard Frear)

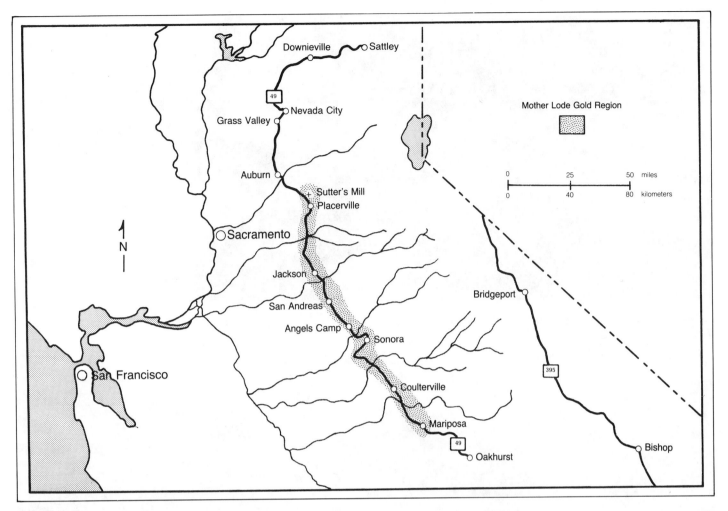

Figure 9.3 Sierra Nevada Range, showing the Mother Lode region with key towns and routes. (Richard Crooker)

ography. Likewise, seashore development has not been totally lacking, as Sea Ranch in the Mendocino area demonstrates.

Nevertheless, from the foggy northwest seacoast to the inland volcanic moonscapes, the predominant spirit is deliberate and calm. If expansion and change are to occur, the people are determined to control such development themselves. Accustomed as they are to the quiet and natural lifestyle, they are unlikely to see a need for precipitous change in the near future.

Argonauts and Mountainmen: Gold Country and Ghost Towns

It is amazing that the most populous state in the Union also contains a back country of astonishing proportions. Ghost towns and Old West communities abound, carrying the colorful frontier past of the state into the present. For the most part, this region of nostalgia is concentrated in the highland block of California known as the Sierra Nevada range, in the communities strung along routes U.S. 395 and California 49, and in parts of the desert (Calico, Daggett, Skidoo; see Fig. 9.3).

Part of the historical romance of California stems from its past role as home of boisterous gold camps and rugged mining sites. The names of present-day sleepy communities give eloquent testimony to the roistering expansion of the 1850s, and crumbling ruins attest to the transitory nature of these boom towns. For the historian

or romantic, however, the Sierra breezes sigh like ghosts of the past, reminding the visitor of an exciting period now vanished.

The greatest modern-day treasure of the region may in fact be just this ambience. Certainly, the Mother Lode area cannot be characterized as a bustling manufacturing or population center. Its charm lies in the very fact that it continues with a relatively slower pace of life that looks back to the past. The primary income of the area comes from modest agricultural activities, from unromantic rock, gravel, and sand mining, from some ponderosa pine and white fir lumbering, and from the tourist-oriented trade. The latter capitalizes on historical sites, winter sports, and wilderness recreation. The nature of this economic activity does not conflict with the yesteryear sense of simplicity and naturalness. This has, undoubtedly, contributed to the modest boom in foothill towns in recent years, with retirees and urban refugees finding the atmosphere they seek in the area.

The advantages of living in this region include distance from the turmoil of big cities, availability of open space and nature, and the presence of historically fascinating sites all around. The area encompasses forested foothill and barren desert, each with its own unique characteristics. The sense of peacefulness, however, pervades both foothill ranches and lonely desert and carries over to the little towns that still exist. Mariposa, Downieville, Garlock, Bodie, and Darwin each slumber and dream of past glories, and a visitor with a good imagi-

Figure 9.4 The romance of the Gold Rush survives in towns such as Amador City. (California Office of Tourism)

Figure 9.5 Panorama view of Calico, a mining ghost town restored by Walter Knott and then deeded to the county of San Bernardino. (Richard Hyslop)

nation can populate the lonely stretches of U.S. 395 and 49 with prospectors and cowboys (Fig. 9.4).

The sense of history is also evident in colorful places such as Fiddletown, Angels Camp, Mormon Bar, and Mokelumne Hill. Columbia and Calico (Fig. 9.5) have been turned into restored Western towns for tourist consumption exclusively, and their success is evidence of the popularity of commercialized history.

Many more of the Mother Lode cities now serve as gateways to the popular wilderness areas of Sequoia, Kings, and Yosemite National Parks and other state and local wilderness settings. In the warm season, providing services for hiking, fishing, hunting, and camping constitutes the mainstay of these towns. In cold weather, skiing becomes the prime attraction. Tourists and temporary visitors move on, but residents continue to enjoy their peaceful environment and historical past. For this region has much to offer: Architectural treasures of the

past, magnificent wilderness locations, quiet, open land and low population density are attributes that hold the loyalty of the people. They take pride in their frontier heritage, and few would trade their lifestyle for one that required them to move to Los Angeles or San Francisco.

A State Without Wine Is Like a Day Without Sunshine: California Vineyards

Wine has become a sophisticated, respected, and palatable business in California. From its early and simple beginnings with the vines brought by Franciscan padres, the California grape has matured into a well-traveled and widely consumed product. In fact, it has become a multimillion dollar industry.

The term "Wine Country" popularly refers to the Napa-Sonoma area northeast of San Francisco. This is a somewhat misleading designation since respectable vineyards have also grown up in many other locations throughout the state. The Central Valley and the southern counties now produce most of the state's wine. The Napa-Sonoma region, however, is still Wine Country to most Californians, and the region takes great pride in this identity even though it now produces only about 20 percent of California's total wine output.

The California wine industry is a remarkable success story. Currently holding a share of the total American wine market in excess of 80 percent and enjoying an extensive foreign export market, the business is solid and growing. Directly and indirectly, viticulture in the state owes much to the contributions of European winemakers. The immigration of experienced wine experts brought first of all a new expertise to the state. During the 1850s, the German vineyards at Anaheim and the Italian Swiss Colony at Asti began their efforts. Contributions by Charles Krug, Etienne Thée, Charles Lefranc, and Agoston Haraszthy took the infant industry further toward fulfillment and demonstrated the significant impact of immigrants. The hard work of these new Californians resulted in expanded vineyards throughout the state, especially in the Napa-Sonoma region.

Indirectly, Europe helped by providing vine cuttings of quality and endurance. The infusion of this established stock enabled California wines to grow in popularity and quality. Continued expansion of the industry was assured, and new wineries sprang up in such diverse locations as Fresno, Madera, Modesto, Cucamonga, Rutherford, and Saratoga. Although Prohibition caused major financial damage to the California wine industry, it returned stronger than ever with the passage of Repeal.

Today, the wine country of California reflects mature respectability. Nowhere is this more evident than in the Napa-Sonoma region. In architecture, cultivated hillsides, and temperament, the area exudes a flavor of the Old World. It is a region of cultivated serenity and traditional values. The plethora of family vineyards lends a stable social order to the area. The feel of the culture is found in the orderly sense by which the long rows of cultivated vines march across most of the available land. It is a peaceful setting, even during the autumn harvest. The tranquil, scenic nature of the area is not even significantly disturbed by the presence of visitors touring the many tasting rooms. Indeed, the courtesy and charm characteristic of this wine country is evident in the care with which the old family wineries treat their guests. If there is an old aristocracy in California, one is tempted to look for it here, although many of these rustic, homey-looking wineries are now owned by international corporations.

Recently, the controlled nature of the agricultural landscape of the Napa-Sonoma area has been copied somewhat in the efforts of the people to prevent uncontrolled residential sprawl. Concern over spread of the Bay Area population has led to zoning efforts to retain the traditional mood, lifestyle, and flavor of the region. With its history of controlled environment, the region is likely to fight hard to retain its romantic and tranquil existence (Fig. 9.6).

The Bay: San Francisco Sophisticate
"The City" has acquired a rare and enviable reputation as a place of ups and downs, views, breezes, and fog. To

Figure 9.6 Christian Brothers winery. (Wine Institute)

a certain degree, the entire Bay Area shares this romantic image; it is an environ of ethnic mixes, cultural
plenty, self-conscious snobbery, refurbished Victorians,
experimental thinking, cluster housing, and dramatic
skyline (Fig. 9.7). It is at once historical and modern,
hurried and calm, artsy and staid. It is unique, its self-
image one of quintessential sophistication.

The San Francisco Bay Area is, of course, more than
the simplified version promoted by songwriters or chambers of commerce. Here is a greater metropolitan region
that encompasses all or part of nine counties in an in-
terconnected web of bedroom communities, residential
tracts, shopping centers, diversified industrial-retail developments, and concrete highways. Though the Oakland–East Bay area and the San Jose–South Bay area
form overlapping centers of residential and commercial
activity, the main hub of this urban web is San Francisco.
The City provides the emotional fix and overall identification for the entire region.

The diversity of the Bay Area is phenomenal. It may
be seen in the variety of architectural styles ranging
from Chinese and Asian influences to refurbished Victorian splendor to leapfrogging tracts to palacial estates
to tidy, middle-class, ranch-style homes. It can be seen
in the obvious extremes of economic affluence from
wealthy Hillsborough to troubled central Oakland, with
every shade in between.

The ethnic makeup of the Bay Area is likewise notable. San Francisco's Chinatown is one of the most celebrated in the country. Oakland and Richmond represent
two very high concentrations of black population. Inner
San Francisco has obvious enclaves of East European

A

Figure 9.7 San Francisco's changing face. Victorian houses and
cable cars and views of Alcatraz are reminders of the city's past (A).
Modern skyscrapers rise against hills and bay to create a
spectacular skyline (B). (A: San Francisco Visitors Bureau, Richard
Frear; B: San Francisco Visitors Bureau, Craig Buchanan)

B

groups, Filipinos, blacks, Japanese and other Asians, Chicanos, and other Spanish-speaking populations.

The climate carries out the theme of diversity in an astonishing fashion. Owing to its watery surroundings, San Francisco itself enjoys climatic conditions entirely different than those experienced by most of the rest of the region. Meanwhile, across the Bay, temperatures and conditions can stand in dramatic contrast—sun versus fog, heat versus cool, dry versus damp. Landscape varies immensely within a very limited geographic region. Urban settings alternate with agriculture; flat marshlands contrast with precipitous hillsides.

A brief tour of the region, starting with the city/county of San Francisco and radiating outward, quickly reveals this diversity: To the east, across the Bay and connected by the Bay Bridge, is the Contra Costa–Alameda complex. This populous, urbanized concentration provides much of the industrial production of the Bay Area. In particular, the Oakland-Richmond complex is a key terminus for rail, ocean, and truck transport. Although metropolitan Oakland has a large minority population, there is a less obvious ethnic mix as one moves south and west from the Oakland core. Similarly, where Oakland appears crowded and congested, shading out and away from the city are typically suburban cities like Walnut Creek, Hayward, Fremont, Concord, and Livermore.

Moving southward from the hub along the peninsula, the entire area stretching from South San Francisco to Palo Alto is a rapidly growing corridor. Neighboring peninsular cities such as Daly City, San Bruno, San Mateo, Redwood City, Menlo Park, and Palo Alto have struggled with the problem of expansion. They have met with mixed success in controlling the development of the peninsula, which now reflects a blend of residential, retail, and diversified light industry.

To the extreme south of the peninsula begins the cluttered sprawl of San Jose and the Santa Clara Valley. Here is one of the most typically disarranged of California urban areas. A region of mixed development, decaying inner city, spreading tract housing, and bustling industry, the South Bay region is experiencing problems coming to terms with itself. The successful industrial capacity of this locale is typified by the major aerospace establishment of Sunnyvale. Meanwhile the supporters of the rural, agricultural lifestyle battle to maintain a hold against the ever-expanding residential tract developments. Moving further south and east from this point, the Bay Area identity begins to weaken until finally the agricultural Central Valley takes over.

To the north of San Francisco, across the famed Golden Gate Bridge, is the North Bay and the Marin County peninsula. The confused and unattractive urban sprawl is less evident in this area, which is a mix of mostly higher-income residential and open land. The wealthier socioeconomic structure here has helped to preserve much of the open marshland, recreation areas, and beautiful green terrain. A quieter, more peaceful section of the Bay Area, it gradually merges into the wine country, not far from the waters of the Bay itself.

Today, the greater San Francisco Bay region is undergoing some traumatic transitions. Long known for its commercial potential, the area continues to support extensive rail, truck, and port facilities. The challenge of the growing southern portion of the state, however, has created some competition for this economic base.

The widespread reputation for charm and sophistication has continued. The international character of San Francisco endures in the culinary, architectural, and cultural choices available. Political and social tolerance is still fostered in the open acceptance of alternate sexual preferences and lifestyles. The appeal of ocean, climate, cable cars, gingerbread houses, theaters, restaurants, and fog continues to draw people to the city.

With the growing demands of a burgeoning population, however, the Bay Area also faces many challenges to the old ways and assumptions. Faced with many of the same problems as the south, San Francisco can no longer look with carelessly veiled contempt on Los Angeles. The difficulties and growing pains of Southern California are increasingly becoming the reality in the Bay Area. The challenge will be to resolve these problems without repeating the mistakes of the south.

Nashville West: Bakersfield, the Central Valley, and the Farm Belt

Agriculture is an important reality in California; a huge portion of the state's land is dedicated to food production. In few places is this more evident than in the Central Valley. Comprising most of the heart of the state, the Central Valley stretches for about 470 miles from Bakersfield north to Redding and lies between the coastal ranges and the western Sierra Nevada. Fertile productivity is the hallmark of the region, and long, flat, open expanses of combed and cultivated land are the common landscape. It is a region of farmers, truckers, and fieldhands, characterized by wide expanses of cultivated fields, diverse crops, and agribusiness operations. It is the source of California's leading position in American agricultural production and income.

To begin to appreciate the magnitude of this richness, few better ways can be found than to drive the length of California 99 or I-5 between Los Angeles and Sacramento. The route passes through extensive agricultural land and is unbroken for hundreds of miles by any significant urban setting. The variety of crops visible along this route is great enough to astonish the most sophisticated agriculturalist. A world apart from the populous bustle of the major urban centers, the Central Valley reflects yet another side of the state in both ecological and cultural terms.

There are few large cities located in the region. Those that do exist unmistakably reflect the priorities of the farm. The large farm city of Bakersfield is a perfect case in point. Driving into Bakersfield, one encounters Montgomery Ward's, truck stops, farm implement dealers, gas stations, cafés, and honky-tonk bars. The uncomplicated strains of country-Western music floats through the air from bars and truck radios. Values in the songs are simple and direct, mirroring the attitudes of the residents of this region. This is a town that is "close to the ground," without pretensions. It exists to serve the agricultural needs of the area with its shipping facilities and stores. Its merchants cater to the farm population, providing services, products, and entertainment for evenings and weekends off the farm. Dubbed "Nashville West," the reputation of Bakersfield as the Western home of country music is well known.

What is true of Bakersfield is true also of the few other farm area cities. Although Sacramento is the state capital and contains immense governmental operations, it makes no pretense of being a cosmopolitan center. In fact, it is an agriculturally oriented city located in the midst of a rich delta farming area. Sacramento is really a farm town; it just happens to be the state capital. Visalia came into being and continues to prosper due to its role as a farm-service community. Likewise Fresno, though it is a big city that reflects many of the benefits and ills of a large urban area, also exists because it serves the needs of the Central Valley farms that surround it. Stockton is equally a product of agriculture; it came into being due to the Gold Rush but stayed alive due to its role as a major agricultural service center.

These cities owe their existence to the agrarian wealth of the state, and most of their residents reflect pride and awareness of the role of farming in California and the nation. If their values seem a little more basic and old-fashioned than those of the big city, and if their music is the music of the country, and if their lifestyle is more sedate, so much the better.

Although not physically a part of the Central Valley, the Imperial Valley in the far south shares the same values, attitudes, and priorities. Like the Central Valley, the Imperial Valley is a highly productive region because of the long growing season, diverse soil conditions, extensive irrigation, and advanced technological applications. Many of the same problems face the area, including urban encroachment and agribusiness consolidation. Economically, socially, and culturally, it is a continuation of the farm belt.

Taken all together, the farming portion of the state is quite significant. It is responsible for mass production of cattle and dairy products, poultry, grapes, vegetables, hay, nuts, cotton, and fruit. The hard work and efficiency of the California farmer in producing these and other crops has made the state a leader in the world. Certain problems do exist, however.

Even with the increased demand for food, urban-residential land uses are cutting into productive agricultural land. The trend toward consolidation and incorporation of agribusiness has brought new complexity to the lives and attitudes of the farm population. Unionization of farm workers and advancing agricultural technology are bringing about a shift in numbers of persons attracted to this way of life. Critical changes are facing the California farming community, which may force this conservative, fundamental culture to reexamine some of its goals. But even if some changes do occur, the farm belt will continue to exert significant influence on the economy, environment, and culture of the state.

Neon Glitter: Southern California and Los Angeles

On occasion, Southern California has had a rather shady public image. Characterized as the last stronghold for assorted faddists, nuts, kooks, and misfits, it cannot be accused of being dull! Congestion, freeways, smog, cars, trucks, recreation vehicles, and rows of identical tract houses typify much of the south. The urban tide of Los Angeles has spread in an almost continuous flow down through Orange County, up through part of Ventura, and across through large portions of Riverside and San Bernardino.

The greater Los Angeles metropolitan area takes in a huge portion of the land and population of the south. The city limits alone comprise more than 450 sq mi, but the Los Angeles influence extends far beyond even these extensive bounds. In terms of its sphere of influence, the Los Angeles metropolitan region extends to the ocean on the west, to the San Fernando Valley and Ventura County on the north, to Orange County on the south, and to the "Inland Empire" of Pomona, Riverside, and San Bernardino on the east. The problems, concerns, and orientations of these areas are a part of the greater entity of Southern California. Los Angeles itself provides the unifying link and shared bond.

Population alone directs much of the focus of the state on Los Angeles. Over half of the state's total population is found in Southern California, with well over 30 percent in Los Angeles County. The trend shows no sign of shifting, and so in terms of population the culture of Los Angeles is the majority culture of California.

As a culture of diversity, Los Angeles and Southern California represent an astounding range of urban-suburban environments. Within one metropolitan area can be found miles of beautiful beaches and blocks of decaying urban jungles. Cool mountain resorts look out over bleak desert landscapes. The plastic glitter of Hollywood contrasts sharply with the air-conditioned luxury of corporate Century City skyscrapers (Fig. 9.8).

Similarly, the mix of racial and ethnic groups is equally diverse. The south now has large and significant populations of blacks, Hispanics, Asians, and others. Most of these are tossed together in an interesting cultural salad bowl called the Los Angeles Basin. Indeed, the *Los Angeles Times* reported in 1980 that the Glendale School District contained children speaking 44 languages. The *Times* further reported that 1980 had marked the point of ethnic shift in Los Angeles, wherein the Anglo population now numbered less than 50 percent.

The southern portion of the state is clearly a land of plenty. There is an abundance of people, money, stores, cars, freeways, motorcycles, billboards, noise, recreation vehicles, shopping centers, gas stations, parking lots, restaurants, lights, colleges and universities, fast food chains, theaters, houses, condominiums, apartments, and real estate salespeople.

The nature of this abundance can be traced to many of the factors that originally drew the population to the region. The military and aerospace industry attracted people with jobs. The movie industry attracted people with glamor. The Mediterranean climate promised health. The romance of the state was touted by the tourist and service industries who relied upon masses of people for their success. Once people arrived, they stayed.

In recent years, a boom in foreign ownership of major downtown Los Angeles properties has contributed to the healthy characterization of the area. Such prominent landmarks as the Bonaventure Hotel, Crocker Plaza,

Figure 9.8 Famous intersection of Hollywood and Vine. The Capitol Records building, designed to look like a stack of records, is one of many fanciful buildings in Southern California. (Greater Los Angeles Visitors and Convention Bureau)

The Park, Pacific Financial Center, The Biltmore, One Wilshire Boulevard, California First Bank, and 800 Wilshire are now owned by foreign corporations.

The Los Angeles and Southern California region does have problems. The mobile, independent, bustling state of mind so common to the population of the region has helped to foster some of its difficulties. An exaggerated sense of individualism has encouraged a political environment in which efforts to achieve mass transit and air standards for industry can be thwarted. Thus, air quality has become a crucial issue at the same time that the population clings to its imagined independence by commuting one-to-a-car. The anarchistic sense of self has made local government decision making a morass of confused, contrary, and involved arguments. The interaction of ethnic and racial groups is uncomfortable at best. The desire to pursue unique notions and lifestyles has not fostered a commitment to planned or controlled development, and monotonous and ugly suburbs attest to this fact.

All the clichés concerning the cultural wasteland of Southern California bear careful examination, however. In spite of the crush and confusion of a booming popula-

tion, Los Angeles has achieved enviable progress as well. The abundance of quality private and public universities and colleges has made Southern California a recognized leader in the field of education. Here can be found some of the world's most impressive programs of collegiate extension courses. Offered in a multitude of locations, subjects, and time slots, these programs have made higher education truly a public pastime. Southern Californians may study virtually any subject, take educational tours to most parts of the world, and participate in the learning experience for as long as they wish. Also, with the impetus of military and government contracts, the Los Angeles metropolitan area has become a center for scientific research and development with such sites as the Rand Corporation and the Jet Propulsion Laboratory in Pasadena.

Certainly there has been a dramatic, and often spectacular, effect on much of the natural landscape of the region. The natural coastal sagebrush and semiarid terrain has been converted in many areas into beautifully groomed suburban neighborhoods. Here proud homeowners have planted, nurtured, and experimented with all manner of exotic plant life, shrubbery, and trees from all over the world, and carefully watered, manicured, and pruned estates are the result.

There has been a serious commitment to the arts, with the Music Center, County Art Museum, and various dramatic companies the envy of much of the rest of the nation. Contrary to the comments of many critics, the Los Angeles area has extensive participation in cultural activities. Numerous private museums supplement the public offerings, with the Norton Simon and the J. Paul Getty museums being only two obvious examples. On almost any sunny weekend, one can find outdoor art shows by thousands of amateur painters, sculptors, and other craftsmen and artists. Likewise, community support for the arts ranges from local theater groups to shows sponsored by savings and loan institutions to local library presentations. A slightly different form of art can be seen in the profuse displays of architectural experimentation found in both private and commercial edifices, from shopping centers to hideaway retreats in the hills.

In terms of its awareness of the world and its cosmopolitan image, Los Angeles has become the rival of New York City as a news capital of the country, both in television and print media. In 1980, *Newsweek* identified the *Los Angeles Times* as one of the three best metropolitan newspapers in the country. In the electronic media, Los Angeles has become a top assignment.

The ethnic contributions to the culture of the region are significant. Like San Francisco, the Los Angeles metropolitan area has an extensive mix of ethnic groups, making its population and style highly diverse. Although the various ethnic cultures are mixed well into many areas of the Los Angeles Basin, there are some notable concentrations that have become largely synonymous with the various ethnic populations.

Watts is one of the sections clearly identified with the black population. Receiving nationwide attention in the late 1960s for the riots that occurred there, Watts has subsequently attempted to achieve a more cohesive sense of black identity, self-direction, and pride. Certainly the yearly Watts Festival and other events have focused attention on the contributions of the black population to the culture of the state and the nation.

East Los Angeles has long been identified with the growing and important Mexican-American or Chicano community. The influence of this ethnic group is, of course, evident throughout California and the Southwest. East Los Angeles, however, has long been identified as a Spanish-speaking *barrio* or community, and the area has provided a cultural home for this population. The growth of the Latino population of the area has accelerated even more with the modern influx of undocumented aliens who are drawn to this neighborhood by the familiarity of a Latin-based culture.

On the other end of the city is West Los Angeles. Here is an area that reflects a strong Jewish influence. Delicatessens and synagogues are more evident here, and the names on stores and buildings reinforce this cultural identity.

Many other sections of the greater Los Angeles region reflect diverse ethnic-cultural influences. A growing Southeast Asian population has swelled the size of the city's Chinatown and Little Tokyo and has also established itself in other outlying regions such as Orange County. Finally, American Indians, immigrants from South Pacific islands, relocated English and Canadian citizens, and many others help provide the dynamic cultural diversity to be found in Los Angeles.

In all, Southern California has largely outgrown its provincial image and has moved into the forefront of the nation as a true center of culture, politics, economics, ethnic awareness, and power.

Beachboys, Boating, and Body Beautiful: Southern Coastal Playgrounds

Most of the image of California seen in posters, media, and popular movies is the beach and seashore scene of the southern coastal playgrounds. A common scene is that of surfers dramatically swooping toward shore in foaming surf while acres of bronzed and beautiful flesh bake on the sand. The glamor of sunny California is also portrayed in pictures of trim sailboats lolling off the coast or bobbing lazily in tidy marinas.

This imagery is not created purely for export consumption; living within this particular culture has its effects on the residents as well. Frequently the stereotype creates a sense of obligation to fulfill the expectation. What Southern Californian would not feel embarrassed to be seen pale and white in shorts or bathing suit? In fact, the region exudes a self-conscious pride in staying beautiful, bronzed, healthy and trim. It is an attitude that permeates the culture and does not stop with youth, as two or three hours of casual observation at Venice Beach quickly reveal.

The Southern Californian beach scene is a fascinating subculture with great outward display and little depth. There is a peculiar arrogance that encourages conspicuous displays of wealth. It rewards with admiration a tan acquired by wasting countless hours lying indolently in the sun and further compounds its vanity by supporting tanning clinics that preserve and protect the deep-baked tan. It is a wealthy, smug, sensual, gaudy, indulgent, and social subsociety.

The area included in the southern coastal playground begins around Santa Barbara and moves southward along the coast through Los Angeles and Orange counties and into San Diego County. This long stretch of coast includes a remarkable variety of beach and coastal headlands as well as an equally broad range of affluence and styles. Santa Barbara is a wealthy, exclusive, and self-contained community that retains a flavor of old Spain in its "Queen of the Missions" and Moorish courthouse. Tidiness and order are the style here, and expensive ranchos and urban mansions are typical. The frantic pace of the big city is missing in both Santa Barbara itself and in the countryside around. The quaintness increases moving inland to the fertile, lush, green coastal valley farmlands. The Scandinavian tourist town of Solvang (Fig. 9.9) is just one additional interesting landmark of the Santa Barbara region, where stability, homely virtues, and good living are evident.

Other selected communities along the southern coastal shoreline share the exclusive, wealthy security of Santa Barbara. Corona del Mar, Lido Isle, Palos Verdes, and Emerald Bay take quiet pride in their expensive lifestyles. These are not transient, brash beach communities but rather the strongholds of the consciously affluent.

In contrast to the orderly, quiet, wealthy beach towns are the socially active and popular beach areas where the fast life prevails. Malibu and Newport, Santa Monica, Venice, and Marina del Rey share a sense of preoccupation with youth, parties, the body beautiful, and novelty. Sports cars, surfboards, sailboats, and sexual experimentation are evident in all quarters; transience and frantic motion are the standards.

Between these two extremes are various other styles of oceanfront atmosphere. Surfing, pier fishing, and oil wells share space with middle-class economic display in Huntington Beach. Tidepools, tourists, art, and scuba diving typify such areas as Laguna Beach, Catalina, and La Jolla. All along the coast, high-rise condominiums and apartment complexes compete for space with exclusive restaurants and growing financial centers. The older beach areas of Seal Beach, Manhattan Beach, Dana Point, and San Clemente are feeling the impact of new money on old lifestyles, and old rag-tag houses are being replaced by expensive residential and business edifices.

The fast-paced demands of growth and affluence have inevitably changed the face of the southern coastal area. The frantic presence of disco, skating, boating, dining, shopping, and corporate enterprise is crowding out the peaceful sense of marching surf. Only the quiet, persistent, and inevitable pier fishermen, and the inaccessable, rocky, rugged bluffs of Palos Verdes attest to the peaceful past.

Country Clubs, Conservatives, Military, and Mexico

Vacation, recreation, and retirement are the crucial draws of modern San Diego. They have made the city one of California's leading metropolitan areas while giv-

ing it a unique flavor at the same time. Building upon its climate and geographic location, San Diego made of them an art, a lifestyle, and a justification for existence.

Starting with one of the best ports on the coast and a location rich in beauty, mild weather, and natural variety, San Diego has capitalized fully on these assets. The favorable coastal profile has made possible a heavy maritime orientation, with the extensive naval facilities exerting a strong social, economic, and political influence. Likewise, the advantages of an excellent port have supported a significant shipping industry and a large commercial fishing fleet. The extensive naval and private marine activities have in turn helped foster related light manufacturing industries as well as a respectable aerospace program. Typically, this type of economic base is associated with a conservative and traditional outlook in the general population. San Diego is no exception. A conservative, no-nonsense attitude is evident in most of the cultural character of the area.

Politically, the region has long been known as a conservative stronghold in the state. Economically, *laissez faire* doctrine is still popular and admired. Socially, the values of small-town America are highly cherished.

On the other hand, San Diego has a lighter side to its collective personality—a single-minded dedication to play! The same factors that encourage and support a maritime and naval presence have also created a strong recreational spirit. The seaside environment has nurtured numerous ocean-oriented pastimes and entertainments. Mission Bay has been developed into a posh and scenic locale. Here, Sea World and its tourist shows draw visitors by the thousands (Fig. 9.10). In addition, the extensive marina, hotel, and restaurant facilities have made this area a major recreation center. Coronado Island caters to those who prefer Victorian-style buildings, dining, and lodging. Deepsea sport fishing is a recognized

Figure 9.9 Solvang, a picturesque tourist-oriented town. (Solvang Chamber of Commerce, photo by King Merrill)

Figure 9.10 Bottlenosed dolphins somersault through the air at Sea World in San Diego. (Sea World)

tourist attraction. Recreational boating, water skiing, surfing, swimming, and skin diving round out the pursuits available in the area.

Location and climate are also part of the playground requisites of the San Diego region. Proximity to the Mexican border places the novelties of bullfights, *jai alai,* and foreign trade at the fingertips of tourists. Mild weather enhances the appeal of scenic Del Mar racetrack, various golf courses, numerous state parks, famous Balboa Park with its Shakespearean Festival and museums, Torrey Pines State Park, respected San Diego Zoo, Wild Animal Park, Old Town, and many other leisure activities. The city and its surroundings cater to the tourist trade. The abundance of motels, hotels, restaurants, picnic grounds, shops, and amusement parks is eloquent testimony to its success.

Historically, San Diego has undergone some interesting changes. From its beginning as a sleepy mission and presidio, the region has evolved into a more aggressive and sophisticated locale. In recent years, the expansion of the region has been dramatic. As a new rapid growth area of residential settlement, the area has seen a shift in the average age pattern. Although retirement-age persons are still attracted to the region, the increase in young families is noticeable. This has created a rising demand for schools, playgrounds, and additional housing. Much of this expansion is occurring in outlying areas such as Escondido, Oceanside, and La Mesa.

Some of the earlier pastoral nature of the region can still be found in the back country areas. Peaceful farm communities like Julian, Banner, Aguanga, and Santa Ysabel alternate with picturesque agricultural valleys and hillsides. This experience is a temporary respite, however. The dominant trend in the San Diego region is toward growth and expansion. As both a residential

and a resort area, San Diego is committed to a process of serving the people who live and visit there. It is equally determined to build its reputation as a place to relax and enjoy the pleasures of California.

MAD DOGS AND CALIFORNIANS

To state that California has its unique and peculiar cultural phenomena is to express the obvious. Although this aspect of the state has been overplayed by Eastern commentators, residents of the state do seem to take pride in forging new fashions and fads, social arrangements, and entertainments. Experimentation has never been a process feared in this state. When these experiments are successful, they are admired by outsiders. When they fail, they are cited as evidence of the basic craziness of Californians. What begins in the Golden State, however, frequently spreads to the rest of the nation and becomes part of American popular culture.

Creating Dreams: Disney, Knott, and Others

Technology has brought numerous benefits to American society. Greater leisure time is created with advancing technology. Likewise, technology usually brings a higher degree of affluence. With leisure and affluence, public literacy and sophistication generally rise. The end in this chain of development is a demand for amusements to fill up the new leisure time. California has certainly met this challenge.

The forms mass amusement and entertainment take in this state are wide-ranging. The traditional forms of television and movies are popular, of course. In the major urban areas, cable and subscription television have become significant multimillion dollar operations, providing first-run movies, sports events, and soft core pornography. Movies continue to provide a source of entertainment, with drive-in theaters holding their own on the West Coast. California has become expert in providing less prosaic forms of amusement, however.

Theme parks have become a popular customer attraction. Californians have proven willing to spend millions of dollars for an afternoon of created experiences in nostalgia, adventure, the Old West, futurism, romanticism, or combinations thereof. Although the original Disneyland in Anaheim may be the best known of these parks, it is certainly not the only one. Knott's Berry Farm and Ghost Town (Buena Park), advertising itself as "America's oldest amusement park," offers a variety of adventures and experiences. Marriott's turn-of-the-century Great America in Santa Clara offers nostalgia and some amusement; Six Flags Magic Mountain in Valencia provides white-knuckle rides and experiences as well as music and entertainment. Universal City Tours brings the movie world to the customer, or vice versa. Other parks provide similar adventures where technology and imagination are combined to satisfy customer needs (Fig. 9.11).

A particular offshoot of theme parks is the wildlife-nature amusement park. In these seminatural settings, wildlife and sealife are displayed and often provide shows for the guests. San Diego has its Sea World and

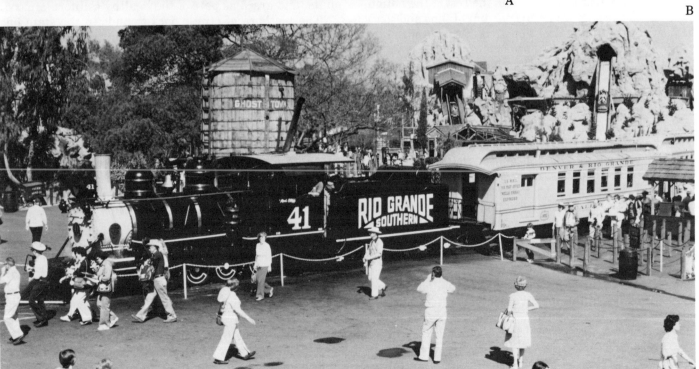

Figure 9.11 Disneyland (A) and Knott's Berry Farm (B) are two of California's major tourist attractions, drawing millions of visitors each year. (A: © Walt Disney Productions; B: Knott's Berry Farm)

Wild Animal Park. The Bay Area has its Marine World and Africa U.S.A. Orange County has Lion Country Safari, and Los Angeles has Hanna-Barbera's Marineland. Most of these attractions attempt to create an illusion of natural setting, which distinguishes them from the more traditional and still popular zoos.

History serves to entertain California. In many cities, major tourist attractions are "Old Towns" from the Spanish days (Sacramento, San Diego) or historical beginnings locations (Olvera Street, Cannery Row). Similarly, the California missions build upon this historical sense to draw tourists. Where true history may not be available, enterprising California businesspeople have created a subgenre of commercial *kitsch*—popularized, if not accurate or aesthetically appropriate, history. Here, stylized plastic history is merchandised in restaurant-shopping-entertainment complexes. San Francisco's Pier 39 or the Cannery or Ghirardelli squares are joined by such consciously quaint tourist towns as Sausalito or Carmel-by-the-Sea or Knott's Berry Farm's replica of Independence Hall and similar cultural expressions.

Finally, there are a variety of other miscellaneous forms of entertainment available in the state. These range from convention center presentations to concerts held in stadiums to programs put on by local theater groups and colleges. Elite culture appears in opera houses, music centers, symphony orchestras, museum, and art shows. Discos, bars, country-Western clubs, jazz halls, and rock concerts provide yet another dimension of the multilayered entertainment available to Californians.

Eating Your Way to Nirvana—By Railroad, Bistro, Pub, and Drive-in

Food is a special form of amusement for Californians. As with other forms of entertainment, this does not make the state unique or different from the rest of the nation, except in degree. Based on the amount of time and space dedicated to eating, it does appear that food is one of the primal urges in American society, especially in its relation to all forms of recreation. Whether it be drinks at the concert, snacks at the game, or junk food at the park, food seems to be a necessity for most recreation.

This becomes even more interesting when we consider that the act of eating itself has become major entertainment for huge numbers of people. In the late 1970s, as much as one out of every three food dollars was spent on dining out. According to *Newsweek,* the food service industry had grown to over $87 billion a year in the country. California alone accounted for a gigantic portion of this growth. Various factors have contributed to this growth, including increases in leisure time, growth in disposable income, higher percentages of single and childless adults, and the rise in the numbers of working women. California has some additional unique factors that have made dining out even more feasible and popular.

First, the weather of the state usually does not pose any significant obstacle to an evening out. Mobility, an assumed and accepted part of California culture, facilitates the restaurant phenomenon. The casual and experiential lifestyle encourages culinary adventures; since Californians frequently seek or create novelty, the varieties of dining experiences are extensive.

Logically, in a state wed to the automobile, speed, and mobility, fast food restaurants head the list in popularity. The fast food establishments have been able to achieve such a prominent position because they fulfill certain needs: The food and menu is standardized and predictable; the product is relatively inexpensive; and the service is fast and, in many cases, does not even require leaving the car. Because there are so many fast food spots, a wide option in food choice is available.

The hamburger, fries, and soft drink establishments are king, with the golden arches leading the pack. California-style Mexican food is a major competitor, selling what has been called "pasteurized Mexican food" for Anglo tastes. A variety of other fast food types round out the choices, offering fish, chicken, pizza, roast beef, hot dogs, and other less familiar dishes. All share the one vital characteristic of serving the lifestyle of a people always on the move who desire cheap, fast, and edible food (Fig. 9.12).

Holding a more prominent position as entertainment are the vast array of theme restaurants. Here the entertainment function or the gimmick is often as vital as the food. Depending on whim, mood, or pocketbook, the diner may choose from railroad cars, seafood havens, family boardinghouses, English pubs, ranchers' tables, mining companies, gypsy dens, or plantation mansions. If you can imagine a theme, there is a restaurant in California catering to this concept. The key is the "experience" more than the food; if the food is tasty, so much the better.

California also reflects some unusual styles that are made possible by its cultural environment. Natural or health food establishments build upon the idea of selling a California lifestyle. Thus, Golden State gastronomics support avocados, bean sprouts, alfalfa shoots, fruit, nuts, and grain as part of the healthy California mood.

The plethora of ethnic backgrounds in the state has made possible an ethnic restaurant business unsurpassed in the country. In Los Angeles alone, over 750 noteworthy ethnic restaurants compete favorably for the dining dollars of hungry Californians.

The state's long coastline has made seafood a vital part of the diet. The choice of seafood restaurants up and down the coast is extensive, ranging from fancy, expensive bistros to stand-at-the-counter fish stalls.

Another category of serious eater is served by the dinner house approach, which usually features a limited menu in large quantities. Buffets also cater to this clientele by letting the diner fill his or her own plate with any number of salads or starches for a fixed price.

Naugahide and neon are the identifying marks of another familiar category of restaurant. This is the coffee shop or café, which has the enduring advantage of always being open for business. For 24-hour mobile Californians, this kind of establishment provides an oasis in the night where coffee and secret sauces combine to keep the diner's eyes open for the next 200 miles.

Another category is the cocktail and candlelight spot, which sells snob appeal and romance. These places can be recognized instantly by their French names or locations atop any tall building. A toned-down version of

Figure 9.12 The choice of fast food establishments and menus is almost unlimited—and while you eat, you might even be a part of a TV or movie filming. (Greater Los Angeles Visitors and Convention Bureau)

this category is the fine-food-by-formula restaurant, where tidy, smiling, college-aged waiters and waitresses serve the specialty (turtle, lobster, or omelet) in a standardized "gourmet" decor.

Perhaps the most salient characteristic of the restaurant experience in California is the choice available. The state has made dining out a recreational activity equal to any Disneyland or Wild Animal Park. Speed, mobility, romance, ethnicity, variety, entertainment, convenience, or image may be purchased at a choice of restaurants usually within a half-hour's radius. All this variety, in addition to food, makes for quite a bargain. If, as the old saying states, "we are what we eat," some interesting speculations could be made about California and American culture generally.

Isolating Age: Leisure World and Age Ghettos

If we find specialization of restaurants and amusement parks in the state, we should not be surprised to find specialized arrangements for living as well. One of the most noticeable of these is the segregation by age in communities within the state. In its compulsion to celebrate youth and beauty, it appears that California culture is embarrassed by wrinkles, age, and gray hair. Thus has evolved a form of age ghetto and segregated living. It also seems that, once started on the process of segregating by age, the people of the state have not known where to stop.

Most identifiable throughout the state are the various restricted communities catering to the elderly only. For-

mally structured closed societies of the aged, labeled euphemistically "Leisure World," are found in several parts of the state. Here, locked safely behind security gates and fences, the elderly can pursue their interests free from outside distraction or bother.

Less structured, but nonetheless equally real, are the informal age ghettos of mobile home parks. These parks are scattered in various locations throughout the state, including dry desert, cool seashore, and dusty urban jungle. Specializing in the elderly on fixed incomes, they provide a central gathering spot for the lower-income aged who can, at least, have each other for company. In these age ghettos, families can visit their grandparents on three or four special occasions a year but be spared the embarrassment and inconvenience of seeing them on a regular basis. Out of sight, the aged can safely be ignored and California can perpetuate its myth of eternal youth (Fig. 9.13).

Another interesting form of age classification is the over-40 adults-only townhouse and condominium development. Growing in popularity, these communities attempt to stratify and structure communal life in such a way as to exclude both the very old and the very young. The ideal residents are the mature couples who have achieved some measure of success, have moved past childrearing age, and now seek to enjoy some of the pleasures affluence can bring. Brought together with other people of similar background and interests, such couples can control and regulate their lives. They can then effectively shut out the irritations of youth and childhood on one hand and senility and infirmity on the other.

Figure 9.13 The "safe haven" of Leisure World in Seal Beach: oasis for the senior citizen or age ghetto? (Ace Aerial Photography, Laguna Hills, CA)

The classic form of age segregation is the young adult or "swinging single" complex. Often recognizable by the fact that they are named after a tree (The Apple, The Aspen, The Pines), these dwellings are California's answer to the search for life in the fast lane. Characterized by frantic efforts of organized mixing, these young adult communities provide a form of family security to otherwise independent youth. It is a snob appeal approach, representing the healthy, free-and-easy good life of California—to those who live there, at least. Marriage usually spells the end of this residential period, since such a permanent relationship implies that one has become too sedate and boring for this community.

Finally, there is a growing form of age segregation that has not been sought by its residents. This is the community for families with small children. For those who can afford the rising costs of suburban living, new housing tracts frequently contain a high proportion of small children. For the less affluent families, apartment or condominium complexes that will accept small children are becoming less common. In practice, those that do accept children eventually become age ghettos themselves, charging families for the privilege of living with small children. Although such segregated patterns have been challenged in the local courts, no definitive answer has been developed.

What the entire process of separating people by age says about California is intriguing. The concept of the traditional nuclear family appears to be seriously undermined in the state. Although similar changes in living patterns have been observed throughout America, nowhere is it more apparent than in California. All the factors that might suggest explanations of the shift are dominant in the state, including mobility, technology, the sexual revolution, expanded recreation, and economic affluence. If California sets styles for the rest of the nation, here is one style that has moved far ahead of the rest of the country.

The Art of Arty California Burial

The ultimate segregation by age is the cemetery. As might be expected, California has found a way to make the process of death unique, unusual, and stylish. The traditional community cemetery is too tame for this state. Rather, California residents can experience the hereafter surrounded by rose gardens, art galleries, statuary gardens, and serene country meadows created especially for the benefit of the deceased. Price is no object!

The most familiar symbol of the California burial must be Forest Lawn. Planned in the early 1900s, this institution set the pattern that others would follow. Rather than conceding death, Forest Lawn and its descendants created a whole cycle of services ranging from marriage chapels to art galleries to a final place of peace and rest for the weary in "slumber rooms" and grassy knolls. In California, one is not buried in a cemetery, one is enshrined in a garden of memory or a heather on the moor or a lawn of oaks or a garden of devotion. How can anyone view such a prospect with terror, especially with the ever-present sun beaming down?

In a strange way, a funeral becomes a semigala event involving an automobile parade and a final chance to use the products for which one was so strongly encouraged to prepay. By selecting ahead of time, one can choose exactly how to spend eternity. This includes piped-in music for those who expect to be bored. Where else but in California would such a healthy attitude exist?

There may be one sad side to the funeral business, however. It should be noted that memorial gardens are not limited to people. A thriving business in pet cemeteries marks the last word in devotion. Pet owners may buy permanent resting places for their dogs, cats, birds, horses, mice, hamsters, turtles, goats, and other exotic animal friends. With names like Good Shepherd and Pet Haven, these institutions cater to the need to preserve the memories of faithful companions. The graves are frequently decorated with flowers, toys, and trinkets, and are visited regularly by the lonely owners. In a culture dedicated to the pursuit of happiness, it is a sad commentary that many can find true friendship only with a pet or its memory.

California's Salad Bowl Culture

Concerning the background nationality and ethnic makeup of the state, much has changed in the past 20 years. As recently as the 1960 Census, the Anglo population constituted 92 percent of the total in California. By the 1980 Census, that figure had dropped to 67 percent. During this brief period, immigration and birth rate patterns have brought about some significant changes. With the rise in numbers of different ethnic populations, Californians have become much more aware of their many contributions to the total unique culture of the state.

In a state as diverse as California, the number of ethnic groups is large. In terms of total numbers alone, however, certain specific groups have become more influential and obvious in the affairs of the state. The largest single ethnic group is that of the Spanish surname, which includes Mexican-Americans or Chicanos, Cubans, and other Latin Americans. During the 1970s and 1980s, this group has grown even more by a significant influx of undocumented aliens who have crossed the lightly guarded border between the United States and Mexico. The 1980 Census shows this group to have grown by a rate of 60 percent since 1970 (when the total California population grew at a rate of 18.5 percent and the Anglo population at a 5 percent rate).

The Hispanic population tends to be clustered more in certain regions of the state. For the most part, the highest concentrations of Hispanics can be found in the Los Angeles Basin, the San Diego region, and the San Francisco Bay Area. This reflects the greater appeal of the urban areas for Hispanics. The agricultural areas of Imperial County, San Benito County, and the San Joaquin Valley, however, have substantial Hispanic populations that are quite visible and influential in these areas. With its rapid growth rate, this distinctive and proud ethnic group has now come to constitute 19 percent of the total California population.

The 1980 Census reveals that blacks, with 8 percent of the total, make up the second largest minority population in the state. This group has seen an increase of 33 percent over the 1970–1980 period. As with most other ethnic groups, the black population tends to be found in greater numbers in the metropolitan regions such as Los Angeles or Alameda County. Although the traditional source of black immigration to California has been states in the Deep South, this pattern has broadened out somewhat in recent years. With its steady growth in size and influence, the black population is a force to be considered in the future of the state.

The third largest ethnic minority group in California is the Asian populace. This widely defined group includes residents of Chinese, Korean, Japanese, Vietnamese, and other Southeast Asian derivation. The 1980 Census reveals that this is the most dramatically increasing group, with a 10-year growth rate of 140 percent. Although the San Francisco Bay Area, Los Angeles Basin, Orange County, and San Diego County account for significant concentrations, people of Asian background are to be found throughout the state, primarily in urban settings. This consolidated category of Asian ethnic peoples now makes up 5 percent of the state's total population, a cultural force that will have increasing impact.

The last ethnic population of statistically important size in California is that of the American Indian, a group that composes 1 percent of the state's population total. The Indians in California are spread between discrete Indian Trust Lands (reservations) and urban locales. Holding approximately 450,000 acres of land in the state, the Indian population has begun to assert its identity and rights in various legal cases, public forums, and economic actions.

The categories noted here are, of course, overly broad clusters that reflect merely the convenience and needs of the Census Bureau. Subsumed within these categories are many other distinctive ethnic groups. These broad categories do, however, provide a convenient and simplified focus for discussion of the cultural contributions of non-Anglo Californians.

In spite of the fact that until recently the Anglo population exceeded 90 percent of the California total, the cultural identity of the state reflects many influences of non-Anglo culture. One need only look around to see the impact of various ethnic groups on the life of California.

On the most obvious level, the physical landscape of California reflects many ethnic influences. Much of the architecture of the state is a tribute to these sources. The tile roofs, mission-style buildings, hacienda-theme houses and tracts, neo-adobe construction, open patio formats, and similar recreations of the mood of early Mexican California abound. Likewise, Asian influence may be found in modified pagoda-style buildings and houses, in ornamental gardens, and in interior decor. In most major cities in the state, one can find echoes of many cultural styles in the buildings and dwelling places.

Certainly, entertainment patterns in California are influenced by various ethnic contributions. Music, restaurants, and dramatic productions can be found catering to every ethnic taste or desire. Mariachi music in Mexican restaurants vies with Jewish delicatessens around the corner from the Chinese Theater. *Ballet folklórico* vies for patrons with Japanese *kabuki* or soul music festivals. Supermarkets and other stores stock a wide variety of ethnic foods and products, and particular neighborhoods of large cities specialize in uniquely exotic markets. Such specialized neighborhoods are particularly evident in the large metropolitan areas of the state.

Many of the businesses in the state reflect an ethnic character in their development and history. The Japanese and Hispanics have traditionally held key roles in the agriculture of California. The Italian influence is evident in the fishing, banking, and wine industries. Southeast Asians are increasingly seeking a greater role in the fishing industry. American Indians control an important amount of acreage in the state, including parts of Palm Springs. Entertainment and sports reflect the presence of a variety of ethnic cultures, the growth in the popularity of soccer giving evidence to this influence.

The growing impact of California's ethnic populations is also being felt in law, politics, literature, religion, lifestyles, language, and general culture in the state. If current demographic trends continue, California's culture will become even more multiethnic.

A final note should be taken of the impact of general immigration into the state by foreign-born citizens. Historically, the countries that have contributed the greatest share of foreign born are, in descending order: Mexico, Canada, the United Kingdom, Ireland, Italy, Germany, and the U.S.S.R. Indeed, well over 25 percent of California's current total population is foreign born, and the pattern is holding firm. Such a continual influx has provided the dynamic and varied culture that has made California such a fascinating and ever-evolving society.

RECREATION OR ELSE

Although some of the more common forms of entertainment in the state have been discussed earlier, the more active forms have not yet been treated. Sedate, family-style amusements are certainly vital, but Californians shine most when they are actively pursuing physical excitement. Recreation is a monumental business in the state and accounts for millions of hours of leisure as well as millions of dollars of profit.

Spectator Spectacles: There's More Than One Coliseum

Sports are big attractions in the entire state. In fact, California has been called the sports capital of the world. Professional sports, college athletics, high school and community sports programs, and individual participation all are widely popular throughout the state. Several things contribute to this advanced position in the world of sports. Climate permits almost year-round competition and activity. Affluence and mobility make most spectator and participant sports easily accessible to the majority of citizens. Some unique geographical characteristics expand the number of sports and recreation activities available. California can support any activity that desert, mountain, or ocean creates.

On the spectator level, there is much to choose from. The number of stadiums, arenas, speedways, parks, courses, sports areas, and tracks in California is stupendous. Large, medium, and small towns all have their attractions loyally patronized by fans. Professional sports draw wide followings in football, baseball, soccer, auto and boat racing, boxing, bowling, golf, horse racing, hockey, tennis, rodeo, and some lesser sports. Alumni, students, and general public support for amateur athletics makes possible extensive spectator programs at schools, colleges, and universities ranging up and down the state. If spectator sports are your particular love, there is no shortage of choices to fill your needs. In person, by television, radio, or cable transmission, an in-

Figure 9.14 All season long, L.A. fans pack Dodger Stadium. (Los Angeles Dodgers)

Figure 9.15 One of California's favorite activities: camping (King's Canyon National Park). (National Park Service, photo by Richard Frear)

terested Californian can satiate the most eager appetite (Fig. 9.14).

Active Play: Everybody Is a Star

If spectator sports and activities are a passion, participant recreation is a compulsion. In a culture where awareness of the body is a fetish and concern for health has become a religion, active pursuit of play is a necessity. Happily, California can provide almost any recreational experience imaginable.

One broad category of active recreation involves the "cult of the body." This includes those activities that call for displays of the body and awareness of the strenuous exercises needed to keep in shape. Conscious effort is exerted to accomplish the goal of having a desirable and healthy body, and exercise classes, weight lifting, nudism, and other similar activities are directed to this end. The widespread appeal of this approach is evident in the multimillion dollar industry that has sprung up to satisfy these needs. Health clubs, spas, racquet ball courts, and athletic clubs can be found almost any place where busy executives, workers, housewives, and students can slip away to the club for an hour's strenuous workout. It is no coincidence that California is the emotional heartland of Jack LaLanne.

Another form of popular activity utilizes the wealth of natural settings available in the state. Numerous federal and state parks offer the challenges of roughing it in the open air. Hiking, swimming, camping, fishing, boating, and hunting may be pursued in various parks, forests, wilderness areas, deserts, and mountains. One can climb Mount Whitney or explore Death Valley, experience Yosemite National Park or wander through Lava Beds National Monument. Skiing at Mammoth or Tahoe or houseboating on the Sacramento River Delta are still further outdoor experiences. Between the federal and state public lands and waters, the resident or tourist has a wide choice of natural settings to explore and enjoy (Fig. 9.15).

A more common and accessible form of recreation familiar to California is the localized sports activity. Many Californians regularly schedule weekly golf games or tennis matches. Even more can be seen during early morning or late evening in their jogging togs. Neither rain, sun, smog, Thanksgiving, nor Christmas can stop these devotees from doing their daily mile or more. The relative importance of these sports can be assessed easily by comparing the price of golf, tennis, or jogging shoes with normal street wear: One pair of prestige jogging shoes can underwrite a couple of pairs of excellent leather dress shoes! That certainly reinforces the importance attached to the healthy recreational activities pursued by the majority of Californians.

Of course, other forms of active recreation are available. With as many tastes, styles, personalities, and preferences as exist within the state, no one needs to feel ignored. In the area of recreation too, California is a culture of diversity.

10

THE FARM: AGRICULTURAL CALIFORNIA

The most remarkable attributes of the contemporary California cultural landscape are farms and cities. By any measure, be it value, yield, or variety of product, California farm output is unsurpassed among the 50 states. This agricultural dominance derives largely from the productivity of some 12.5 million acres of *prime land*—land having obvious locational and physical advantages such as proximity to city markets and services, relatively level or gentle topography, good drainage, ample water supply, fertile soil, long growing season, optimal microclimatic condition, and minimal development costs.

At the same time, with 24 million people, California claims the nation's largest and most urban population: Nine out of every ten Californians live in cities and towns of 2,500 or more population and are consequently classified as *urban* by the U.S. Bureau of the Census. In the context of spatial expansion, urban California manifests itself in a scattered, hit-and-miss sprawl over the landscape—a housing tract here, a shopping center there, an industrial park somewhere else, and patches of undeveloped land and freeways everywhere. California cities seem to grow in every way imaginable, except compactly.

This *urban sprawl* might not be anything to get too excited about were it not for the fact that it is absorbing copious amounts of a precious and scarce resource: the state's 12.5 million acres of prime agricultural land. Estimates vary wildly, but some place the rate of conversion of prime land from agricultural to urban use at close to 50,000 acres a year. For the reasons just cited and as Figure 10.1 demonstrates, urban development and agriculture generally compete for the same prime land. But in a relatively free land market economy like California's, where urban land uses are considered "highest and best" (actually, most valuable in generating revenue), agriculture almost inevitably loses the competition.

Given the magnitude and geography of both agriculture and urbanization in California, it is little wonder, then, that the conflict between the two is escalating. In fact, the impact of rapid urbanization on land in Cali-

fornia presently devoted to intensive irrigated agriculture may well be the single most significant problem facing the state's natural resource complex. The exceptionally favorable combination of landform, climate, and soil that is responsible for California's intensively cultivated, highly valued agricultural commodities is a limited and high-demand resource not only to the state and the nation, but to the world as a whole. Once the paving of California reaches the point of rendering the state a net importer of food and fiber, then what? The answer is painfully clear: A world already suffering from hunger in too many places will have lost its single most productive agricultural region. Save for the nagging probability of droughts, there is no prime agricultural environment comparable to California's anywhere on earth. It seems unconscionable that this bountiful resource is slowly but surely dwindling away.

So that these complex issues may be better understood, this and the next chapter will examine land utilization on California's farms, in its cities, and in between in the rural-urban fringe.

AGRICULTURAL RECORDS, RESOURCES, AND COMMODITIES

The recordsetting performance of California agriculture over the years can be viewed in a variety of ways. California, with its farms producing $10.4 billion worth of commodities in 1978, was the very first state to surmount the $10 billion plateau in annual gross cash receipts from agriculture. Not only is Iowa or some other Midwestern or Southern state usually a distant second in this regard, but no other state or even region in the United States produces the variety of farm commodities California does.

The physical resource base for the state's national leadership in the production of 46 different commercial crop and livestock commodities is found in an abundance of prime valley flatlands, proximity to the ameliorating influences of the Pacific Ocean, lengthy growing seasons, an extensive latitudinal range of climates, and other environmental amenities discussed in Chapters 3 through

7. Some of the state's agricultural environments are unique to the point of rendering California almost the sole producer in the nation of more than a dozen major crop commodities. Obviously, the conversion of prime land to nonagricultural uses in many of these rare environments is of the utmost concern.

In all, 68 different types of crops are grown in California and yields per acre for many of them are unmatched anywhere else in the world. California annually accounts for about 10 percent of the total value of U.S. agricultural production and by itself exported nearly $3.5 billion worth of food and fiber in 1978 to other states and nations. Agricultural exports each year comprise about one fourth of the state's total value of exports and thus significantly reduce a trade deficit caused by the import of largely nonagricultural products. Agriculture's role as the most valuable primary industry in the state looms all the more prominent when California's position as the seventh largest "nation" in the world in terms of gross national product is brought to mind.

Production costs and thereby net income seem to vary more in farming than in most major California industries. And again, drought appears to impact the situation more than any other environmental, economic, or human influence, although the Mediterranean fruit fly, or Medfly, crisis took precedence in 1981. In the last year of the 1975–1977 drought, for example, production costs soared as a result of expanded well drilling operations and increased investment in irrigation equipment. Consequently, for the first time in many years, net farm income in the state declined slightly. Increased energy, fertilizer, labor, machinery, and pesticide costs also contributed to the 1977 decline. It should be noted here that many fertilizers and pesticides as well as fuels are petroleum based, and thus energy costs as a whole will play a greater part than ever before in determining farm profits and losses. In 1978, however, the rains returned and so did farm profits, registering an estimated $3.06 billion out of $10.4 billion in gross sales. In 1980, California farm commodity sales hit approximately $13 billion, with net income estimated at about $3.5 billion. Although these figures were new highs, increasing production costs caused net farm income to drop about 6 percent from 1979 to 1980.

To talk solely of gross cash receipts and net profits from the sale of farm products is to understate agriculture's broad impact on the California and national economy. As with any other industry, agriculture consumes goods and services from other sectors of the economy as well as supplies them. For instance, when farmers purchase harvesting machinery and have it serviced regularly, their income is added to the income of the suppliers of these capital goods and services, who in turn increase their consumption outlays because of higher income. Thus, a chain reaction of spending and respending, known as the *multiplier effect,* is set off in the form of increased demand for consumer goods and services. Technically, the multiplier effect is defined as the ratio of a change in output to a change in *aggregate demand,* or the total flow of cash expenditures in an economy during a year or other specified time period.

Agricultural economists have worked out quite different multipliers for crop agriculture and livestock agriculture; the two, however, average out to about 2.7:1. If this ratio is applied to the value of agricultural production in 1978 of $10.4 billion, it could then be said that the monetary impact of California agriculture that year was more than $28 billion. Such an estimate is rough at best and should be scrutinized in the light of economic variables such as propensity to consume, propensity to save, and taxation. But however it is expressed for an industry that year after year sets new income and expenditure records, taking into account agriculture's multiplier effect unquestionably presents a more holistic view of its economic impact.

Still another ancillary aspect of agriculture that impacts the state economy is *value added by manufacture* as is created by the multibillion-dollar-a-year food processing industry. Along with aerospace and electronics, food processing shares the manufacturing spotlight and for the most part derives its raw materials from California farms. Although in-state consumption is growing rapidly, the bulk of processed products, like canned and frozen fruits and vegetables, is exported to U.S. and international markets. In the realm of manufacturing employment, the processing industry employed about 10 percent of nearly 2 million California factory workers in 1980.

Other indicators of California's agricultural success are found in a comparison of the number, size, and ownership characteristics of its farms with those of the nation as a whole. The nationwide trend to fewer and larger farms continues unabated, as it has now for decades, but the proportional changes are significantly different for California compared to the rest of the country. Between the 1964 and 1974 censuses of agriculture, the total number of farms in the United States declined 21.7 percent, from 2,165,176 to 1,695,047, whereas California farms declined by only 11.4 percent, from 57,289 to 50,763.[1]

This meant that average individual farm size grew more rapidly in the United States than in California— nearly 20 percent in the U.S. (from 446 acres to 534 acres) versus less than 4 percent in California (from 608 to 632 acres). Thus, it would appear that the relatively large California farm with its economies of large-scale operation is rapidly being emulated throughout the nation.

When farm size is measured in terms of sales rather than acreage, California is again the leader, with nearly 95 percent of its total agricultural output in 1974 coming from the largest farms—those producing $40,000 or more in annual sales. Nationwide the figure was 79 percent. Whether size-by-acreage or size-by-sales criteria are used, it should be remembered that California farms produce a great variety of specialty crops that have relatively high per-acre sales value. Many of the state's fruit, nut, vegetable, and horticultural commodities simply cannot be grown anywhere else in the country, except perhaps in hothouses.

As to what kinds of organizational units control agricultural land and production in California, families

---

[1]A "farm" in this context has annual sales of $2,500 or more. The U.S. Census Bureau's *1978 Census of Agriculture Preliminary Report for California* showed an increase in the number of farms so defined from 50,763 in 1974 to 57,247 in 1978. The amount of land in such farms, however, declined from 32.1 to 31.5 million acres.

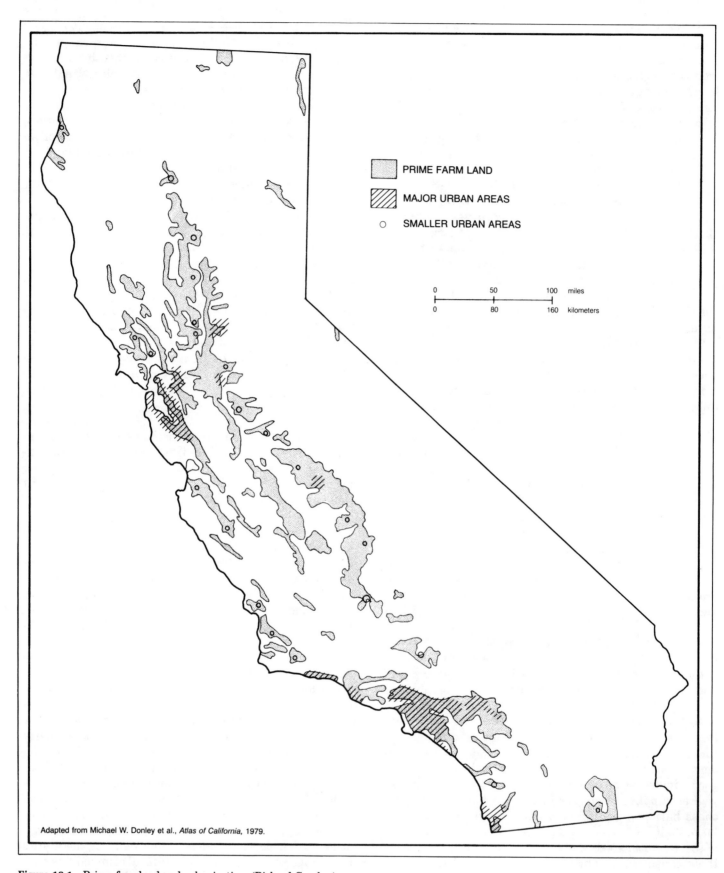

PRIME FARM LAND

MAJOR URBAN AREAS

○ SMALLER URBAN AREAS

| 0 | 50 | 100 | miles |
| 0 | 80 | 160 | kilometers |

Adapted from Michael W. Donley et al., *Atlas of California*, 1979.

Figure 10.1 Prime farmland and urbanization. (Richard Crooker)

were in charge of 58 percent of all the farm acreage and produced 41 percent of all agricultural sales in 1974. A little over half of all California farms are owner operated. These were somewhat below national figures showing family operation of over 75 percent of all farmland and families generating 68 percent of all commodity sales.

Given the advantages of keeping a farm in the family while at the same time limiting financial liability, however, a trend may be developing in California in the direction of more farm families forming limited corporations and partnerships. In 1974, for instance, corporations held 19 percent of the state's farmland and accounted for 36 percent of agricultural sales; partnerships held 22 percent and 23 percent, respectively. Corporate farms obviously produce more income from less land than do farms run by single proprietorship families or partnerships; nevertheless, the family presence in corporate farming in California may be on the increase. Moreover, there is some evidence that multiproduct corporations and even some agribusiness giants are moving out of food and fiber production in California because scarce capital resources can earn better rates of return in nonagricultural sectors of the economy.

The U.S. Supreme Court's June 1980 ruling regarding the quarter section limitation on the use of federal reclamation project water mentioned in Chapter 3 will also have a bearing on farm ownership and production trends. There is no question that corporate farming operations with relatively vast capital resources have outcompeted and thereby contributed to the demise of the small family farm, but this long-standing trend may be weakening.

At the very heart of California agriculture's unprecedented productivity are its human resources, which represent a marshaling of expertise from as far away as Europe and the Orient and from as near as Mexico and the Midwest. In 1980, some 300,000 Californians, or about 2 percent of the total work force, were employed in agricultural pursuits: two thirds as laborers, one fourth as owner-operators and tenant farmers, and the remaining one tenth in managerial and research and development roles.

Much of the field labor force migrates from place to place, depending on what seasonal harvest is at hand. Also, the ranks of the field work force swell considerably with both legally resident green card holders and undocumented alien workers during peak harvest seasons—there would undoubtedly be a serious labor shortfall if these people were not available for this back-breaking form of stoop labor. But passage of the Agricultural Labor Relations Act, increased mechanization, and other events of the last decade are expected to result in an increasingly industrial pattern manifesting itself in the farm labor market in the 1980s. Thus, even though seasonal demands for labor will continue with some crops, farm laborers in general will be more skilled, more steadily employed, and more organized. An unfortunate aspect of this emerging industrial pattern is the increasing displacement of farm workers by farm machinery and the attendant social costs, an issue we shall address again as we next discuss the "what, where, and why" of California's major agricultural commodities.

LIVESTOCK PRODUCTS AND FEED CROPS

Since the dawn of commercial agriculture in California, livestock products have been the state's most valuable farm commodities. Two out of three of California's billion-dollar-a-year commodities, the state's number one and two commodities ranked by value, and one fourth of all the state's agricultural revenues come from two livestock products: beef and milk. In 1978, beef cattle and calves grossed $1.3 billion in sales and milk and cream $1.2 billion. Yet in neither commodity is California a national leader, with those honors going to Texas in beef production and Wisconsin in dairy products output. California's other important livestock products are eggs, averaging nearly a half billion dollars in sales a year, and chickens (fryers and broilers) and turkeys, each grossing about $100 million annually. California does lead the nation in egg production and is usually first or second in turkey raising. Because of a large local population of consumers, isolation from potential markets in the Midwest and East, and perishability, there is little export of any of California's various livestock products.

Livestock production of one sort or another exists in practically every county in the state. More than 4 million head of beef and dairy cattle and some 1.5 million sheep and lambs are likely to be found in California in any one year. This ubiquity owes partly to livestock's and feed crops' greater tolerance of marginal climatic, landform, and soil conditions than is the case with most of California's fruit, nut, and vegetable crops. For instance, Imperial County's hot, dry summers detract little from its being first in the state in feedlot beef cattle production (Fig. 10.2). Likewise, Mono County's rugged Sierras rarely prevent range cattle from finding high country summer pasture (Fig. 10.3). If nothing else, such harsh environments usually do have plenty of nonprime grazing land. Add water, either by importing it via aqueducts or by drilling wells, and almost any habitat becomes suitable for raising livestock.

Although almost every county has sheep, Kern and Imperial claim the largest herds, with 400,000 head between them. Despite the impressive numbers of animals, however, wool and lamb are not among California's more important farm commodities.

Actually, the fact that grains, hays, and other feeds are grown in all but a handful of counties in the state is the real secret to the widespread success of the livestock industry. Figure 10.4 illustrates the strong spatial ties between feed crop growing and livestock raising in the state. It's no accident, for example, that Imperial and Kern counties are first and second in alfalfa acreage, with more than 100,000 acres each, and first and third in the number of feedlot cattle, with 700,000 and 165,000 head, respectively, in an average year.

Another case in point is the concentration of dairy farming in Riverside and San Bernardino counties, where feeds are major local cash crops. Inclusion within the greater Los Angeles metropolitan area market has also contributed to San Bernardino's position as the leading milk-producing county by value in the United States. In 1978, for example, the county grossed $220 million in sales of milk products. With a higher risk or perish-

Figure 10.2 Feedlot cattle and what they feed on are the leading farm revenue producers in several counties. In 1980, the leading commodities in Imperial County, for example, were cattle ($189 million), alfalfa ($161 million), cotton lint ($100 million), wheat ($61 million), and sugar beets ($55 million), these five accounting for 75 percent of gross farm income in the county. (California Cattleman, photo by Phil Raynard)

A

B

Figure 10.3 Range cattle (A) and sheep (B) in Mono County. (Crane Miller)

ability in the transport of fresh milk and cream, the dairy industry tends to be more market oriented in location than the beef industry. Although some final feedlot fattening or *finishing* of cattle near slaughterhouses in the Bay Area and Los Angeles County does occur, it is not nearly as extensive as in Midwestern cities.

The egg industry appears to favor metropolitan fringe production sites as well, with about one third ($130 million in 1978) of the entire state output of laying hens coming from Riverside and San Bernardino counties alone. Even so, chicken, turkey, sheep, and a good share of the state's dairy and beef production are concentrated in a dozen or so Central Valley counties, primarily because of abundances of locally grown feeds and irrigated pasturelands.

Alfalfa, other hays, barley, field corn, sorghum, and several other field crops comprise a raw materials base for the livestock industry that covers nearly one half of all the cultivated land in California. In national com-

modity rankings by value, California is either first or second each year in hay production and second only to North Dakota in barley production. Although droughts diminish production, downpours wipe out whole crops, and inflation does its part, hay and barley annually bring in $600 million and $150 million, respectively. At these rates, hay ranks as the second most valuable crop in the state and barley about thirteenth. Nearly 90 percent of the state's annual barley crop is fed to livestock, with the remaining 10 percent being used in the brewing of beer and other malt products.

Corn, most of which is used directly as grain feed or stored green as *silage* for later use as fodder, annually grosses nearly $100 million and thereby ranks nineteenth or twentieth in value among California crops. Were California ever to give Iowa, Illinois, Indiana, and Minnesota a run for their money in hog production, corn would rank higher in the state. Sorghum, a canelike tropical grass providing both fodder and molasses for

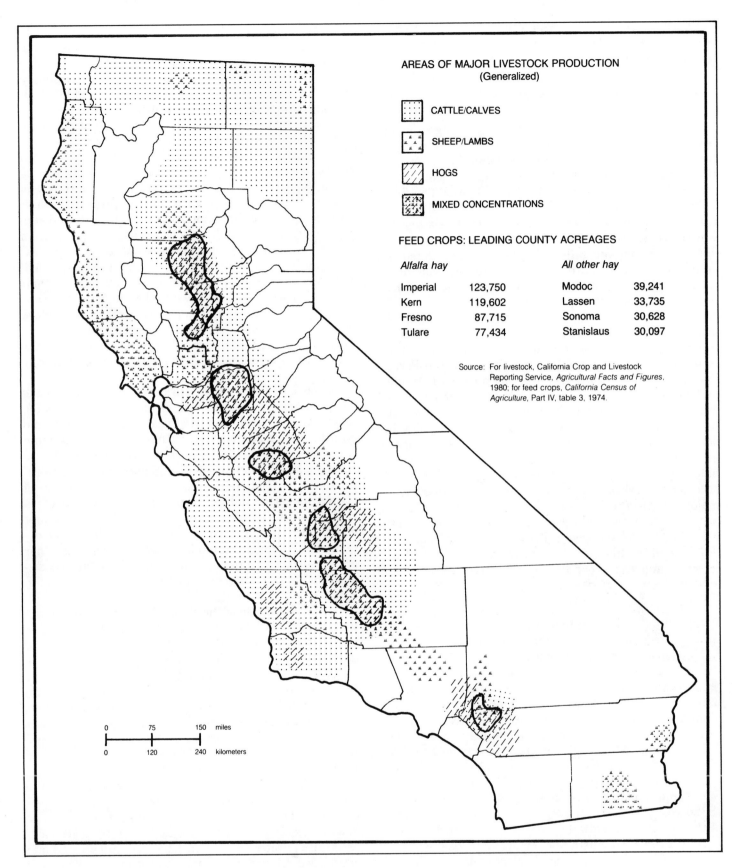

Figure 10.4 Feed crops and livestock production. (Richard Crooker)

livestock, is gaining favor as a feed crop, but California is still far behind Texas, Nebraska, Kansas, and Oklahoma as a ranking grower.

FOOD AND FIBER FIELD CROPS

Field crops, by definition, occupy vast acreages, yield best when irrigated, are generally sown and harvested by machine, and in California include all the aforementioned feed crops plus cotton, wheat, sugar beets, rice, Irish potatoes, dry field beans, and safflower. The first five of these crops each gross more than $100 million in sales yearly and are ranked among the state's top 20 commodities. Cotton, in fact, is California's most valuable crop and the only billion-dollar-a-year crop. As such, cotton is the state's third ranking agricultural commodity behind beef and milk. Nationally, California is second only to Texas in cotton production.

Sugar beets and rice also loom large in the national picture, with California sometimes ranking first in year-to-year production of both commodities. In the growing of Irish potatoes, originally domesticated in the Peruvian Andes, California vies for second place with Maine and Washington while Idaho leads the nation in production. A century ago, California was the leading wheat producer and flour exporter in the nation, but today it does well to place in the top 10 states each year. Higher yielding and more remunerative by the acre, irrigated field crops such as alfalfa, cotton, and rice have simply outcompeted wheat for prime acreage. The state's two major cereal grains, wheat and barley, continue to be *rainfed* (dry farmed), however, and between them occupy 1.5 million acres mapped in Figures 10.4 and 10.5. Safflower, a thistlelike herb that yields both a low cholesterol oil and red dyestuffs, is currently very popular among dieters.

Cotton: King of the San Joaquin

A unique interaction of natural and human forces in the San Joaquin Valley has promoted the rise of cotton as king of California crops. As mapped in Figure 10.5, cotton growing is limited almost exclusively to the southern San Joaquin Valley, which accounts for about 90 percent of total state production. Fresno, Kern, and Kings counties (the leaders in that order) alone contain 800,000 acres of cotton, whereas Imperial and Riverside counties together have only one tenth that acreage.

Four facets of the physical geography of the southern San Joaquin Valley have contributed immeasurably to the success of cotton in the region: (1) This southern part of the valley is essentially a basin of interior drainage in which the Buenavista and Tulare Lake basins (Fig. 10.5 and Chapter 3) have acted for millennia as sumps for the Kern, Kings, and other Sierran rivers and in the process collected a wealth of rich, loamy soils. (2) Local surface runoff and groundwater resources (Chapter 5) are adequate in meeting irrigation demands, except in times of severe drought. (3) The dry summer, subtropical climate of the region (Chapter 4) allows both a long growing season and a rainless harvest period. (4) There was and still is relative freedom from the boll weevil and other pests.

Human ingenuity has added the final touch to modification of the natural landscape, resulting in an optimal environment for growing cotton. The initial reshaping of the land began a century ago with the building of levees by local farmers to reclaim the primeval lakebeds for agriculture. Starting in the 1930s, the federal government stepped in, first with the Bureau of Reclamation's building of the Friant-Kern irrigation canal into the region as part of the Central Valley Project (Chapter 5) and later with the Army Corps of Engineers' damming of the Kings (Pine Flat Reservoir) and Kern (Lake Isabella) rivers for purposes of flood control and water storage. The reservoirs and the Friant-Kern Canal supply thousands of small cotton farmers with irrigation water, but again the big growers had to lobby an exemption from the 160-acre limitation on the use of federal reclamation project water or sell off most of their acreage in order to come down to the limit. Despite such government help or hindrance, privately inspired flood control work continues, as witnessed during the 1969 floods when one large farming firm lined a Tulare Lake levee with several thousand wrecked cars to keep it from being washed away.

Cotton cultivation and marketing date back to the early history of California. Originally domesticated hundreds, if not thousands, of years ago in Central and South America and perhaps in India as well, *Gossypium* was introduced to Alta California in the eighteenth century by Franciscan padres with plantings at several mission sites. But commercial cultivation and export of California cotton did not begin until the Civil War period, when the state government offered prizes for first crops. Once the Confederacy rejoined the Union, the demand for California cotton diminished. Worse yet, other crops proved more remunerative and cotton all but disappeared from California until well into the twentieth century.

With reclamation of the Tulare lakebed already under way, the 1920s saw a resurgence of cotton growing in the southern San Joaquin Valley that persists to this day. Development of the Acala variety of upland cotton, which annually yields half a ton or more an acre in the lakebed *loams* (sand and clay soils high in organic content) and dry, warm climate of the San Joaquin Valley, was another factor in cotton's revival. Acala cotton bolls take well to machine harvesting, and it is said that since the 1950s mechanization in the cotton fields has resulted in the elimination of some 100,000 pickers' jobs.

Cotton *ginning,* or separation of the lint fiber from the seed, takes place in nearby towns such as Tulare and Corcoran. The lint is then baled and sent on its way to distant textile manufacturing centers in the southeastern United States and Japan. The seeds are pressed into cottonseed oil and meal that appeal to a multitude of buyers ranging from paint manufacturers to feedlot operators. Obviously, raw cotton leads all other field crops in value of export. (Rice is the only other significant export among California field commodities.)

Although the state's cotton may find its way back to the garment manufacturing district in downtown Los Angeles or yard goods outlets throughout California, its conversion to textiles within the state has been preempted by lack of any longstanding textile manufacturing tra-

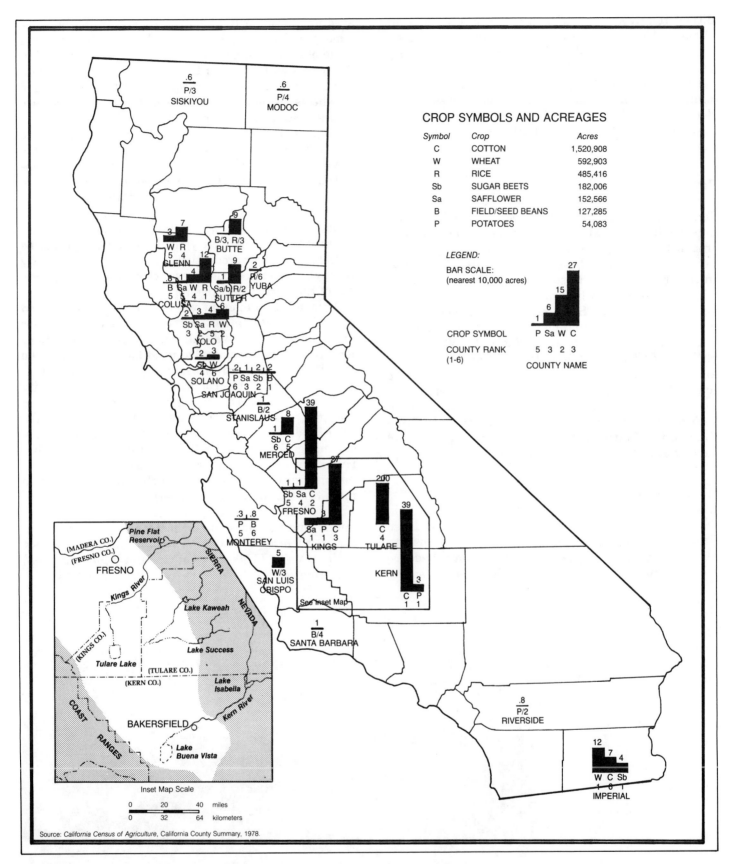

Figure 10.5 Food and fiber field crops. (Richard Crooker)

dition, relatively high industrial labor costs, and dry climate. Along the Carolinas' Fall Line, on the other hand, where Atlantic-bound streams fall from the Appalachians onto the Piedmont, hydropower is always readily at hand and high humidity facilitates the spinning and looming of fabrics such as cotton sheeting and denim. Nevertheless, California fed a virtual flood of raw material to the jeans and urban cowboy fads of the early 1980s.

Rotation Crops

Land producing cotton for too long becomes tired land. To restore moisture, nitrogen, and other soil constituents, fertilizers may be applied and/or alfalfa, barley, or Irish potatoes may be rotated with cotton. Alfalfa, a cloverlike member of the bean family, is especially effective in restoring nitrogen to soil through *nitrogen fixation,* which occurs in soil when one crop replenishes nitrogen depleted by another. Since neither plants nor animals can assimilate atmospheric nitrogen directly, microorganisms do the fixating (Fig. 10.6). When grown on irrigated land, alfalfa yields additional benefits by allowing several crops in a year versus only one crop under dry farming. The advantages of such crop rotations notwithstanding, the demand for California cotton is so great that if federal cotton acreage limitations were lifted, cotton cultivation would in all likelihood spread rapidly at the expense of alfalfa and other field crops.

Rice: Automation in the Sacramento

Driving north out of the state capital on either California 99 or I-5 in the summertime, you can see flooded rice fields stretching out seemingly forever. What you are not likely to see are people tending those paddies, whether during the summer growing season, spring seeding season, or fall harvest. To be certain, there are times when a few workers are on the scene, but in spring some of them will be aloft flying seeding planes and in fall others will be nearer the ground driving *grain combines*—machine harvesters equipped with tracks instead of wheels so they can operate in the mud of recently drained rice paddies (Fig. 10.7).

Contrast this rice-growing landscape with one in the Far East, where the paddies will be teeming with people sowing and later harvesting the crop. The unseen feature of this comparison is the difference in annual per-acre yields of rice: nearly 6,500 pounds in California, but less than 2,400 pounds in Asia. In this country, Arkansas usually leads California in total production but is well behind in annual per-acre yield. Both states export some 60 percent of their production to Asia, California mostly through growers' cooperatives such as those that operate out of the Port of Sacramento.

Although cold-tolerant varieties of *Oryza sativa* had to be developed to allow for the possibility of an earlier and cooler than normal fall, environmental conditions for rice culture are closest to ideal for California in the middle Sacramento River basin centering on Butte, Colusa, Glenn, and Sutter counties. Much of the four-county area is covered with dense, clayey soils and impermeable hardpan, which allows the land to hold water for months after flooding. Evaporation exacts its toll during the dry summer growing season, but the Sacramento and Feather rivers, with the help of state and federal water redistribution projects (Chapter 5), supply sufficient water to maintain the continuous submergence of soil needed in rice production. On the other hand, the low relative humidity and heat of summer hastens the maturation of the crop. For these and other reasons, about 70 percent of the state's 475,000 acres of riceland is found in these four counties.

Figure 10.6 In this photo of *intercropping* (two or more different crops growing simultaneously) on the Oxnard Plain, a lima bean crop is hosting soil nitrogen replenished for a lemon grove. (Crane Miller)

Figure 10.7 Rice fields in Sutter County with Sutter Buttes in the background. Soil parent materials weathered from these volcanic plugs and tightly folded sedimentary formations surrounding the Buttes have contributed to the area's agricultural capabilities. Traps in the sedimentary rocks also hold one of California's large working natural gas fields (see Chapter 3). (Crane Miller)

VEGETABLES, CITRUS, AND AVOCADOS

Name a vegetable, any vegetable, and no doubt it is grown in California. The same can be said for most varieties of citrus *(Citrus)*, avocados *(Persea)*, berries, and deciduous fruit and nut crops. Specifically, California produces more than two dozen different vegetable commodities and leads the nation in the output of artichokes, asparagus, broccoli, Brussels sprouts, carrots, cauliflower, celery, chili peppers, garlic, lettuce, lima beans (Fig. 10.6), onions, Oriental (Chinese) peas and other exotic vegetables, spinach, and tomatoes. In all, *truck crops* or vegetables alone account for about one fifth ($2.01 billion in 1978) of California's annual farm revenue. Even more impressive is California's one-third share of the nation's total vegetable production.

In tropical evergreen tree crops, California is the nation's leading producer of avocados, lemons, and olives but is a distant second to Florida in orange production: The state grows some 20 percent of the country's oranges while Florida boasts 70 percent of national output. Grapefruit, tangelos, and tangerines also number among California's commercial citrus commodities.

Although Figure 10.8 demonstrates the vegetable industry's geographic versatility, many types of produce prefer the mild temperatures and moist air of locations near the ocean, as the case study of Ventura County that follows demonstrates.

Ventura County: California's Fruit and Vegetable Industry in Microcosm

Ventura County offers a unique environment for agriculture, one that may seem common in California but that is altogether too rare on the face of the earth. Few regions anywhere encompass the combination of self-contained mountainous watershed, intermont basins, broad coastal plain, advantageously situated stream and groundwater systems, mild Mediterranean climate, and abundance of deep and fertile lowland alluvial soils that characterize Ventura County. As shown in Figures 10.9 through 10.13, this natural assemblage presents farmers with nearly limitless opportunities for intensive growing of a great diversity of high-value crops.

Long before the turn of the century, when Henry Oxnard established the nation's first permanent sugar beet industry in the county, Ventura was widely recognized for its inherent agricultural potential. Today, that potential has developed to the point that Ventura County mirrors the whole of California agriculture to a greater extent than any other single county. In all, Ventura County farmers produce seven different livestock commodities, six kinds of fruit and nut crops, a dozen major vegetable commodities, fourteen minor vegetable types, seven different field crop types, cut flowers and nursery stock, and apiary products consisting of honey and beeswax. Although several counties far exceed Ventura County's $500 million in annual farm products sales, the county claims leadership in the state and the nation in growing cabbage, green lima beans, lemons, Romaine lettuce, and spinach, and second place in bell peppers, celery, and avocados.

Lemons, which at $100 million in average annual sales are the county's most valuable commodity, find environmental conditions in Ventura County that exist in few other regions of like size in North America. A comparison of the physical geography of Ventura County (see Figs. 10.9 through 10.12) with the distribution of

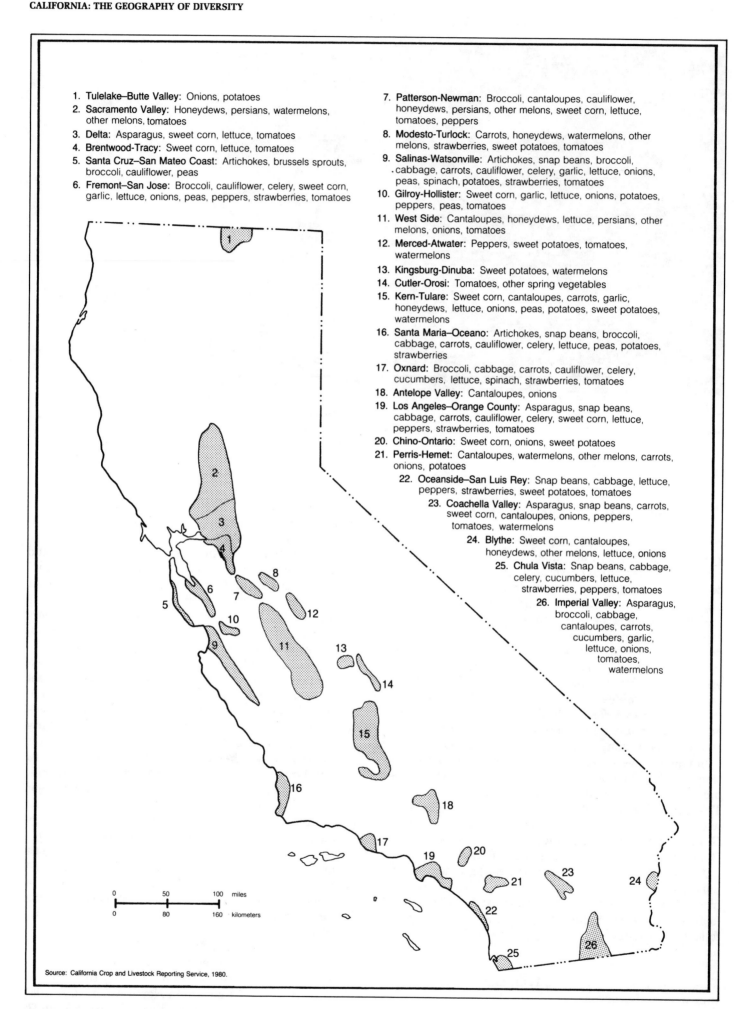

1. **Tulelake–Butte Valley:** Onions, potatoes
2. **Sacramento Valley:** Honeydews, persians, watermelons, other melons, tomatoes
3. **Delta:** Asparagus, sweet corn, lettuce, tomatoes
4. **Brentwood-Tracy:** Sweet corn, lettuce, tomatoes
5. **Santa Cruz–San Mateo Coast:** Artichokes, brussels sprouts, broccoli, cauliflower, peas
6. **Fremont–San Jose:** Broccoli, cauliflower, celery, sweet corn, garlic, lettuce, onions, peas, peppers, strawberries, tomatoes
7. **Patterson-Newman:** Broccoli, cantaloupes, cauliflower, honeydews, persians, other melons, sweet corn, lettuce, tomatoes, peppers
8. **Modesto-Turlock:** Carrots, honeydews, watermelons, other melons, strawberries, sweet potatoes, tomatoes
9. **Salinas-Watsonville:** Artichokes, snap beans, broccoli, cabbage, carrots, cauliflower, celery, garlic, lettuce, onions, peas, spinach, potatoes, strawberries, tomatoes
10. **Gilroy-Hollister:** Sweet corn, garlic, lettuce, onions, potatoes, peppers, peas, tomatoes
11. **West Side:** Cantaloupes, honeydews, lettuce, persians, other melons, onions, tomatoes
12. **Merced-Atwater:** Peppers, sweet potatoes, tomatoes, watermelons
13. **Kingsburg-Dinuba:** Sweet potatoes, watermelons
14. **Cutler-Orosi:** Tomatoes, other spring vegetables
15. **Kern-Tulare:** Sweet corn, cantaloupes, carrots, garlic, honeydews, lettuce, onions, peas, potatoes, sweet potatoes, watermelons
16. **Santa Maria–Oceano:** Artichokes, snap beans, broccoli, cabbage, carrots, cauliflower, celery, lettuce, peas, potatoes, strawberries
17. **Oxnard:** Broccoli, cabbage, carrots, cauliflower, celery, cucumbers, lettuce, spinach, strawberries, tomatoes
18. **Antelope Valley:** Cantaloupes, onions
19. **Los Angeles–Orange County:** Asparagus, snap beans, cabbage, carrots, cauliflower, celery, sweet corn, lettuce, peppers, strawberries, tomatoes
20. **Chino-Ontario:** Sweet corn, onions, sweet potatoes
21. **Perris-Hemet:** Cantaloupes, watermelons, other melons, carrots, onions, potatoes
22. **Oceanside–San Luis Rey:** Snap beans, cabbage, lettuce, peppers, strawberries, sweet potatoes, tomatoes
23. **Coachella Valley:** Asparagus, snap beans, carrots, sweet corn, cantaloupes, onions, peppers, tomatoes, watermelons
24. **Blythe:** Sweet corn, cantaloupes, honeydews, other melons, lettuce, onions
25. **Chula Vista:** Snap beans, cabbage, celery, cucumbers, lettuce, strawberries, peppers, tomatoes
26. **Imperial Valley:** Asparagus, broccoli, cabbage, cantaloupes, carrots, cucumbers, garlic, lettuce, onions, tomatoes, watermelons

Source: California Crop and Livestock Reporting Service, 1980.

Figure 10.8 Major vegetable, melon, and potato-growing regions. (Richard Crooker)

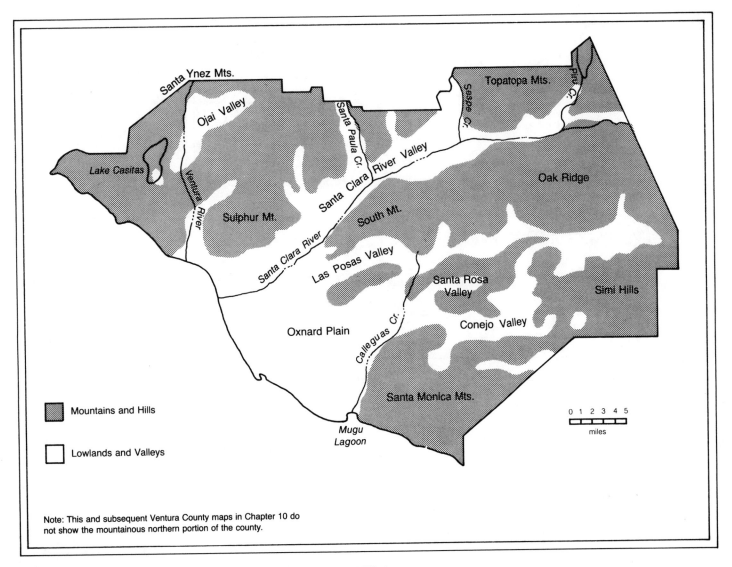

Figure 10.9 Ventura County, landforms and hydrography. (Whitney Miller)

lemon growing in the county seen in Figure 10.13 reveals some of the critical relationships between the commodity and its environment.

Equally significant in understanding the where and why of the success of lemons in Ventura County is a knowledge of their unique climatic tolerances. Since lemons are the least frost-tolerant citrus fruit, most of the acreage is concentrated in the Oxnard Plain and lower Santa Clara River Valley (Fig. 10.9), where a nearly year-round growing season is the rule (Fig. 10.10).

Other aspects of the marine climate conducive to lemon production, especially of the Eureka variety pictured in Figure 10.14, include: (1) higher relative humidity, which promotes a thicker rind yet a fruit that is juicier and more readily squeezed; (2) greater exposure to cooling summer sea breezes, which delay maturity by preventing excessively high temperatures; (3) cooler summer temperatures, which often obviate the use of refrigeration in lemon warehouses; and (4) comparative freedom from wind damage, notably during the fall months when dessicating east winds or Santa Anas often wreak havoc on citrus and other tree crops deeper in the interior of Southern California. The dry winds not only blow down trees and "burn" their fruit but also dry out soil, which necessitates more irrigation, and dehydrate

leaves, which reduces photosynthesis. North-south oriented cypress and eucalyptus windbreaks protect lemon groves from the Santa Ana that occasionally reaches the coast and the brisk onshore winds that often follow winter frontal passages.

Higher humidity and soil moisture on the coastal plain do increase the chance of fungus disease occurring in lemons; fungicides and artificial soil drainage, however, have largely alleviated this problem. Some lemon groves are found in the interior valleys of Ventura County, but only on higher alluvial slopes where there is less likelihood of cold air ponding (Chapter 4) than in valley bottoms. Even in these upslope *thermal belts,* wind machines and orchard heaters (Fig. 10.15) are on hand to break up unusually deep accumulations of dense, freezing air. This phenomenon, which occurs during subfreezing winter nights when there is little or no circulation in the local atmosphere, is known as *cold air ponding* or *drainage.* Meanwhile, temperatures are warmer upslope, creating a classic case of *temperature inversion,* as explained in Chapter 4.

Lemon and other citrus trees generally bear their first fruit four to six years after initial planting as a seedling. Once they have reached bearing age, most varieties of lemon trees will produce fruit the year around. Harvesting of the Eureka variety, however, usually occurs

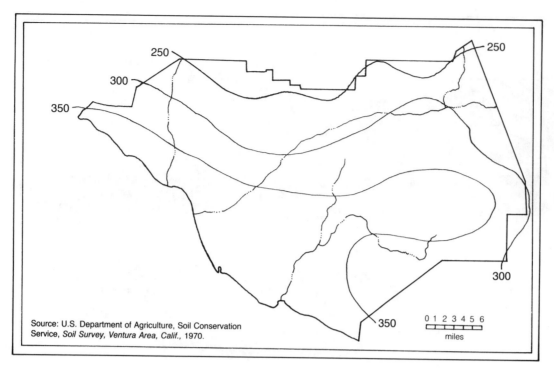

Figure 10.10 Ventura County, average length of growing season (in days). (Whitney Miller)

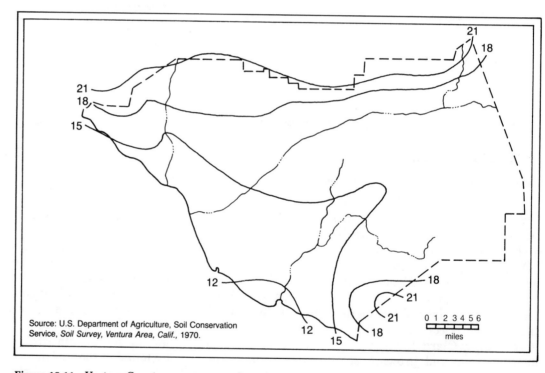

Figure 10.11 Ventura County, average annual precipitation (in inches). (Whitney Miller)

in spring and summer when the demand for fresh and frozen lemonade is greatest. Even lemon by-products, such as oils from the rinds that are used as fragrance bases in everything from furniture polish to shampoo, peak in demand during the warm season.[2] Nevertheless, the ability of the trees to bear throughout the year has strengthened the county's hold on the national market. With a near-national monopoly in production, the Ventura County lemon industry rarely feels the deleterious effects of competitive price bidding.

[2]Frozen lemonade and all the by-products can be stored indefinitely; hence summer peaks are of no real consequence. Since lemons cure for two weeks to six months, marketing time can be easily adjusted.

The high price of fresh lemons in the supermarket reflects the relatively high per-acre value of the crop back on the farm. In 1978, for instance, a bearing acre of lemons produced $4,650 worth of the citrus. When compared to the harvest value per acre in the same year of avocados at $2,215 (Fig. 10.16), grapefruit at $2,155, oranges at $3,150, and walnuts at $410, it is easy to see why growers prefer lemons over other tree crops. Again, given what is tantamount to a national production monopoly and consistently high demand in the marketplace, Ventura County lemon growers can just about name their price. Only strawberries (Fig. 10.17), which generated nearly $9,500 an acre in 1978, are more re-

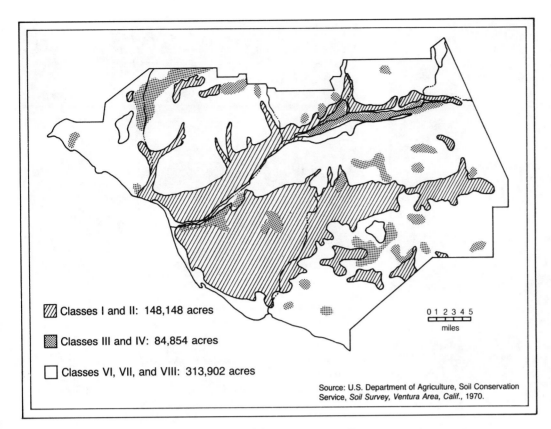

Classes I and II: 148,148 acres

Classes III and IV: 84,854 acres

Classes VI, VII, and VIII: 313,902 acres

Source: U.S. Department of Agriculture, Soil Conservation Service, *Soil Survey, Ventura Area, Calif.,* 1970.

Figure 10.12 Ventura County, soil capability classes. (Whitney Miller)

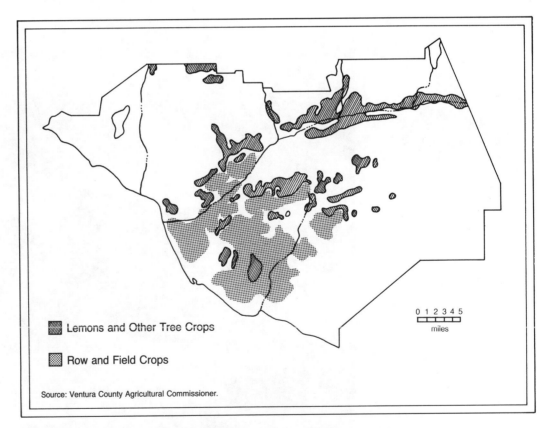

Lemons and Other Tree Crops

Row and Field Crops

Source: Ventura County Agricultural Commissioner.

Figure 10.13 Ventura County, crop distribution. (Whitney Miller)

Figure 10.14 Lemons are first in value among all farm commodities in Ventura County ($122 million out of $484 million total, including livestock, in 1980), and Ventura County is first in lemons among all producing counties in the nation. The all-year-bearing Eureka variety is grown on 19,000 acres in the county, whereas the more frost-resistant Lisbon variety is farmed on only 6,000 acres. Lisbons usually ripen in fall but sometimes can be harvested in other seasons. (A: Sunkist Growers, Inc.; B: Roger M. Rhiner)

Figure 10.15 Wind machines and orchard heaters (smudge pots) diminish frost damage in citrus and avocado groves by dissipating cold air that by its very weight or density (relatively high air pressure) drains downslope into valley bottoms. The upslope location is obviously a favorite planting site of citrus and avocado growers. (Sunkist Growers, Inc.)

Figure 10.16 Avocados, originally domesticated in southern Mexico and Guatemala, have found an ecological niche in Southern California, especially in the Fallbrook area of San Diego County—the number one county in national production with 15,000 acres of bearing trees. La Habra Heights in southeastern Los Angeles County, the Santa Clara River Valley in Ventura County, coastal Santa Barbara County, and thermal belts in San Luis Obispo, Kern, Tulare, Fresno, Orange, Riverside, and San Bernardino counties account for the balance of California avocado production (on 13,000 acres). The Fuerte (strong) avocado is a hybrid of Guatemalan and Mexican varieties; it ripens in winter and is considered the best-tasting California variety. The summer-ripening Hass, a Guatemalan variety, is a tasty competitor of the Fuerte. Besides the Fuerte and the Hass, several other varieties ripen in spring and fall, thereby assuring year-round California avocado production. (California Avocado Commission, photo by Richard Conley)

Figure 10.17 Strawberry fields here on the Oxnard Plain and elsewhere are covered with plastic before the crop is planted so that the soil can be fumigated to rid it of organisms harmful to strawberry plant roots. The polyethylene tarp also fosters plant growth with its greenhouse effect and cuts down on the loss of soil moisture. Early spring and early summer are the prime planting and harvesting (by hand) seasons, respectively. Given the high value of production by the acre, strawberry land forestalls impending urban development better than most other types of cropland and thereby is often seen as the sole surviving form of agriculture in suburbia. (Crane Miller)

munerative by the acre than lemons among all the county's fruit and nut crops.

While citrus production occurs both on the Oxnard Plain and in the interior valleys, vegetable or row crops (Fig. 10.18) are restricted essentially to the coastal plain, where they enjoy the best soils the Ventura County environment has to offer. For 10,000 years, the Santa Clara River has transported alluvium eroded from the mountainous northeast and deposited it to depths of several hundred feet over the Oxnard Plain. Together with other soil-forming agents, the recent alluvium provides the basis for the rich 5-foot deep loamy sands and silty clay loams that presently make up almost 100 percent of the area under irrigation on the plain. When these soils are machine leveled, graded, and furrowed for irrigation, there is minimal loss of fertility because of their inherent organic content, great depth, lack of profile, effective moisture retention, and loamy texture. Few soils anywhere in the world possess this ready adaptability to machine cultivation.

Beside helping accumulate most of the county's prime soils in the Oxnard Plain (Fig. 10.12), the Santa Clara River acts as a vehicle for the supply of nearly all of the plain's groundwater. Most of the normal runoff from the mountains percolates into subsurface water-bearing sediments in the stream course and then flows by gravity down to the permeable alluvial beds of a broad *aquifer* (Chapter 5) that underlies the entire Oxnard Plain. The pumping of confined groundwater from this and deeper aquifers has fostered the expansion of irrigation agriculture to all parts of the plain over the last half century.

Add to a dependable supply of well water a year-round growing season (Fig. 10.10) and plenty of dry season fog, and optimal conditions for growing just about any kind of vegetable are found to exist. Advection fog, commonly caused by the upwelling of cold ocean water and the presence of the cold California Current (Chapter 4), ex-

tends inland for 2 to 5 miles along the Oxnard Plain throughout many a spring and summer day. In effect, the fog acts as a surrogate source of moisture for plants at a time when rainfall does not normally occur. This overcast condition is vital to the growing of summer vegetable crops requiring high atmospheric humidity and restricted sunlight. On the other hand, constant fog works to the detriment of most tree crops in that it promotes fungus and retards growth. Lemons, though, are more fog tolerant than are other citrus and avocados.

Of the some two dozen different vegetable crops grown on the Oxnard Plain, celery and tomatoes are by far the most valuable. Celery sales average more than $60 million a year and tomatoes annually bring in about $20 million. In per-acre value, celery topped the vegetable list in 1978 at $7,075 and cucumbers finished second with $4,185. Tomatoes, as well as broccoli, cabbage, cauliflower, and peppers, each gross about $3,000 an acre in an average year.

Celery and green cabbage are Ventura County's principal winter vegetables and as such are marketed largely in the eastern United States and Canada at a time when supply and demand are at a maximum. An extended dry period from late spring through fall allows for celery transplants to be set out before the first heavy rains. Celery matures rapidly once the wet season arrives, with the harvest often starting before winter and sometimes extending into early summer. To thwart the spread of celery blight by leaf hoppers, celery land is taken out of production for at least three weeks in mid-summer. In the interim, quick-maturing rotation crops such as tomatoes, lettuce, and cabbage are grown. Obviously, rotation by double- or sometimes even triple-cropping makes Oxnard Plain vegetable land all the more valuable.

Given the rotation and marked seasonality of row crops in general, it is not surprising to find that much of the vegetable land in the Oxnard Plain is operated by

Figure 10.18 Row crops on rented land in the Oxnard Plain. Vegetables, in this case string beans, are planted literally in rows with irrigation furrows plowed in-between. Since investment in row crops is remunerated sooner, more quickly, and more regularly than investment in tree crops, row crop land often is rented or leased on a short-term basis by growers. For a long-term income producer and tax shelter, tree crop land seems a better bet. (Crane Miller)

tenant farmers or on short-term leases (Fig. 10.18). On the opposite side of the coin is tree cropland, which represents investment in growing a single crop commodity over many years. Consequently, orchard land is mostly owner-operated.

Tomato Technology, or People versus Machines

The tomato *(Lycopersicon)* is not a vegetable; it is a large, seedy berry that comes in two commercial varieties: (1) the hand-harvested fresh market or *pole tomato,* and (2) the machine-harvested vine or *cannery tomato,* seen being sorted by flotation in Figure 10.19. The latter is one of several California fruit and vegetable commodities at the center of a storm of controversy over mechanization technology and its displacement of farm workers. On one side are growers and University of California (UC) agricultural researchers whose aim is to increase production while lowering costs. On the other are the farmworkers and their collective voice, the United Farm Workers (UFW), who see mechanization permanently forcing more than 100,000 farm workers out of jobs and actually raising consumer prices.

There is no question that in the last 20 years machines have all but eliminated human hands in the canning tomato harvest. From 1962 to 1972, during which time the Blackwelder tomato harvester was developed and put into operation, the number of harvest workers fell from 50,000 to 18,000. Significant expansion of cannery tomato acreage thereafter temporarily reversed the downtrend by adding nearly 10,000 to the work force by 1976. But since then, UC's labor-saving electronic-eye sorter has been introduced and there are fears that it, coupled with further innovations in machine harvesters, will diminish the number of tomato harvest workers to a scant few thousand during the 1980s, or less than 10 percent of the 1962 labor force. If these displaced farm workers could simply switch to harvesting other crops, there would be no problem. But mechanization has invaded the harvesting of everything from almonds to sugar beets and consequently has fomented the growth of a class of unemployed workers perhaps more unfortunate than any to be found in the nation. Already, for example, there are second generation hamlets of chronic unemployment in the San Joaquin Valley that grew out of the automation of the cotton harvest back in the 1950s and 1960s.

The social costs of a large class of able, working-age people on welfare are sobering to contemplate, whether they are as specific as increases in crime rates or as general as a deterioration of the quality of rural life. But the wrenching away by a machine of one's lifelong occupation and thereby one's dignity seems among the cruelest of setbacks. Machines do free us from toil, but they can also sever us from the only gainful occupation we know. One cannot help wonder, though, if some kind of turnabout might not be in store if fuel prices rise to prohibitive levels. Even now, the energy crunch has forced some cattle ranchers to abandon trucks and jeeps and revert to using horses to carry out roundups. There are those who scoff at using our own two hands or other forms of animate energy as stepping back into the Dark Ages, but what better way is there of conserving inan-

Figure 10.19 Canning, cannery, or processing tomatoes are California's fifth most valuable crop, averaging more than $300 million annually over the last few years. Nationally, tomato processing is a $2-billion-a-year industry, with California garnering 90 percent of the market. The state is the nation's leading grower. Production is centered in Yolo (more than 60,000 acres) and other counties peripheral to the Delta region of the Central Valley. Here tomatoes find the irrigation water and well-drained soils they need. (Crane Miller)

imate energy than by substituting something in its place? On the other hand, a totally automated society might give those of us who could afford it good reason to toil away at the local fat farm.

Another victim of tomato technology is the small farmer. During the onslaught of mechanization from 1962 to 1973, the number of tomato growers declined from some 4,000 to less than 600. Many growers simply could not muster the financial resources to buy a mechanical tomato harvester, which now costs in the neighborhood of $75,000. Small farm operators in general, as well as UFW officials, feel that UC agricultural research monies going into the development of the Blackwelder and other machine harvesters should benefit both small and large growers and their workers, especially since UC is a public, tax-supported institution. Instead, the agribusiness giants stand to gain the most from UC research because they have the dollars and/or credit to buy the latest in equipment. Sadly, comparative lack of capital is rapidly propelling the small farm operator down the road to oblivion.

There is, of course, a bright side to farm mechanization. Dramatic increases in production probably comprise the most impressive array of benefits, at least to consumers. In the 11-year period mentioned earlier, for example, statewide tomato production rose from 3.2 million tons to 6 million tons annually. Consumers would be even more impressed were the rise in food prices diminished by farm mechanization. Unfortunately, this is not always the case. The price of machine-harvested tomatoes, for instance, rose by 111 percent between 1964 and 1975, whereas the price of hand-picked strawberries and lettuce increased only by 41 and 70 percent, respectively, in the same period—though one could argue that if machines had not replaced people and hand pickers' wages had risen sufficiently, the price of cannery tomatoes would have gone up as much or even higher than 111 percent. Also, the state's canning tomato industry might have fled to Mexico were it not for labor-saving machinery.

Another measure of the benefits of farm automation is the gross social rate of return (GSRR), whereby an estimate of the dollar rate of cost reduction in output resulting from the adoption of new technology over time is calculated. In the case of the diffusion of new tomato harvesters from 1965 to 1972 in California, an estimated GSRR of $9.29 per dollar of research and development (R&D) was calculated by UC agricultural economists. Whether or not a net social rate of return (NSRR), which takes into account the social costs of displaced workers, was realized was not indicated in the study. The study did indicate, however, that "it is doubtful that the NSRR to tomato technology would approach zero."[3] If the NSRR just happened to be above zero, the twin goals of improving efficiency and maintaining full employment might be realized. Unfortunately, the social costs of worker displacement are not easily determined and, in any case, the displaced farm laborer all too often comes out with less than zero.

DECIDUOUS TREE CROPS

A certain Southern state advertises on its license plates that it is the "peach state" when, in actuality, California is the leading producer of this deciduous fruit in the nation. In fact, California outproduces any other single state in all major commercial categories of stone or pit fruits except for cherries. Thus, California's dominance in *Prunus* production embraces almonds, apricots, nectarines, plums, and prunes as well as peaches. Rounding out the state's first-place ranking in deciduous tree crops are English walnuts *(Juglans regia)* and pears *(Pyrus communis)*.

Annual farm gate sales of all these fruits and nuts hover around half a billion dollars, with almonds, peaches, and walnuts each regularly exceeding the more than $100 million-a-year mark. Export of these commodities depends on whether they are sold as fresh produce or canned, frozen, or dried, the latter three forms finding markets throughout the United States and Canada. This is especially true with bagged or bottled walnuts, for California grows nearly 100 percent of the North American crop.

A look at Figure 10.20 reveals the preference of deciduous fruit and nut crops for the cooler, more northerly climes of California. Most of these crops were introduced by the Franciscans in the late eighteenth century and prospered reasonably well as far south as Mission San Diego. A hundred years later, Ventura County, still in sunny Southern California, was on its way to becoming the leading apricot and walnut producer. As commercial production began to expand significantly in the mid-twentieth century, however, the focus of almost all new plantings of deciduous fruit and nut trees turned to the San Joaquin and Sacramento valleys. Here in the northern interior, where the winters are longer and colder and the summers hotter and drier than in coastal Southern California, deciduous trees are more likely to lose all their leaves before the cold season has completely passed. With peaches and pears (Fig. 10.21), for example, the lack of chilling that accompanies too mild a winter results in delayed spring foliation, few flower and fruit sets, and eventual death of the trees. Moreover, the dry summer heat of the interior valleys and high deserts encourages sugar or fructose production in the fruits and wards off bacterial blights, viruses, and fungi.

VITICULTURE AND WINEMAKING

California's national prominence in viticulture and winemaking is unrivaled. The state produces 100 percent of the country's raisins, about 95 percent of its table grapes, and some 75 percent of all the wine consumed in the nation, which all adds up to a $600-million-a-year industry utilizing 650,000 acres of vineyard (Fig. 10.22). The majority of the grapes picked each year are crushed at California wineries, the latter in turn producing more than a billion dollars worth of wine, brandy, and brandy spirits annually.[4] Thus, it is in the production of wines and brandies that viticulture ultimately generates the greatest revenues.

Winemaking

The production performance of California winemakers is indeed impressive and warrants a brief review before we delve into the history of the industry. Suffice it here to consider winemaking as it applies to the production of California's finest wines, the *table wines*—so named because they should be served at the dinner table with the day's main meal.

The process starts with the mechanical destemming and crushing (Fig. 10.23) of the fall harvest of grapes, which involves breaking the grape skins but not the seeds. Next, the *must*, or juice and pulp, is conveyed to fermenting vats for the production of red wines—dark-skinned grapes imparting natural color to the wine. If white wine is desired, the juice is separated from the skins before fermentation.

Although grape juice inherently contains ferments or yeasts (*Saccharomyces* spp.), the wild yeasts are inhibited by the addition of sulfur dioxide (SO_2) to the must. The sulfured must is then pumped into a tank and in-

---

[3]Refugio I. Rochin, "Farm Mechanization Research: Assessing the Consequences," *California Agriculture* 32, 8 (August 1978): 8–10. *California Agriculture* is a University of California Division of Agricultural Sciences report on progress in research carried on by the UC Agricultural Experiment Station and Cooperative Extension. NSRR is calculated as follows:

$$NSRR = \frac{GSR - cost\ of\ displaced\ workers \times 100}{R\&D\ costs}$$

[4]With 165 establishments reporting, the *1977 Census of Manufactures for California* gave the following figures for the production of wine, brandy, and brandy spirits for the year: (1) cost of materials: $745.7 million, (2) value added by manufacture: $405.6 million, (3) value of shipments: $1,109.3 million, and (4) new capital expenditures: $43.8 million. Significantly, the most popular table fruit grape variety, the Thompson Seedless or Sultanina, is also the favored raw material among California winemakers. About one third of all the state's wine is made from this seedless grape.

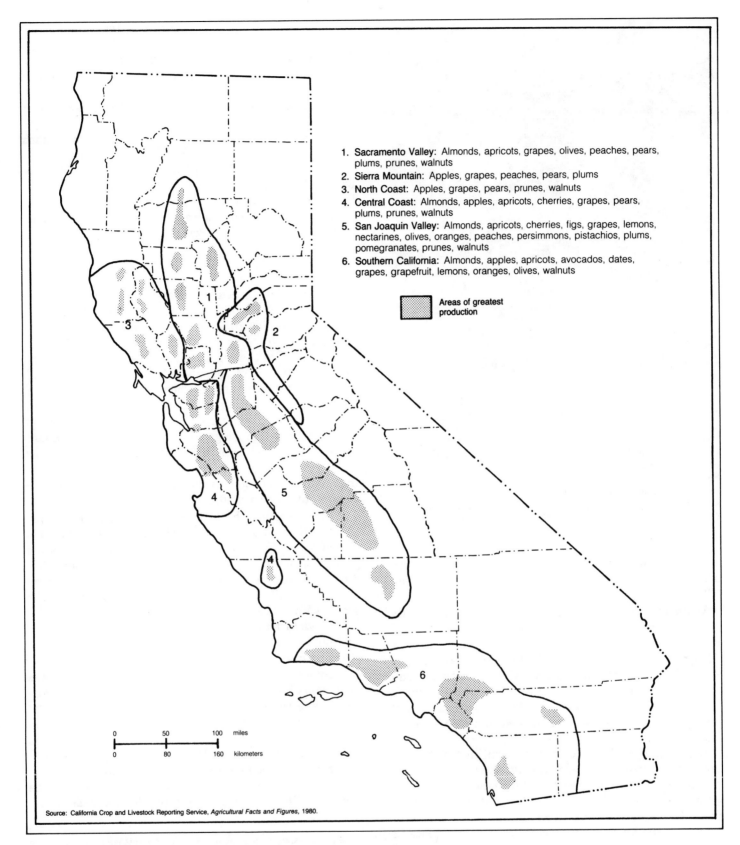

1. **Sacramento Valley:** Almonds, apricots, grapes, olives, peaches, pears, plums, prunes, walnuts
2. **Sierra Mountain:** Apples, grapes, peaches, pears, plums
3. **North Coast:** Apples, grapes, pears, prunes, walnuts
4. **Central Coast:** Almonds, apples, apricots, cherries, grapes, pears, plums, prunes, walnuts
5. **San Joaquin Valley:** Almonds, apricots, cherries, figs, grapes, lemons, nectarines, olives, oranges, peaches, persimmons, pistachios, plums, pomegranates, prunes, walnuts
6. **Southern California:** Almonds, apples, apricots, avocados, dates, grapes, grapefruit, lemons, oranges, olives, walnuts

Areas of greatest production

Source: California Crop and Livestock Reporting Service, *Agricultural Facts and Figures*, 1980.

Figure 10.20 Fruit and nut crops: major producing districts. (Richard Crooker)

Figure 10.21 Lake County Bartletts are said to be the world's best-tasting pears. Bartlett variety production centers in the pear capital community of Kelseyville, located just west of Clear Lake and volcanic Mount Konocti. Windward and lakeside microclimatic conditions and cool winters, as well as rich volcanic soils, no doubt contribute to Kelseyville's prominence in pears. Lake and Sacramento counties, each with some 7,000 bearing acres, are the leaders in the output of all commercial varieties of pears in the state. Other important California varieties include Anjou, Bosc, Comice, and Winter Nelis. (Crane Miller)

oculated with wine yeasts, which, when exposed to air, act to convert grape sugar to alcohol and carbon dioxide (CO_2).

While the temperature of the fermenting mass rapidly rises, the CO_2 escapes into the air and the ethyl alcohol content of the new wine builds to a maximum of about 14 percent. As far as the finished product is concerned, state regulations require that red wines contain between 10.5 and 14 percent alcohol by volume and white wines between 10 and 14 percent. At the prescribed alcohol level, all sugar supply is exhausted and fermentation stops.

Depending on the volume of fermenting must, local air temperatures (the cooler the air, the slower the fermentation), and whether red or white wine is being made (white wine needs more time to ferment than red wine does), fermentation lasts anywhere from two to several weeks on the average. Fermentation can take place in vats made from one of a number of different kinds of material, including redwood, oak, stainless steel, or concrete. Given California's relatively warm and short vintage season (two to three months) in which all the table wine for the year is made, large wineries usually require elaborate cooling systems to keep fermenting musts from exceeding 90°F for red wines and 70°F for white wines.

Following fermentation, the new wine is placed in storage cooperage to be clarified, racked (removal of sediment-freed wine to smaller containers), and aged prior to bottling. Thereafter, some premium table wines may be bottle-aged at the winery for up to two years. Wine, it is said, gains character with time and a fine wine "should not be sold before its time." Even once a fine table wine is ready to be consumed, it should be uncorked and allowed to "breathe" somewhat before dinner: an hour before if it is red wine, and a half-hour before if it is white wine.

Modern wine production as just described owes much to Louis Pasteur and his fellow chemists, who little more than a century ago helped transform the age-old art of winemaking into the science we know today as *enology*. But what was the state of the art and science of *winegrowing*[5] in California more than a century before Pasteur and associates' discoveries?

The Mission Grape

Although native species of grapes had grown wild for millennia in California and perhaps even been pressed into wine by aboriginal people, it befell the Franciscan missionaries to carry the first vines of the Old World wine grape into the region. Given the urgency of establishing production of a dependable supply of sacramental wine, Father Serra and the other padres no doubt wasted little time in planting the first cuttings and/or raisin seedlings of *Vitis vinifera* after their July 1, 1769, arrival at the Mission San Diego de Alcalá site. The abundance of wild grapes here and at subsequent mission sites as far north as Sonoma (Fig. 10.24) signaled the padres that Alta California had the makings of an optimal environment for viticulture.

While awaiting the bearing of *vinifera's* first fruits, they even attempted making wine from the native species of *Vitis*. The Monica variety of *vinifera* or Mission grape,[6] which came to California from Spain and Sardinia via Mexico, eventually became the viticultural mainstay of all 21 missions. One Mission grape vine, the Trinity Vine at Mission San Gabriel Archangel, continued to yield fruit for 170 years. The Old World grape had obviously found an ecological niche of grand proportions in California.

Commercial wine grape growing had somewhat less auspicious beginnings in California, although the Mission grape remained the principal raw material of the industry for many decades following the secularization of the missions in the mid-1830s. Joseph Chapman, who arrived at Monterey in 1818 and was only the third American to become a permanent resident of Alta California, planted the first commercial vineyard in the province. Chapman was a ship builder by trade, but a

---

[5]The term "winegrowing" actually refers to a cottage-industry type of winemaking that still exists in many parts of the world, though largely absent from California since the advent of modern production techniques. Given that they are located in out-of-the-way rural areas and that their harvested grapes will ferment and spoil on their own, such winegrowers will often make their own bulk table wine and sell it, rather than their grapes, to wholesale brokers. In turn, the brokers sell the wine to local vintners, who blend it with other growers' wines. Obviously, quality control suffers in such an operation and the wine is likely to be below par. See M. A. Amerine and V. L. Singleton, *Wine: An Introduction,* 2nd ed. (Berkeley: University of California Press, 1977).

[6]By other accounts, Criolla (also developed in Mexico) was the first variety of *vinifera* introduced by the Franciscans and thus is said to be the forerunner of the Mission grape.

Figure 10.22 Varietal wine and applesauce come from the white Chardonnay grapes and Gravenstein apples seen growing here in western Sonoma County. Both are deciduous crops and do well in this coolest (Region I, Fig. 10.26) of grape-growing climates. Chardonnay or Pinot Chardonnay wines number among California's premium dry white table wines having a distinct varietal aroma. One nearby winery produces an unusual white wine known as Gravenstein Blanc, but there is no apple juice in it. (Crane Miller)

Figure 10.23 These modern Wilmes presses gently extract as much juice as possible from crushed grapes without breaking the seeds. The press on the right with doors removed stands ready for loading. A rubber bag in the center of the press is inflated to gently squeeze the grapes against the press's inside walls. A continuous screw conveyor brings the grape "must" from the crusher. These presses are typical of the modern equipment used in California's wineries. (Wine Institute)

Figure 10.24 Mission San Francisco Solano and the first Sonoma vineyard were established by the Franciscan fathers in 1823 and 1825, respectively. The pueblo of Sonoma was founded in 1835 by General Mariano Vallejo, two of whose daughters later married two sons of Agoston Haraszthy, the father of California winemaking. Although one of California's oldest and largest family wineries, Sebastiani Vineyards came to the region much later. In 1904, Sebastiani bottled its first varietal wine, a Zinfandel. Red Zinfandel grapes prefer the warmer climes of this eastern interior part of Sonoma County and neighboring Napa County (Regions II and III, Fig. 10.26). (California Department of Parks and Recreation, photo by John Kaestner)

change in profession was in the offing when in 1834 he set out some 4,000 Mission vines near the pueblo at Los Angeles. Chapman was probably encouraged by Father Sanchez and other Franciscan viticulturists at nearby San Gabriel mission, where 100,000 vines were annually yielding some 500 barrels of wine and 200 barrels of brandy. By the end of the decade, Chapman's and the padres' Mission wines had gained a favorable reputation among travelers from Mexico and the United States; remoteness from potential markets and a chronic shortage of bottles, however, all but dashed hopes of significant exports of California wines.

The first professional *viticulturist* to come to California was Jean Louis Vignes, a native of France's Bordeaux wine district. He arrived in Monterey in 1829 and by 1831 had moved to Los Angeles. His first sight of the vast vineyards of the Franciscans, plus those of Chapman and five other minor wine growers, led him, in 1833, to purchase 104 acres of potential vineyard land centered on what is now the site of the Los Angeles Union Station. His land was soon planted, mostly to Mission vines, but also with some experimental cuttings of French grape varieties. Vignes was the first person to bring foreign cuttings to California, for the Mission grape by that time was considered a California grape. He constructed a commercial winery near a large alder, the tree's presence inspiring him to name the rancho El Aliso, and his neighbors to call him Don Luís del Aliso.

Vignes's first vintage was in 1837; by 1843, he was producing 40,000 gallons of wine a year, the bulk of it from Mission grapes. His sole major competition was

William Wolfskill from Kentucky, who in 1838 bought several vineyards in what is now the heart of downtown Los Angeles. By the time of statehood, Vignes and Wolfskill had practically cornered California wine production. Their wineries were producing nearly 60,000 gallons yearly and the Mission grape was the raw material of their success.

The Green Hungarian

Count Agoston Haraszthy, a Hungarian, was no newcomer to the art and science of wine grape growing in California. The appellation "Green Hungarian" refers to a white table wine and the white grape that produces it, the latter of which may have been one of the 300 different varieties of *vinifera* that the count collected in Europe and brought to California in 1861. If Haraszthy was not Green Hungarian's originator in California, he was certainly its principal promoter. This was but one of many viticultural feats performed by Haraszthy, who is considered the father of modern California viticulture.

As with his predecessors, Haraszthy started with the Mission grape. He planted his first vineyard near San Diego shortly after his arrival in California in 1849. But Haraszthy's stay in Southern California was as short-lived as his use of the Mission grape. In 1852, he headed north and bought 211 acres of ex-Mission Dolores land in San Francisco at the southern end of present-day Market Street. Here he planted two new European grape varieties: (1) Zinfandel, which is of Italian origin; and (2) Muscat of Alexandria, direct from Málaga, Spain. By

1854, Haraszthy had more than tripled his grape acreage on the San Francisco peninsula and the future appeared promising. But in the ensuing three years he was accused and later acquitted of embezzlement while in the employ of the U.S. Mint and his vineyards suffered both from neglect and the frequency of peninsular fog. All this prompted him to sell out in the Bay region and move even farther north to Sonoma.

The Sonoma Valley proved to be the environmental niche that Haraszthy and *vinifera* were looking for: Fungus-causing fog was not the problem it was nearer San Francisco, yet the valley was close enough to the Pacific to allow a long growing season. Moreover, Franciscans and their Mission grapes (Fig. 10.25), Indians working ex-mission vineyards, and General Vallejo's wines and brandies had already gained some measure of viticultural repute for Sonoma. Nevertheless, it was Haraszthy who would make the valley famous. By the end of his second year (1858) in the valley, he had seen to the planting of 165 different varieties of *vinifera*, the building of a winery and storage cellars, and the founding of Buena Vista Vineyards. In 1863, Haraszthy and eight others incorporated the Buena Vista Vinicultural Society (Fig. 10.25) with holdings of 6,000 acres planted to nearly all the 300 varieties of *vinifera* he had earlier collected in Europe. The corporation's plan was to be producing 2,260,000 gallons of wine annually by 1873.

Sadly, Haraszthy never saw his dream come true, for in 1868 he went to Nicaragua to build a distillery and returned only once briefly to San Francisco before his mysterious disappearance in 1869. Supposedly, he was devoured by alligators in a stream on his own Nicaraguan property. This Hungarian's "greenness" in a hostile tropical milieu undoubtedly led to his undoing, but not before he had forever modified California's wine-growing landscape.

Agoston Haraszthy's contemporaries and successors in California viticulture—Frohling, Gallo, Kohler, Krug, Masson, Mondavi, Petri, and Wetmore, to name but a very few—followed his lead in supplanting Mission grapes with all manner of European varieties. What Haraszthy had visualized as essential to the attainment of variety and quality in California wines has been accepted and implemented by the industry over the last hundred years.

Vinifera's Enemies

First there was *Phylloxera,* then there was Prohibition. The former was naturally and probably accidentally introduced to California in the 1850s, whereas the latter was strictly a cultural imposition, thrust upon the state with enactment of the 18th Amendment to the U.S. Constitution in 1920. Both nearly dealt death blows to California wine growing in their time, but both would eventually be vanquished as the industry rebounded to new levels of international prestige.

Phylloxera is a vine disease transmitted to either the leaves or the roots of a grape vine by a species of vine louse or aphid known as *Phylloxera vastatrix*. The *Phylloxera* insect is a native of the eastern United States that was introduced to Europe in the mid-nineteenth century

Figure 10.25 Agoston Haraszthy's press house at his Buena Vista Winery just east of the town of Sonoma. Not to be called or confused with BV (Beaulieu Vineyard) in nearby Napa Valley, Buena Vista was founded in 1857 and for several years was the world's largest winery. Later, phylloxera, the 1906 earthquake, and Prohibition teamed up to close down Buena Vista. But restoration began in 1943, and today the winery is both a state historical landmark and a producer of premium wines. Although Monterey, Santa Clara, and several San Joaquin Valley counties provide keen competition, the triumvirate of Sonoma, Napa, and Mendocino claims nearly 100 wineries and is considered California's premier varietal wine district. (Buena Vista Winery & Vineyards, photo by Matrix/Sexton)

when native eastern American vines *(Vitis labrusca)* were sent there for grafting to European vines. The less resistant European *Vitis vinifera* quickly fell prey to phylloxera and by 1865 most of Europe's vineyards had been ravaged. It is now known that phylloxera had indirectly made its way to California, via European cuttings, in the 1850s; but it was not until 1876 that the disease was considered a major threat to California wine growing. First and hardest hit was Sonoma County, where by 1879 more than 100,000 vines had to be uprooted. Still, by 1880, the majority of California wine growers were apathetic to taking any meaningful action. Consequently, the *Phylloxera,* which by this time had evolved to its winged form, spread throughout the counties of Napa, El Dorado, and Placer, as well as Sonoma. Vineyardists affected were losing an estimated $1,000 a day. The disease struck the older vines the hardest, all but wiping out the Mission grape in northern California. The newer European varieties of *vinifera* were hard hit, too, but eventually enough were saved to provide the base for a resurgent wine industry. Even all the European varieties would have succumbed to phylloxera had it not been for the efforts of three men.

Charles Wetmore, Professor Eugene Hilgard of the University of California College of Agriculture, and Professor George Husmann were, in the main, the developers of the only practical means of combating phylloxera. Led by Husmann, the three concluded and proved that if resistant native American vines were used as root stocks for *Vitis vinifera,* phylloxera would not attack such vines. At first *V. californica* and *V. labrusca* were grafted to *vinifera;* however, more recently ·hybridized species of *V. riparia, rupestria,* and *berlandieri* have proved most effective as root stocks. Thus by 1890, phylloxera had ceased to be a major problem and a major relocation of grape varieties had been completed: European varieties became dominant in Northern California, but the Mission grape remained supreme in Southern California, which had remained relatively unaffected by phylloxera mainly because of the sandy soils found in its vineyards.

No sooner had phylloxera been quashed than the rumblings of impending national prohibition of alcohol began to be heard and take their toll. Eight years before Prohibition became law, California wine production had peaked; thereafter, it went into a deepening slump. By 1919, the state's wine production had declined to less than half of the 1912 mark. Prohibition was in fact only the enemy of the wine grape, for raisin and table grape acreage increased until by 1927 the state showed its largest acreage in history, 648,000 acres. The effect of this switch in cultivation was to create an imbalance of table and raisin grapes over wine varieties.

Prohibition's worst effect, then, was to cause a dearth of wine grape varieties by the time of eventual repeal. When the 21st Amendment was passed in 1933 and the repeal of Prohibition finally did come, an oversupply of the wrong varieties of grapes, dilapidated wineries, unsound cooperage (storage tanks), inexperienced personnel, and lack of capital blocked the rebirth of the California wine industry. But reborn it was, for wine connoisseurs the world over remembered the excellence of California wines. The real problem through the rest of the 1930s was keeping supply up with demand, and this despite the worst economic depression in history. Eventually, such difficulties as too much sweet wine and not enough table wine production were overcome, and since the 1940s California has accounted for about 80 percent of all domestic (U.S.) production. *Viniculture* alone, or growing wine grapes, exclusively occupies 330,000 acres of the state's farmland. Today, New York is a distant number two producer of wine in the nation.

The needs for standardization within the industry and for advancement of sales of domestically produced wines were ameliorated in 1934 by three separate events: (1) organization of the Wine Institute as a nonprofit association of more than 80 percent of the nation's wine growers to prevent the marketing of unsound and misbranded wines and to advertise wine as a food product; (2) establishment of the Federal Alcohol Control Administration to originate and implement standards of competition and promote stability within the industry; and (3) assignment of the California Board of Public Health to the task of establishing minimum standards of quality for wine.

Wines, Varieties, and Climates

Post-Prohibition standardization within the U.S. wine industry brought with it recognition of the classification of wines into three general categories: generic, proprietary, and varietal. *Generics,* or *semigenerics* as they are called under U.S. regulations, are identified by geographic origin, such as Burgundy from France or Rhine wine from Germany. Generic wines have obviously long since lost their original regional significance and are consequently labeled according to their actual place of production, such as California Mountain Burgundy. A *proprietary* wine, such as Thunderbird or Silver Satin, is narrowly exclusive by comparison, denoting on its label the name of a wine that no other winery can make. But of the three types, the *varietal* label is the one to be most trusted by the wary wine buyer. For if the label reads Cabernet Sauvignon or Pinot Noir or Sauvignon Blanc or one of dozens of different varieties of *vinifera* grown in California, one is assured that the majority or perhaps all of the grapes used to produce that wine are of the variety on the label. By law, California varietals contain at least 51 percent of the grape variety listed (75 percent by 1983). However, more expensive varietal wines are produced exclusively or nearly so from the variety labeled. One can conclude that the environmental parameters for growing fine varietal wine grapes are more confining than those required of varieties used in the production of ordinary table wines and so-called jug wines.

Of the ecological constraints on wine grape growing, climate in general and temperature in particular are most significant. The white Palomino or Golden Chasselas variety, used mostly to make sherry, provides a case in point. Any grape, including the Palomino, requires a given number of sunny, warm days to grow to full size and then to ripen. During early growth, the acid content of the grape will increase until the fruit reaches half of its full size. Then, shortly before ripening begins, acidity will start to decrease. All during the ripening period, sugar content increases.

The Palomino follows this maturation pattern throughout except that it is an early-ripening variety and therefore develops a comparatively low acid content. Its underacidity renders the Palomino poor material for making dry table wines. Given enough time, however, the Palomino will develop a relatively high sugar content and thus be readily suitable as the basic ingredient of fortified (with brandy) dessert wines and apéritifs, such as sweet and cocktail (dry) sherries. Consequently, more than 80 percent of all of California's 6,000 acres of Palomino grapes grow in the Central Valley where the summers are long, hot, and dry. The remaining Palomino vineyards are found in inland coastal valleys where they must contend with summers that are just a bit too short, cool, and humid for optimal maturation of their fruit. Winter, on the other hand, is rarely a problem in either the coastal valleys or the Central Valley, for the deciduous vines have lost their leaves and are ready for some cold and wet weather.

Perhaps the best argument for temperature as the most critical climatic element in wine grape growing is seen in Figure 10.26, a map of M. A. Amerine's and A. J. Winkler's degree-day regions of California. A couple of decades ago, these two University of California enologists set about collecting different varieties from every principal grape-growing district in California. The grapes were converted to wine, which was analyzed chemically and subjected to periodic tastings. From thousands of analyses and tasting records, they were able to form a basis for classifying the capabilities of hundreds of grape varieties according to local temperature regions. In their studies, Amerine and Winkler considered other factors, such as rainfall, fog, humidity, and duration of sunshine, but found that these only had a minor effect upon the balance of the composition of the fruit at maturity. The major factor was temperature, or *heat summation,* as they termed it.

Amerine and Winkler established five regions, based solely on the summation of heat as degree-days above 50° F for the period from April 1 through all of October. Simply stated, this is the total amount of heat that is available to a vine during its growing season and is

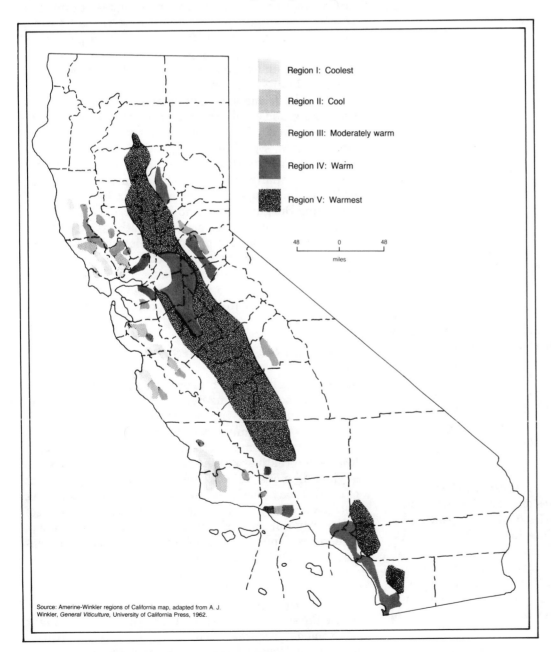

Region I: Coolest

Region II: Cool

Region III: Moderately warm

Region IV: Warm

Region V: Warmest

48   0   48

miles

Source: Amerine-Winkler regions of California map, adapted from A. J. Winkler, *General Viticulture,* University of California Press, 1962.

Figure 10.26 Degree-day regions. (Brett Wilson)

calculated as follows: If the mean temperature over a five-day period were, for example, 70° F, the summation would be 100 degree-days, or $(70 - 50) \times 5 = 100$. The ranges of degree-days for each of the Amerine-Winkler regions shown in Figure 10.26 are: Region I, the coolest, with less than 2,500; Region II, cool, with 2,501–3,000; Region III, moderately warm, with 3,001–3,500; Region IV, warm, with 3,501–4,000; and Region V, the warmest, with 4,001 or more.

A rough rule of thumb application of the heat summation system would probably find the drier, higher tannin varietal wine grapes doing best in Regions I and II and the sweeter, less astringent types coming from Regions IV and V, with a mix of fruitier semidry and semisweet varietals growing in Region III. The following table provides a listing of some of California's better known varietal wines and the degree-day regions in which the growing of grapes used in their production is greatest:

Red Varietals

Barbera (III, IV)
Cabernet Sauvignon (II, III)
Gamay Beaujolais (I, II)
Merlot (II, III)
Petite Sirah (II, III, IV)
Pinot Noir (I, II)
Ruby Cabernet (III, IV, V)
Zinfandel (II, III, IV)

White Varietals

Chardonnay (I, II)
Chenin Blanc (III, IV)
French Columbard (III, IV, V)
Gewurztraminer (II, III)
Pinot Blanc (I, II, III)
Sauvignon Blanc (I, II)
Sylvaner or Franken Riesling (II, III)
White Riesling (I, II, III)

In using this list, it should be made clear that: (1) dates on bottles are significant in denoting the age of some varietals; but not in terms of *vintage* (best year or years), for practically every year is a vintage year in California; (2) either red or white generic wines are produced from a blend of different varieties of grapes growing in any of the wine districts in California; and (3) there are only two true colors in wine, red and white. So-called rosé wines are best made from red grape varieties, the skins imparting color to the wine while being allowed to remain in contact with the must during fermentation. Nonetheless, rosé wines can also be made by blending red and white grapes or red and white wines.[7] The more popular red varieties (and their growing regions) used to make rosé wines include Carnelian (IV, V), Grenache (IV, V), Napa Gamay (III), and Zinfandel. This does not necessarily preclude a rosé wine's having varietal qualities. It is true, though, that the varietal-like character of a rosé is diminished when the must is removed from the skins after only about 15 hours of

[7]Amerine and Singleton, *Wine: An Introduction*, p. 124.

fermentation in order to keep the wine from becoming too dark. Among the more esteemed rosé "varietal" wines are California Grenache and California Gamay.

Moving from the realm of still wines to that of sparkling wines, California must give some ground to New York. The Finger Lakes district of upstate New York is second only to the wine districts of California in producing the nation's finest champagnes. In both states, the better champagnes are all produced in the same manner as those of Champagne, France—by means of secondary fermentation in the bottle (Fig. 10.27). Such naturally fermented champagnes should develop in the bottle for at least a year before they are marketed; those with dates from several years back are usually at their peak of quality.

All this time and added expense can be saved by employing the *bulk* or *Charmat* process, wherein champagnes are made by fermentation in large tanks and then bottling under pressure. Cheaper and quicker still is artificial carbonation, accomplished by addition of CO_2 to the wine as in the manufacture of soft drinks. Bulk or Charmat process wines are champagnes but must be labeled accordingly, whereas labeling carbonated wines as champagne is expressly forbidden. In these poor man's sparkling wine types, the gas fails to become a component part of the wine and consequently they go flat all too quickly after opening.

Naturally fermented champagnes enjoy the character that aging adds and are made from the choicest grape varieties. Depending on whether they are California Champagnes, Sparkling Burgundies, or Pink Champagnes (Sparkling Rosés), the state's finest sparkling wines are usually made from Chardonnay, Pinot Blanc, or Pinot Noir grapes. When California Champagne and Sparkling Burgundy are combined to produce Cold Duck, a concentrate of Concord grapes from the state of Washington may be added to produce a relatively sweet sparkling wine. Generally, though, champagne aficionados prefer their wines on the dry side, ranging from *brut* (very dry; less than 15 grams of sugar per liter) to *sec* (medium sweet; 17 to 35 grams of sugar per liter).

ODDITIES IN COMMODITIES

Marijuana cultivation, because it is illegal; turf production, because most of us perceive lawns as being born, growing up, and living out their lives in one place; Christmas tree farming, because nothing edible or buildable will come from the trees; and energy crops, because few people realize that food and feed crops are capable of yielding motor vehicle fuel—these are rarely thought of as everyday, garden-variety types of agriculture. Yet not only are they bonafide agricultural products like beef and barley, but some of them are also beginning to nudge aside more familiar kinds of crops on the California agricultural landscape.

"Where's the Pot?"
While the subject of spirits is still fresh in mind, it might be deemed appropriate to dwell for a moment or two on another of California's euphoria-inducing agricultural

Figure 10.27 Korbel Champagne Cellars is situated among towering redwood trees along the banks of the lower Russian River. Immigrants from Bohemia, the three Korbel brothers began their enterprises in this part of western Sonoma County in the 1860s with a redwood lumbering operation whose basic purpose was to supply wood for their cigar box factory in San Francisco. But soon they were planting vines among the redwood stumps and importing eastern oak from around Cape Horn to build their *cooperage* (wine casks, collectively). In 1954, the Heck family acquired the Cellars and furthered the already well-established reputation of Korbel champagnes and brandies by expanding vineyard acreage and improving the *riddling* process (whereby champagne bottles are placed neck down in a rack so that the unspent yeast cells and sediments collect next to the caps), among other improvisations. A signature of quality on Korbel Champagne labels reads: "Naturally fermented in this bottle." (F. Korbel & Bros., Inc.)

commodities, albeit an illegal one. Marijuana, known unscientifically as "pot" or "grass" and scientifically as *Cannabis sativa* (an annual herb of the mulberry family), has become one of California's most valuable crops. Because the cultivation and sale of marijuana are felony offenses in California, the annual value of the crop can only be guessed at. Such guestimates usually range from $100 million to more than $600 million. If one takes the higher-priced end of the range as gospel truth, then marijuana could be said to be in the same league as cotton and grapes in terms of the annual value of the crop. A more conservative estimate by the U.S. Drug Enforcement Administration placed pot tenth among California farm crops with a value of $186 million in a single year late in the last decade.[8]

For obvious reasons, no attempt is made here to map pot-growing regions, although such a geography of marijuana in California might become a bestseller.

Other than on condo balconies and in backyard gardens, however, where is most of the "commercial" crop grown in the state? Many a smoker and lawperson will point to the northwestern counties, where a highly potent variety of *sativa*, known as *sinsemilla* (meaning "seedless"), is widely cultivated. Actually, counties from one end of the state to the other that offer isolation,

[8]John Hurst and Phil Garlington, "Pot: The Price and Potency Are 'Way Up,'" *Los Angeles Times*, November 25, 1979, pt. 1, 20.

rugged terrain, clayey soils, and a reasonably lengthy growing season are likely candidates for marijuana's cultivation for income. Although cities and suburbs constitute the major markets for the drug, growing it in urban areas is more for private consumption than for profit. Be it in a rural or urban milieu, however, pot production is expanding and California is rapidly moving towards self-sufficiency and a diminishing need for imports. Too bad the same can't be said for some of the state's legal natural resources and manufactures, such as oil and natural gas or Chryslers and Fords.

While efforts at decriminalization of marijuana in California have made some inroads, dreams of eventual legalization have so far gone up in smoke and are likely to remain there in the foreseeable future. One wonders, though, to what degree the state's pot farmers would support legalization. At some point in any gradual legalization, income from marijuana production would become legally reportable and the Franchise Tax Board, the Internal Revenue Service, and other public agencies would begin cashing in on their share of the trade. Such revenues could conceivably lower the overall tax burden of nonsmokers but more likely would be spent on rehabilitation programs and keeping high drivers off the highways. Whatever its legal fate might be, the funny-smelling stuff has subtly become an important part of California's agricultural landscape.

Figure 10.28 Turf grass grown in the Santa Clara Valley finds its major market just a few miles away in the San Jose metropolitan area. (Crane Miller)

Another Kind of Grass

This is the kind that is mowed, not smoked, and it too is increasing its share of the state's agricultural output. As seen in Figure 10.28, turf grass occupies relatively large tracts of land and must be irrigated. But turf grass is a highly remunerative crop, with several counties each producing more than a million dollars worth a year. Markets for rolled turf range from country clubs and nurseries to race tracks and city parks departments.

What is curious about nonedible nursery stock in general, which includes the growing of ornamental flowers (Fig. 10.29) and Christmas trees as well as turf grass,

is that it is prospering from urbanization rather than hurting from it. Obviously, urbanization has created new markets for horticultural products. The same could be said for agricultural products. What is really happening, however, as we will see in Chapter 11, is that agriculture is giving ground to urbanization while at the same time gaining increased sales from it. In a sense, Peter is being robbed to pay Paul.

Christmas Tree Farming

Commercial Christmas tree farming is more correctly deemed *silviculture* than agriculture; but however described, it is increasingly happening on prime land formerly used to grow food and feed crops. The economics of supply and demand and diminishing returns may check this trend; should it continue unabated, however, world food supplies would be that much more in jeopardy. Today, Christmas tree production on former agricultural land in California is becoming a multimillion-dollar-a-year industry.

From the farmer's viewpoint, though, the conversion from agriculture to silviculture has its merits. Take, for instance, the hypothetical case of a citrus grower turned Christmas tree farmer. No longer will our erstwhile citrus farmer need to drill wells or import water, for Monterey pines and most other Christmas tree varieties are rainfed crops (Fig. 10.30). Not only will water cost nothing, but the farmer will no longer have to maintain an expensive irrigation system either. Labor savings will appear attractive as well, especially if the farmer charges the same price for every tree, regardless of size, and lets customers cut their own. The buyers attracted

Figure 10.29 Ornamental flowers and nursery products now constitute a more than $500-million-a-year business in California; the state leads the nation in production. The Lompoc Valley in northern Santa Barbara County is the commercial flower seed capital of the United States, while several other coastal counties account for the bulk of the state's nursery stock and cut flower production. Their nearly year-long growing seasons give these California counties a decided advantage in the production of horticultural commodities. (Denholm Seeds)

Figure 10.30 Christmas tree farm in Palo Alto. (Roger M. Rhiner)

through local newspaper and radio ads will probably not have forestry degrees or experience, but all will no doubt gravitate to the largest trees on the farm. Our farmer can then sit back and watch customers go about the selective cutting of the forest. Drought or fire or disease might destroy this dream farm, but in the meantime the farmer is realizing higher profits and fewer ulcers than when he or she was in citrus. And when winter frosts strike, it's not necessary to get up at night to light orchard heaters.

Energy Crops: A Sweet Solution?

Agrifuels, such as ethyl alcohol or *ethanol* distilled from plant sugars, may be California's best answer yet to OPEC's outrageous petroleum pricing policies. Such carbohydrate-rich crops as barley, corn, potatoes, sugar beets, and wheat grow by the hundreds of thousands of acres in California and their production could be doubled or tripled in rather short order. So far, *gasohol*, a 90-octane mixture of 90 percent gasoline and 10 percent ethanol, is the only major agrifuel product available to the motoring public. But as technology could have it, we might soon be burning pure 200-proof ethanol in our engines. After all, racing drivers have been using alcohol fuel in their specially designed engines for years and getting up to 18 percent more power than from gasoline. Another source of crop energy now being tested involves *biomass conversion*: in particular, the manufacture of producer gas from crop and other plant residues. If and

when a major conversion from hydrocarbons to carbohydrates comes about, we would find that the latter also supplies a host of by-products ranging from lubricants to paint bases.

Before we become too enthusiastic about agrifuels, it would be well to examine some of their shortcomings. For instance, environmentalists and air resource people point to more smog if gasohol replaces gasoline. They say that gasohol evaporates more readily than gasoline, with most of the additional evaporation emanating from gas tank spouts and carburetors. Fuel-injected engines unquestionably run more efficiently on gasohol, but carburetor-equipped cars outnumber them. Worse yet, emission control devices in nearly all cars are unable to capture the resulting increase in hydrocarbons from evaporating and burning gasohol. Consequently, the more gasohol used in existing cars, the greater the amount of hydrocarbon emissions reaching the atmosphere, although emissions of oxides of nitrogen will diminish. With agrifuel production in general, the other major difficulty will be coping with hidden energy costs. Think of how much energy might be spent on cultivating new cropland, running new equipment, and producing more pesticides and fertilizers. Lastly, much fuel is needed for converting crops into ethanol.

As we now leave the farm and venture into the city in Chapter 11, it would be well to recall that urban California constitutes the major market for the state's agricultural products and as such has contributed immeasurably to the prosperity of rural California.

11

THE CITY: METROPOLITAN CALIFORNIA

The preceding chapter and this one might well be jointly dubbed "The Farm and the City: A Tale of Two Places," for the continued well-being and development of rural California is inexorably linked to that of urban California. More than 95 percent of California's land area is occupied by farms, forest, wilderness, and other nonurban uses, but most of the population and most decision making are found in the cities.

Regional agglomerations of cities have coalesced into metropolises, and they in turn may one day form great, or not-so-great, megalopolises. To gain a clearer understanding of how metropolitan California has grown, what its functions are, and where its impacts on prime agricultural land have occurred and are likely to take place is the purpose of this chapter. The connection between farm and city is, after all, a two-way street, and the sooner we appreciate the geographical bond involved, the better.

PATTERNS OF METROPOLITAN GROWTH

In California and elsewhere, the metropolitan community is largely a product of the twentieth century and, as such, represents a relatively new type of living unit. In comparing the metropolitan community to the city, Amos Hawley makes this distinction: "The city is the creature of the nineteenth century [in North America]; its successor in the twentieth century is the metropolitan community. This new urban unit is an extensive community composed of numerous territorially specialized parts, the functions of which are correlated and integrated through the agency of a central city."[1] In somewhat similar terms, Raymond Murphy defines the metropolitan area as consisting of "a recognized, substantial population nucleus and the adjacent areas of countryside and scattered urban development that have

a community of interest with the nucleus."[2] In a sense, the metropolitan area is analogous to the central city and its suburbs, except that the former is not necessarily limited to a contiguous built-up area.

The U.S. Bureau of the Census also has its definition of metropolitan, designating a county or group of contiguous counties that contain at least one city of 50,000 inhabitants or more a *Standard Metropolitan Statistical Area* (SMSA). Figure 11.1 maps 17 such SMSAs in California as of the 1980 Census; because of their delineation according to county boundaries, however, they are in many instances depicted covering huge tracts of land that are anything but metropolitan. For example, Ontario–Riverside–San Bernardino is the nation's largest SMSA in area but one of the smallest in population. Actually, most of it is sparsely settled desert. The Bureau's *urbanized area*, as defined in Chapter 1 (Fig. 1.17), presents a truer picture than the SMSA of what is actually populated urban land. Obviously, the SMSA serves more as a data-gathering unit with fixed boundaries than as anything else.

Historically, the development of the metropolitan community is a relatively recent phenomenon in North America and, as such, is to a large degree a function of modern technology. Until the turn of the century, urban growth was confined to compact *centripetal* or inward-growing communities, but with the twentieth century came dramatic advances in agricultural and industrial productivity that soon revolutionized the nature of cities. The climb of the automobile industry to a position of dominance in an expanding industrial economy was a key factor in the areal explosion of cities and the emergence of suburbia. Notably in California, but throughout the metropolitan United States as well, the automobile quickly became the major mode of mass commuting to and from work. This is evidenced by the phenomenal rise in automobile registrations in the nation: from 8,000 in 1900 to 40,333,591 by 1950.

[1]Marion Clawson, R. Burnell Held, and Charles H. Stoddard, *Land for the Future* (Baltimore: Johns Hopkins Press for Resources for the Future, 1960), p. 55.

[2]Raymond E. Murphy, *The American City: An Urban Geography* (New York: McGraw-Hill, 1966), p. 15.

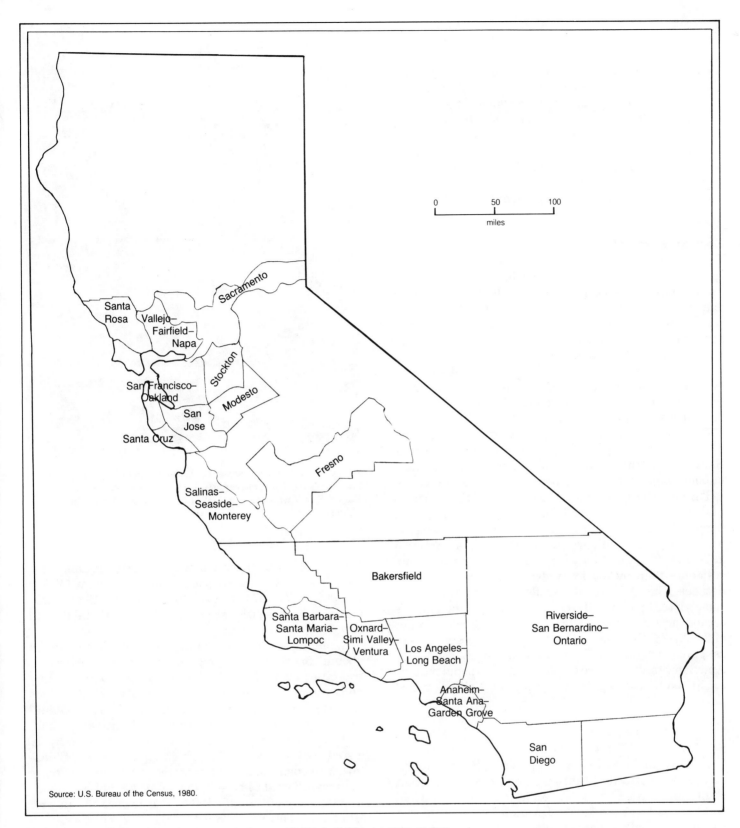

Source: U.S. Bureau of the Census, 1980.

Figure 11.1 Standard metropolitan statistical areas (SMSAs), California, 1980. (Jeff Dunn)

Accompanying technological progress was a rapid increase in personal income levels, with per-capita disposable income rising from $682 in the first year of the Depression in 1929 to $3,089 thirty years later. The standard of living of Americans improved so dramatically that residing in the suburbs was no longer the exclusive province of the wealthy, but could now be enjoyed by people from a broad range of socioeconomic backgrounds. In short, the forces of technological progress and the concomitant rise in living standards allowed a relaxation of the centripetal forces that largely precluded metropolitan development in the nineteenth century.

Shrinking Central Cities

One of the unique demographic features of metropolitan growth is the propensity of the urban fringe or hinterland to experience a population growth rate that exceeds that of the central city. In fact, this tendency has so accelerated in recent decades as to suggest that the metropolitan area explosion is in essence a suburban explosion. Between 1950 and 1960, for example, 12 of the nation's 20 largest cities actually experienced a population decline within city limits, but all showed a significant increase in total metropolitan population because of suburban growth. In the same decade, 96 percent of the national population increase occurred in Standard Metropolitan Areas (SMAs were the predecessors of SMSAs), and three quarters of this increase took place outside the administrative boundaries of central cities.

Through the 1960s and 1970s, the central city depopulation trend has intensified. Chicago is perhaps the biggest loser in the nation, at least in a relative sense according to preliminary 1980 census data. Between 1970 and 1980, the Windy City lost 644,072 people, more residents than moved away during the two preceding decades. Chicago's recent loss also saw Los Angeles become virtually tied with the Windy City as the nation's second largest city, with a preliminary 1980 census count of 2,952,198. Even sprawling Los Angeles posted a modest gain of only 140,397 new residents during the 1970s. And San Francisco, once California's most populous city, continued to lose population during the 1970s as it had during the 1960s.

San Francisco's Depopulation

Originally founded in 1835 as Yerba Buena, which rather prophetically translates to "good grass," San Francisco reigned as the state's largest city from Gold Rush times until the 1920s. During that 70 years, the city was leveled on more than one occasion by fire and/ or earthquake, yet revive it would each time, only to assume greater urban prominence (Fig. 11.2). San Francisco seemed destined to grow in spite of the worst disasters and hazards imaginable, and when it ran out of horizontal space (Fig. 11.3), it reached for the sky. Today, Baghdad-by-the-Bay puts other California metropolises to shame as a skyscraper-filled,[3] cosmopolitan urban cen-

[3]In 1974, San Francisco ranked sixth in the United States in skyline height, with New York first and Los Angeles nineteenth. See Larry Ford, "The Urban Skyline as a City Classification System," *Journal of Geography* 75 (1976): 154–164.

Figure 11.2 California Street holds the distinction of being San Francisco's longest cable car street, the tracks stretching from Market Street westward and uphill to Van Ness Avenue. (Roger M. Rhiner)

ter, and one with hardly a trace of air pollution. Why, then, has San Francisco's population slipped from 740,300 in 1960 to 715,674 in 1970 to 674,063 in 1980, while other California cities seem to buck the national central city depopulation trend?

Explanations of San Francisco's population losses abound, many of them symptomatic of depopulating central cities throughout the United States. Deteriorating and overcrowded residences in inner city neighborhoods constitute one of the most serious problems. In Chinatown (Fig. 11.4) alone, 60 percent of the housing is substandard. This may be significant in explaining why, in a study completed in 1980, a higher proportion of Chinatown's residents suffered from some sort of mental illness than were found to be so afflicted in the midtown Manhattan study of the late 1960s. Out toward the Bay on Hunter's Point, where much of San Francisco's sizable black population resides, a mix of old and new low-cost housing exists, but accommodations often are spartan at best.

Some Chinese are relocating in the more affluent northwestern part of the city close to Golden Gate Park while black families are doing likewise nearby in the older Haight-Ashbury district. Appropriately dubbed "Hashbury" back in the 1960s, the district became a self-styled hippie haven, but by the 1980s that reputation had faded and Haight-Ashbury had reassumed an image of residential stability. Anywhere in San Francisco, though, affordable housing is at a premium, albeit the

Figure 11.3 Air photo of San Francisco. Except for Presidio Park (upper left or northwest) and rectangular Golden Gate Park, the University of California's San Francisco campus, Buena Vista Park, and Twin Peaks (all lower left or southwest), this U-2 vertical view displays wall-to-wall city at the northern end of the San Francisco peninsula. With the main boulevard, Market Street, diagonally offsetting the directional orientation of the rectangular street pattern, the pattern itself tends to flatten or obscure the very hilly terrain: 40 hills and elevation changes ranging from sea level to 929 ft. (NASA)

Figure 11.4 Chinatown, here viewed northward along Grant Avenue, covers some 16 blocks of east-central San Francisco and houses a larger Chinese population than any other place in the world outside China and Singapore. (Roger M. Rhiner)

hilly terrain affords a plethora of view-site residences. An apparently increasing number of blacks who work in San Francisco now commute in from across the Bay, whereas the Chinese population by and large seems to prefer continuing both employment and residence entirely within the city.

Inner city crime could be said to be a major deterrent to settling in San Francisco, were it not that every American city seems similarly plagued. In the evening, in fact, the streets of San Francisco are probably safer places to be than in downtown Los Angeles or Sacramento. Choice restaurants, theaters, museums, and night life in general are active around the clock and well diffused throughout the city, thus reducing the presence of dark, lonely, and out-of-the way streets and back alleys. The old adage that "when the lights go up, crime goes down" seems to apply here.

San Francisco's position nearly on top of the San Andreas fault has been cited as contributor to depopulation. But again, residents seem "unmoved" by this horrendous environmental hazard. This finding was borne out in a recent hazard perception study in which not a single respondent in the sample group queried identified earthquakes as a disadvantage of living in San Francisco.

Finally, there is the simple lack of space, which is probably a more substantive reason for San Francisco's population loss than any thus far mentioned. Bounded on three sides by water and on the fourth by its border with San Mateo County, San Francisco City and County had long ago seen almost every square inch of its 60 or so square miles developed to urban land uses, including parks. The city then had nowhere to go except up. But

vertical development has its limitations, too, especially when building finances become scarcer and danger of the San Andreas fault acting up becomes greater. Los Angeles, Sacramento, San Diego, San Jose, and other big California cities each have four or five times or more area for development than does San Francisco. Moreover, none of these cities sits right on the San Andreas, although San Jose may be a bit too close for comfort. In short, San Francisco's high-density population and high environmental hazard risk are evidently proving increasingly oppressive to residents, even though some won't admit it until after they've moved away.

Where have former and even would-be San Franciscans gone? At first, they moved across the Bay to established cities like Oakland, Berkeley, and Richmond, and then down the East Bay to populate newer bedroom communities such as Hayward and San Leandro. A closer migration reached directly down the Peninsula, populating a string of old and new cities from Burlingame and San Mateo southward to Sunnyvale and San Jose. There were times during the 1960s and 1970s when Sunnyvale was the nation's fastest-growing city and San Jose was the state's second largest city in population. There seemed an inexhaustible supply of former prune orchard land available for urbanization in the South Bay–Santa Clara Valley region (Fig. 11.5). And northward from San Francisco and the mountainous Marin peninsula lay thousands of acres of valley bottomland just waiting for the bulldozer and urban development. In the 1970s and 1980s, the San Francisco–Oakland metropolitan area has spread to Napa and Santa Rosa, with vineyards and orchards coming down and housing

Figure 11.5 Santa Clara Valley: rural and urban. Not to be confused with Ventura County's Santa Clara River Valley 300 miles south, the Santa Clara Valley fronts on the southern end of San Francisco Bay and Peninsula near Palo Alto and from here extends southward nearly 50 miles to Gilroy. Santa Clara County, with its predominantly urban population of 1.3 million but still with significant agricultural production, bore the brunt of the 1981 controversy over how to rid California of the crop-destroying Mediterranean fruit fly. The controversy served to point out the incompatibility of urban and agricultural land uses existing side by side, especially in this valley where urban sprawl has left isolated patches of farmland still in production. (Crane Miller)

tracts and shopping centers going up in their place at an unbelievable rate. Physically binding this supercity together is a equally unbelievable network of trans-Bay bridges, commuter rail lines, freeways, and BART (Bay Area Rapid Transit). Politically trying to keep the whole thing under control is California's very first Council of Governments (COGs), the Association of Bay Area Governments (ABAG). The more than 4 million residents, 85 incorporated cities, and seven counties within ABAG's jurisdiction give us some sense of the enormity of metropolitan San Francisco's expansion. More than any other central city in California, however, San Francisco remains the cultural and financial heart of its metropolitan area.

Suburbanization

The suburbanization movement is an escape from congestion like San Francisco's, as well as a response to create more space for burgeoning city populations. The population explosion alone would have caused such a movement, but the concomitant migration to lower-density living makes the spreading of cities proceed at a more rapid rate and causes it to cover more territory. As a result, the main characteristic of suburbanization is the thin, often discontinuous distribution of population over broad expanses of land. This low density of development, which often takes rise in a mixture of developed and vacant land, is the essence of urban sprawl.

Los Angeles: Suburbs in Search of a City

Founded in 1781 as a Spanish pueblo, the growth of *el Pueblo de Nuestra Señora La Reina de Los Angeles,* both as a city and a metropolitan area,[4] contrasts markedly with that of San Francisco. The differences in physical setting (Chapter 3) alone would no doubt have caused Los Angeles to develop in quite a different direction from San Francisco. Originally situated more than some two dozen miles upstream from the Pacific along the intermittent Los Angeles River, the City of Angels could expand for dozens of miles in almost any direction over relatively level land. But in its first 100 years, Los Angeles hardly took advantage of any of its breathing room, although it did become the most populous pueblo during both the Spanish and Mexican periods, reaching 1,500 residents by 1836. A dozen years later, though, San Francisco, given its proximity to the Sierran Gold Rush and a huge natural deepwater harbor to boot, temporarily stole the urban limelight from Los Angeles.

[4]Although the Los Angeles–Long Beach SMSA and L.A. County are one and the same, with an area of 4,000 sq mi and a 1980 population of 7.4 million, the Los Angeles metropolitan area could be said to at least include all the counties that border Los Angeles County except Kern County, which is physically set apart by a formidable mountain range. Such a metro area, then, would also include Orange County (1.9 million), Riverside County (660,000), San Bernardino County (877,481), and Ventura County (528,000). Orange County is one of California's fastest-growing counties, posting a 500,000 gain from 1970 to 1980. Los Angeles County, on the other hand, is one of the slowest gainers, with an increase of only about 400,000 for the 1970s. Early in the decade, Los Angeles County actually lost population, dropping from 7.0 million to 6.9 million, but it recovered by about 500,000 between 1975 and 1980. The COGs for Los Angeles and adjoining counties is the Southern California Association of Governments, or SCAG.

By contrast with its first century, Los Angeles started its second 100 years with the "Boom of the Eighties,"[5] a boom that would ebb and flow right to the present as the metropolis heads into its third century. The advantages of Los Angeles's physical geography, principally an abundance of developable terrain (Chapter 3) and the mildest of Mediterranean climates (Chapter 4), had become legend to Midwesterners and Easterners by the 1880s. So westward they came, most via recently completed transcontinental railroad lines, but some by old wagon trails, others by ship around the Horn, and few by a trek over the Isthmus of Panama. Egged on by news of the hastened subdivision of vast Mexican-era ranchos, everyone from real estate speculators and retirees to fledgling citrus farmers and petroleum wildcatters flocked to the southland.

By about the turn of the century, the newcomers had firmly set the pattern for America's first sprawling metropolis: Farflung irrigation colonies from Anaheim to Pasadena had begun their transition to fashionable suburbs. Edward Doheny had struck oil west of Figueroa near downtown Los Angeles. William Mulholland had launched a search for desperately needed water that would end successfully in faraway Owens Valley (Chapter 5). The southland's first and last interurban rail transit system, the Pacific Electric Railway Company, had incorporated. Fashionable Bunker Hill had been connected to the rest of downtown Los Angeles by a funicular railway, later known as Angel's Flight. And the City of Los Angeles proper had passed the 100,000 mark in population.

The 1 million mark was attained by the 1920s, when Los Angeles again assumed the status of the state's most populated city, and the 3 million plateau was nearly reached during the 1970s, as the City continued to maintain its number one position.

Today the City of Los Angeles spans 456 sq mi and has indeed radiated outward from its civic center (Fig. 11.6) in every direction imaginable. To the west, many a boulevard has helped bring the city all the way to the shores of Santa Monica Bay (Fig. 11.7). Truly the most incredible of these arteries is Wilshire Boulevard, a 25-mile corridor of hotels, office buildings, high-rise condominiums, banks, and exclusive department stores stretching from downtown Los Angeles through affluent Beverly Hills to the palisades of Santa Monica.

Southward, the city again reaches for the sea, culminating its southerly development in the finest of manmade harbors at San Pedro (Fig. 11.8).

Occupying much of the older residentially developed territory between the city and its port is Watts-Willowbrook, home of California's largest black community, as well as a new and growing Latino population. The Coliseum (Fig. 11.9), Sports Arena, Museum of Science and Industry, Exposition Park, and the University of Southern California also occupy considerable territory as a contiguous unit in south Los Angeles.

East of downtown Los Angeles, longer-established Latino neighborhoods or barrios (Fig. 11.10) dominate the cultural landscape, although the occasional Eastern Eu-

[5]See Glenn S. Dumke, *The Boom of the Eighties in Southern California* (San Marino: Huntington Library, 1944).

ropean and Asian enclaves are also to be found. Many suburbs east of the Los Angeles River originated along transcontinental rail lines in the days when passenger trains were in vogue. Pasadena, Arcadia, Downey, Norwalk, and other bedroom communities to the northeast and southeast first developed quite independently of any early transportation linkages with Los Angeles or the rest of the nation.

Finally, far to the north of downtown Los Angeles lies the city's last and largest residential frontier, the San Fernando Valley. Readily accessible by freeways over the Hollywood Hills (Fig. 11.11) and through Glendale Narrows, the San Fernando Valley was unbelievably quick to transform from a verdant farmscape of citrus groves and row crops to an indifferent expanse of rooftops, commercial strips, schoolyards, and parking lots. In the quarter century following the close of World War II, the valley's population exploded from less than 100,000 to more than a million.

Although the ethnicity of the valley population has diversified in recent years, whites are still much in the majority in the outlying more affluent suburbs. This situation, and distances sometimes exceeding 50 miles between San Fernando Valley public schools and those in inner city minority neighborhoods, have caused no end of frustration in efforts to implement court-ordered busing of students throughout the Los Angeles Unified School District. Institution of bilingual education, es-

pecially for the some 45 percent of the District's student body who are Latinos, represents still another effort at improving integrated education throughout this impossibly large city.[6] Whether or not these and other attempts at diffusing Los Angeles's highly polarized ethnogeography ever work, the day is fast approaching when once again a majority of the citizenry are Spanish speakers.

URBAN CALIFORNIA AT WORK AND PLAY

By some measures, agriculture dominates the economic landscape of California, but by other parameters, and certainly in urban California where most of the people live and work, it is outdone by manufacturing and tourism. Despite rural California's geographic attractions, such as a great number and variety of resource-based factory sites (near sources of raw materials and energy)

[6]Larger in area than the City of Los Angeles, the District services 710 sq mi, 637 schools, and 540,000 students. It is the nation's second largest school district in population. In 1981, mandatory busing was demanded when the state Court of Appeal and the California Supreme Court ruled that antibusing Proposition 1 (1980) was constitutional and applicable in the Los Angeles case. Meanwhile, the District is proposing voluntary desegregation programs and must still contend with strong minority opposition to such proposals and the possibility that federal courts may overturn state court rulings. By the opening of the 1981–1982 academic year, District enrollments were approximately 45 percent Latino, 25 percent black, 23 percent white, 7 percent Asian-American, and less than 1 percent American Indian.

Figure 11.6 Los Angeles Civic Center lies just north and up Bunker Hill from downtown Los Angeles. The nighttime view from the Music Center's reflecting pool is impressive. The Center houses three theaters: the Mark Taper Forum, the Ahmanson Theatre, and the Dorothy Chandler Pavilion, the latter hosting the Academy of Motion Picture Arts and Sciences Annual Oscar Award ceremonies as well as a regular schedule of internationally known stage and concert productions. (The Music Center Operating Company)

A

B

Figure 11.7 Santa Monica Bay and the Los Angeles Basin as scanned from Landsat at more than 500 miles altitude (A). The dark area left of center and fronting on the bay is the chaparral-covered Santa Monica Mountain range. The eastern extension of the range, the Hollywood Hills, separate Beverly Hills, Hollywood, and downtown Los Angeles on the south from the urbanized San Fernando Valley to the north. The three intermittent rivers flowing out of the southeast (lower right) portion of the basin are, from left to right, the Los Angeles, San Gabriel, and Santa Ana. Concrete-lined flood control channels for the most part, the river courses are sometimes mistaken for freeways in aerial and satellite images. View (B) shows Santa Monica Bay from the ground. Except for the hills of Palos Verdes Peninsula, the Baldwin Hills in west Los Angeles, and the hills of East Los Angeles, Monterey Park, Montebello, and Whittier, the Los Angeles Basin south of the San Gabriel Mountains is relatively flat and largely urbanized. (A: NASA; B: National Park Service, photo by Richard Frear)

Figure 11.8 Los Angeles–Long Beach harbors include Terminal Island peninsula (just east of Palos Verdes Peninsula in Fig. 11.7), which is connected by the Vincent Thomas Bridge to San Pedro on the Palos Verdes Peninsula. Los Angeles's city limits were extended southward to include the waterfront communities of San Pedro and Wilmington; dredging of an inner harbor was begun in the opening decade of this century. (Port of Los Angeles)

A

B

Figure 11.9 Los Angeles Memorial Coliseum hosted the 1932 Olympic Games and is the home stadium of the Los Angeles Raider and USC Trojan football teams. The professional Los Angeles Rams shifted their home turf from the Coliseum to Anaheim Stadium in Orange County after the 1980 season. When the Dodger baseball team first came from Brooklyn, New York, they played in the Coliseum but soon built and occupied Dodger Stadium just north of the Civic Center. (A: Richard Hyslop; B: Crane Miller)

Figure 11.10 The Million Dollar Theater across the street from the famed Bradbury Building in downtown Los Angeles at Third and Broadway. This Spanish-baroque-style theater was one of the first movie palaces in the country. Much of this portion of downtown Los Angeles has developed a predominantly Spanish-speaking population—as the theater marquee shows. (Richard Hyslop)

Figure 11.11 Hollywood is an older, medium-density residential community. Actually, many Hollywood apartments have been converted to condominiums, much to the chagrin of senior citizens on fixed incomes who cannot afford to buy instead of rent. Incorporated into Los Angeles in 1910 and seeing its first motion picture studio established a year later, Hollywood has of late become more of a production center for television than for movies. But a walk on the starred sidewalks of Hollywood Boulevard or a visit to Grauman's Chinese Theater leaves many tourists with the impression that Hollywood is still the movie capital of the world. (Greater Los Angeles Visitors and Convention Bureau)

and a seemingly boundless diversity of scenery, manufacturing and tourism are largely urban-oriented industries in the state. The reasons for this range from the existence in the city of a large, affluent buying public and skilled labor supply to the availability of more and better convention, entertainment, lodging, eating, and transportation facilities. In a very real sense, Californians' hard work and hard play have earned them national leadership in most aspects of manufacturing and tourism.

California's prominence carries over into almost all other aspects of the national urban economy as well. For instance, the *1972 Census of Retail Trade* showed California leading the nation with $48.893 billion in retail sales, whereas New York was a distant second with $39.173 billion. Much of the retail trade industry's outstanding performance in this state is owing to the popularity of suburban shopping centers; shopping centers, however, have gained in favor at the expense of older downtown and ribbon (along boulevards) retail trade areas.

In the closely related category of wholesale transactions, the *1972 Census of Wholesale Trade* listed the Golden State with $68.6 billion second only to the Empire State with just over $100 billion. California wholesalers, as in the case of the state's retailers, are displaying

increasing preference for locating their distribution centers in suburban rather than central city sites. Given the largest and one of the most prosperous populations in the United States, a wealth of natural resources, and other geographic amenities, is it any wonder that California is at or near the top as a revenue and/or employment producer in the above and other urban-dominated economic activities, including construction (Fig. 11.12), education (Fig. 11.13), entertainment (Fig. 11.14), financial institutions (Fig. 11.15), government, medical services, research and development (Fig. 11.16), sports (Fig. 11.17), and transportation?

Manufacturing

Every five years, when the national census of manufacturing establishments is conducted, California registers impressive, and sometimes unprecedented, gains. The *1977 Census of Manufactures for California* was no exception, showing value added by manufacture increasing from $31.175 billion in 1972 to $54.862 billion in 1977, or by 76 percent in the five-year period. The number of employees in the 45,289 establishments reporting in 1977 was 1,751,500, a gain of 13 percent over the 1,546,000 figure for 1972. In 1972, only New York with 1,679,000 manufacturing employees was ahead of Cal-

Figure 11.12 Residential construction slowed to a snail's pace in the early 1980s, mostly because of the highest mortgage interest rates ever seen in the country. For instance, in September 1981 in 10 Southern California counties that often lead the nation as a group in housing construction, total new residential construction was valued at $286,338,000, or 48.2 percent less than it was in September 1980. The ripple effect of the slowdown proved economically devastating to the lumber industry, but at least some redwoods, firs, and other commercial conifers in northwestern California received a new lease on life. (Roger M. Rhiner)

Figure 11.13 Stanford University in Palo Alto is one of the world's largest and finest privately endowed universities. The "Farm," or 8,200-acre campus, centers on Hoover Tower, which houses the Hoover Institution on War, Revolution, and Peace, and was named after the thirty-first president of the United States, a graduate of Stanford. The two-mile-long Stanford Linear Accelerator, which explores atomic particles, is considered to be the largest scientific instrument ever constructed. (Stanford University)

Figure 11.14 Hollywood Bowl fills to its 17,599-seat capacity during many a summer symphony under the stars. To improve acoustics in the natural amphitheater of the Bowl, architect Frank Lloyd Wright was retained to design the orchestra shell seen here. The Bowl, the nearby Greek Theatre, and the Universal Amphitheatre form a triumvirate of Hollywood Hills outdoor concert areas that features internationally known entertainers, bands, and symphony orchestras every summer. (Greater Los Angeles Visitors and Convention Bureau)

Figure 11.15 Banks are a high profile component of the California urban landscape, especially now that so much space is needed to accommodate drive-up teller services. Along many a commercial thoroughfare, such as Wilshire Boulevard here, banks, savings and loans, insurance companies, and other financial institutions appear to be replacing retail trade businesses. California-based banks, such as the Bank of America and Security Pacific National Bank, are among the world's largest banks in total assets. Some, like First Interstate Bank, have extended their services to include branches in other states. (Roger M. Rhiner)

Figure 11.16 Research and development (R&D), such as for the space program at Jet Propulsion Laboratory (associated with the California Institute of Technology) in Pasadena, is an area of high achievement for Californians. (Jet Propulsion Laboratory)

ifornia. Since the 1977 census, these two states have run neck and neck for first place in manufacturing employment in America. California's leading manufacturing categories by employment in 1977 were transportation equipment, electric and electronic equipment, machinery (nonelectrical), and food and kindred products.

Four counties, two in Northern California (Alameda and Santa Clara) and two in Southern California (Los Angeles and Orange), accounted for 73 percent of all manufacturing employment and 72 percent of value added by manufacture in the state in 1977. As apparent

in Table 11.1, manufacturing in those four counties is well *diversified* and to a large degree *market oriented*, thus avoiding the pitfalls of *overspecialization* (Fig. 11.18) and remoteness from markets (Fig. 11.19).

Derived from the U.S. Bureau of the Census's *1977 Census of Manufactures for California*, the data in Table 11.1 contain both obvious and hidden comparisons well worth highlighting. Of 350,000 manufacturing establishments (each employing one or more persons) included in the census nationwide, 13 percent were located in California. Of the Bureau's 20 major Standard Industrial

Figure 11.17 Spectator sports facilities, comprising a major part of the California metropolitan landscape, are significant revenue producers. Imagine what might be spent by 40,000 racegoers on a weekend day during the winter meeting at Bay Meadows or Santa Anita Park on admissions, bets, food, beverages, and other services. Other spectator sports in California, whether amateur or professional, also generate impressive crowds and revenues. In all, California could fairly lay claim to being the sports capital of the world. (Bay Meadows Race Course, photo by Doug Murchison)

Classification (SIC) groups, 19 were represented in the four counties listed in Table 11.1. Obviously, the diversity theme applies to manufacturing as it does to just about everything else in California. Lastly, the stellar performances tabulated here were to a considerable degree responsible for: (1) San Jose becoming America's fastest-growing city, according to the preliminary *1980 Census of Population and Housing*[7]; (2) Orange County (coextensive with the Anaheim–Santa Ana–Garden Grove SMSA; see Fig. 11.1) becoming California's fastest-growing county as of the 1970 census; (3) the Los Angeles–Long Beach SMSA (coextensive with Los Angeles County; see Fig. 11.1) strengthening its third place ranking behind the New York and Chicago SMSAs in manufacturing employment; and (4) the Los Angeles–Long Beach SMSA ranking among the national leaders in petroleum refining, an example of a *capital-intensive industry,* and apparel manufacturing, an example of a *labor-intensive industry,* with 78,200 employees and value added by manufacture in 1977 of $1.355 billion (compare with item 19 in Table 11.1).

[7]The City of San Jose, which is in Santa Clara County (the county is coextensive with the San Jose SMSA), showed a 1970–1980 growth rate of 36.1 percent and a 1980 population of 628,106. This moved San Jose from twenty-ninth to seventeenth and ahead of Cleveland, Ohio among the 30 largest cities in the United States. Second in the nation was El Paso, Texas with a growth rate of 31.7 percent and a 1980 population of 424,522 for ranking in the twenty-eighth position. Other 1980 national rankings of California cities were: Los Angeles, third (by 1981, Los Angeles was ahead of Chicago and took second place); San Diego, eighth; and San Francisco, thirteenth.

To distinguish between capital-intensive and labor-intensive industries, note that the labor-intensive industry (apparel, in this case) employed more than eight times as many workers as the capital-intensive industry (petroleum refining and coal products; see Table 11.1), but value added by manufacture for both industries was about equal. Moreover, new capital expenditures in petroleum refining and coal products manufacture ($81.5 million) were more than triple those in apparel manufacturing ($25.1 million) in 1977. It is noteworthy that petroleum refining alone accounted for nearly 90 percent of value added by manufacture and new capital expenditures in the petroleum refining and coal products manufacture category in Los Angeles County in 1977.

Tourism

California is a fun place. It would have to be to attract $19.1 billion tourist dollars in 1979 and thereby perpetuate its leadership in travel and tourism over second-place Florida, third-place New York, and fourth-place Texas. Since tourist dollars are here defined as revenue generated from the expenditures, employment, and tax revenues by travel 100 miles or more away from home, $19.1 billion is undoubtedly an understatement of the total impact of the tourist industry on the California economy in 1979. But regardless of any additional impact a multiplier effect might have had, the $19.1 billion was spent approximately as follows: 53 percent on trans-

Table 11.1
California Manufactures: Four Selected Counties, 1977

County and Industry	Number of Establishments	Number of Employees (thousands)	Value Added by Manufacture (million $)
Alameda (total)	2,057	87.0	3,098.9
1. Food and kindred items	167	13.4	658.5
2. Apparel and other textiles	99	2.1	25.4
3. Lumber and wood products	57	1.1	29.3
4. Furniture and fixtures	61	2.0	44.6
5. Paper and allied products	48	3.6	109.6
6. Printing and publishing	276	4.3	106.9
7. Chemicals and allied products	120	5.9	312.2
8. Rubber and plastic products	74	1.8	54.2
9. Stone, clay, and glass items	88	4.7	127.0
10. Primary metals	64	4.2	142.4
11. Fabricated metals	273	9.8	361.5
12. Machinery, except electrical	314	10.4	288.2
13. Electric and electronic equipment	89	4.2	113.6
14. Transportation equipment	80	10.9	660.5
15. Instruments and related items	67	1.3	36.1
16. Miscellaneous manufacturing	74	0.7	11.9
17. Administrative and auxiliary	70	6.4	—
Los Angeles (total)	21,119	825.5	24,701.8
(Industries 1–16, total)	20,758	806.0	23,173.7
18. Textile mill products	272	10.3	211.5
19. Petroleum and coal products	89	9.2	1,316.6
Orange (Industries 1–2, 4–16, total)	4,703	177.5	5,280.9
Santa Clara (Industries 1, 3, 5–16, total)	2,671	181.4	6,205.7
Four-county total	30,550	1,271.4	39,287.3
State, 58-county total	45,289	1,751.5	54,862.4
Four counties as percentage of state	67	73	72

Figure 11.18 Santa Clara County manufacturing is well diversified, ranging from agriculture products processing to electronic circuit printing. The manufacture of transistors and other electronic equipment using *semiconductors* (a substance like silicon and lead sulfide whose electronic conductivity lies between that of copper wire and glass insulators) is so widespread in the Santa Clara Valley that the valley is now widely known as Silicon Valley. Firms in the area benefit from proximity to research-oriented Stanford University. Nearby in Sunnyvale, NASA-Ames at Moffett Field is a further boon to R&D in the region. Were Santa Clara County to become overspecialized in the area of electronics and that industry to suffer a slump, regional unemployment and recession could be quite severe. (Santa Clara Chamber of Commerce)

Figure 11.19 Orange County firms find markets both at home and around the world, the latter exemplified here by the Fluor Corporation in Irvine. Fluor is a megaproject construction company involved in energy fuel and petrochemical development in such places as Alaska and the North Sea. Fluor is conveniently located adjacent to the San Diego (I-405) Freeway and John Wayne Airport and, as pictured here, has its own heliport. In all, Orange County manufacturers represent 15 different industial categories and claim a potential 24 million consumers within the state alone. (Crane Miller)

portation (cars, buses, planes, and trains), 23 percent on food, 12 percent on lodging, and 12 percent on entertainment, recreation, and incidentals.[8]

It is in examining the geography of tourism in the state, or where the $19.1 billion was spent, that we see how urban-oriented the industry is. Five urban counties alone accounted for $13.7 billion in tourist expenditures in 1979. They were: Los Angeles ($5.8 billion), San Francisco ($2.5 billion), San Mateo ($2.3 billion), San Diego ($1.7 billion), and Orange ($1.4 billion). Four busy airports, including Los Angeles International (LAX) in Los Angeles County, San Francisco International (SFO) in San Mateo County, San Diego International (SAN or Lindbergh Field) in San Diego, and John Wayne Airport in Orange County, account for a good deal of this prominence.

According to the *1977 Census of Service Industries,* however, the thousands of California's 1,527 hotels, 3,839 motels, and 24,000 amusement and recreation service businesses found in the five counties generate the bulk of their tourist revenue. California is ranked first and far ahead of second-place Florida in these three accommodation and service categories.

In the realm of urban amusement attractions, Disneyland (in north Orange County), Knott's Berry Farm (in northwest Orange County), San Diego Zoo and Wild Animal Park (two locations in southern San Diego County), and Universal Studio Tours (in the southern San Fernando Valley in Los Angeles County) were among the 10 leading amusement parks in the nation

[8]Except where sources are actually quoted, most of the data in this section are derived from the Research Department, Security Pacific Bank, *Monthly Summary of Business Conditions in Southern California* 60, 5 (May 31, 1981); U.S. Travel Service, *1977 National Travel Survey;* and State of California, Office of Tourism studies.

in attendance. The four parks annually draw more than 21 million visitors, which are more visitors than frequent the nation's gambling capital, Las Vegas, Nevada, in a year.

Although tourists in California often chance "get rich quick" side trips to Las Vegas or Tahoe-Reno, urban California has its own legalized gambling attractions in the form of city-licensed poker palaces, such as in Gardena in western Los Angeles County, and parimutuel wagering at horseracing tracks, such as Santa Anita (Fig. 11.17) and Hollywood Park in Los Angeles County, Los Alamitos in Orange County, Del Mar in San Diego County, Bay Meadows in San Mateo County, Golden Gate Fields in Alameda County, and numerous county fair tracks. Another significant aspect of urban tourism is convention activity, in which San Francisco, as noted in Table 11.2, led all other major convention cities in expenditures in 1979. Most of the remainder of California's urban tourism ($1.1 billion in 1979) occurs in the Great Central Valley, principally in Fresno, Kern, and Sacramento counties.

Although the majority of tourists in California each year are state or U.S. residents, several million are foreigners. The largest groups of non-U.S. resident visitors are from Canada and Mexico followed by Japan, the United Kingdom, West Germany, and France. Tourists from north and south of the border come by and large to visit friends and relatives, whereas those from Europe and Asia come largely to see the sights. The port of entry for nearly half of the state's foreign visitors is Los Angeles, which curiously enough is the "fourth largest Canadian city in the world" (behind Toronto, Montreal, and Vancouver). With a Mexican-American population of about 2 million and a Canadian-American population approaching .75 million, greater Los Angeles (the county)

Table 11.2
Conventions in California[a]

	California	Los Angeles	Anaheim	San Diego	San Francisco
Number of conventions	5,800	216	147	1,239	781
Attendance (thousands)	4,300	702	476	553	743
Estimated expenditures (thousands of $)	1,000,000	149,845	154,700	199,100	338,000
Average number of delegates per convention	741	3,250	3,238	446	951

[a]Figures for 1979. Derived from data gathered by the California Association of Visitors and Convention Bureaus.
Source: Security Pacific Bank, *Southern California: Monthly Summary of Business Conditions* 60, 5 (May 31, 1981).

is uniquely North American cosmopolitan and as such will continue to draw millions of visitors each year from the continent's three largest nations: Canada, Mexico, and the United States. Table 11.3 expands on this human side of tourism in California and Los Angeles, Orange, and San Diego counties in 1977.

Finally, which California counties are most dependent on tourist dollars? When tourist spending is calculated as a percentage of total personal income, San Francisco and San Mateo led the pack in 1979 with 29 percent each, which was far above the state average of 8.4 percent. By contrast, tourism's share of personal income in the same year was 7.7 percent in Los Angeles, 7.1 percent in Orange, and 10.8 percent in San Diego. Of nearly half a million people employed in the tourist industry in California in 1979, 60 percent were in the labor-intensive food service and lodging industry and the majority were employed in these four counties.

THE IMPACT OF URBAN SPRAWL ON AGRICULTURE

Judging by the recent spate of articles, books, editorials, and other commentaries on the subject, there is steadily mounting concern over the urban encroachment on farmland and its ultimate impacts on the agricultural resources of the state and the nation. Views on the gravity of the situation range from alarm to complacency and, consequently, a number of controversial questions have been raised over the issue: Does the metropolitan area explosion and the conversion of farmland pose any real threat to the food supply or at least some elements of that supply? On the other hand, hasn't the growth of population and cities so broadened the market for agricultural products that more land has come into production than been taken out, and, if anything, great food surpluses have resulted?

In another sector, has the forced retreat of farms to areas farther and farther removed from urban markets noticeably affected the cost of food by putting more distance between producer and consumer? And, too, hasn't the urban market for agricultural products spread? Or have capabilities in processing and transporting of food so improved that the actual location of agricultural production in relation to its markets is of little importance?

In this regard, are there not vast areas of potentially good cropland in California literally waiting to be put into production? Yet doesn't the distinct possibility abide that the production of some specialty crops, which require optimum conditions of soil and climate found only

in or near certain metropolitan areas, may soon cease altogether in the nation? On the other hand, if the market continues to demand such products, will it in essence ever really let them disappear?

Lastly, what do we make of the environmental implications of urban sprawl and the disappearance of agriculture? Should we allow the land and the air in rich farming regions, such as once existed in the San Fernando, San Gabriel, and Santa Clara valleys, to be paved over and become befouled with smog? To preclude this possibility from happening, should agriculture be preserved and thus subsidized in metropolitan areas as an open space or greenbelt amenity? Or has agriculture already received more than its share of subsidies such as those gained through price supports, special reclamation and irrigation projects, and property tax breaks?

The answers to all these questions are likely to be subjective and probably depend to a large degree on one's point of view. Chances are that developers and urban planners would voice opinions that differ markedly from those of ecologists and farmers. But one thing is certain: Prime farmland is objectively definable and there is really not that much of it left on earth. In fact, many nations don't even have any. Sadly, some of these same countries are experiencing unprecedented population explosions.

Land Economics and Land Taxes

Many economists look on the conversion of farmland to urban uses more often than not as an expression of the free land market, doing its job very efficiently. They maintain that supply and demand is affecting the orderly transfer of fringe land simply because the land usually has more value for urban than rural uses. And if agricultural land does become scarce eventually, prices offered for it by those interested in agricultural development could conceivably exceed those offered by urban interests. In the view of Robert O. Harvey and W. A. V. Clark: "If the price of citrus fruits or some other agricultural specialty became sufficiently high to yield a return on the land higher than that earned under an urban use, then a transfer from urban to agricultural uses would take place in contrast to that which typically occurs."[9] James Gillies and Frank Mittelbach look with disfavor on suggestions for preserving agricultural land that would constrain operation of the land market in metropolitan areas, noting that: "These efforts should

[9]Robert O. Harvey and W. A. V. Clark, "The Nature and Economics of Urban Sprawl," *Land Economics* 41, 1 (February 1965): 8.

Table 11.3

Tourism[a]

	California	Los Angeles	Orange	San Diego
Total trips (thousands)	64,207	9,700	2,500	7,600
Main purpose of trip (%)				
Visit friends/relatives	32	38	30	39
Business	17	27	14	19
Entertainment/recreation	33	16	43	21
Vacation trip (%)	43	34	54	30
Weekend trip (%)	39	29	37	35
Traveler characteristics				
Median age	31	32	23	33
College education (%)	38	50	39	38
Retired (%)	10	10	3	6
Transportation (%)				
Motor vehicle	80	66	73	82
Airplane	15	29	18	13
Train and other	5	5	9	5

[a]Figures for 1977. Data provided courtesy of Security Pacific National Bank and the U.S. Travel Service.

Source: Security Pacific Bank, *Southern California: Monthly Summary of Business Conditions* 60, 5 (May 31, 1981).

not be such that they encourage the continued use of land for agricultural production if there is some higher and better alternative use of the land as measured by the capitalized value of its earning capacity."[10]

A point often not stressed by either agricultural conservationists or urbanists is the fact that urbanization, depending on where and how it occurs, usually does *not* pay its social costs. This is especially true "in the case of residential development (the major suburban land use), where new expenditures (particularly for schools and other public facilities) might in fact more than offset the benefits of the increased tax base. Even more so if development occurs at random. Because of leap-frogging development, utilities, sewers, and roads have to be extended in even more uneconomic fashion."[11] On the other hand, agriculture requires comparatively little in the way of services and usually more than pays its own way with regard to social costs. Unfortunately, this contribution of agriculture to the welfare of the metropolitan community is generally ignored in the operation of a free land market. Indeed, in ignoring the social benefits of agriculture, the land market may in fact *not* be doing its job as efficiently as is generally assumed.

Rising land values accompanied by rising taxes on the land come sharply into focus when an expanding urban society extends into a retreating farmland base, a farmland base that has been losing ground in metropolitan

[10]James Gillies and Frank Mittelbach, "Urban Pressures on California Land: A Comment," *Land Economics* 34, 1 (February 1958): 82.

[11]Association of Bay Area Governments, *Bay Area Regional Planning Program–Agricultural Resources Study*, Berkeley, August 1969, pp. 2.15–2.16. Any growing city needs a broad *tax base*, that is, one that includes generous proportions of revenue-producing commercial, industrial, and perhaps even mineral extraction land uses, as well as deficit-producing single-family residential land use. With such a broad land, property, or real estate tax base, a city could then theoretically build an adequate *infrastructure* or internal framework of public service systems (law enforcement, schools, smog abatement, transportation, waste disposal, and the like). Exclusively residential communities, as are commonly found in suburbia, have very narrow tax bases and thus their property owners pay relatively high tax rates. Such cities also depend on state and federal aid to a greater extent than cities with a broad tax base.

California at an annual rate of almost 50,000 acres since the end of World War II. The farmland base in question exists at the rural-urban fringes of metropolitan areas where land supply and demand are greatest. The supply function owes to the availability of more and cheaper land in the rural fringe than in areas closer to metropolitan centers, a circumstance that encourages outlying development. The demand function is attributed largely to a desire on the part of a majority of the home-buying public to reside in a low-density, single-family suburban environment.

Both supply and demand are also affected by the recent skyrocketing index of average farm real estate value versus the relatively declining index of farm income. This is but another sign of impending prime land scarcity at the rural-urban fringe. A dynamic rural-urban fringe land market operates to the benefit of farmers who are desirous of getting out of agriculture, for they can now reap a higher price for their land than at any time in the past. But for farmers committed to staying in agriculture, it works a hardship in the form of increasing tax assessments, which can rise along with other expenses to the point where it is uneconomical to continue farming.

Take, for instance, the hypothetical plight of Farmer Fred illustrated in Figure 11.20. Between 1960 and 1980, the market value of his 100 acres of cropland appreciated tenfold, from $100 to $1,000 per acre. His property taxes, however, increased 30 times, from $125 to $3,750 for all his land. Most of the $3,750 Farmer Fred paid in 1980 went for urban services from which he derives little or no benefit. If anything, Fred probably realizes more disbenefits than benefits from his new suburban neighbors. Tract house owners complain about his noisy tractoring and noxious spraying on weekends while he tries to keep their kids from trampling his vegetables and picking his citrus after school. Worse yet, the city will no doubt annex the neighboring tracts and his land as well, whereby the city tax rate and those of more special districts will be added to his tax bill. Fred is also paying more than he ever did before for labor, machinery, fertilizers, pesticides, irrigation systems, water, fencing, *ad nauseam*.

In face of increased taxes and operating costs and thus declining profits, Fred and thousands of other urban fringe farmers must either sell their land, which is often the only profitable commodity left to sell, or revert to growing only the very highest-value crops. Even this latter alternative is economically feasible only to a certain point. Is it any wonder, then, why thousands of farmers, especially smaller operators, are getting out of the food supply business? Urban sprawl is hardly the sole reason the number of farms in California is diminishing at a rate of about 7,000 per decade, but it may take the heaviest toll.

Urban Shadows

Another pattern to be noticed in Figure 11.20, as well as in Figures 11.21 and 11.22 is urban sprawl's haphazard invasion of rural land and the resultant chopping up of agriculture. This not only disrupts the continuity of farm production, it also creates an *urban shadow* where,

in anticipation of capital gains, land speculators have taken large tracts of farmland out of production long in advance of their planned development. Perhaps the farmer abandoned cultivation of the land well before title passed to the buyer or maybe the developer saw mortgage money suddenly dwindle in supply. Moreover, with the average selling price of new tract houses now around $200,000 in several metropolitan fringe counties in California and mortgage interest rates varying wildly between 10 and 20 percent, the proportion of qualified buyers has shrunk to a few percentage points of the total population.

Obviously, a seriously diminished market will influence developers' decisions on whether or not to build on their land. Higher-density residential development may offer some hope, though even condominiums and townhouses are increasingly out of reach of the buying public. But whatever originally caused the land's vacancy, it may simply sit there for years doing nothing more useful than growing weeds to control erosion and providing an investment tax shelter. Some developers rent newly acquired land back to farmers or farm it themselves until

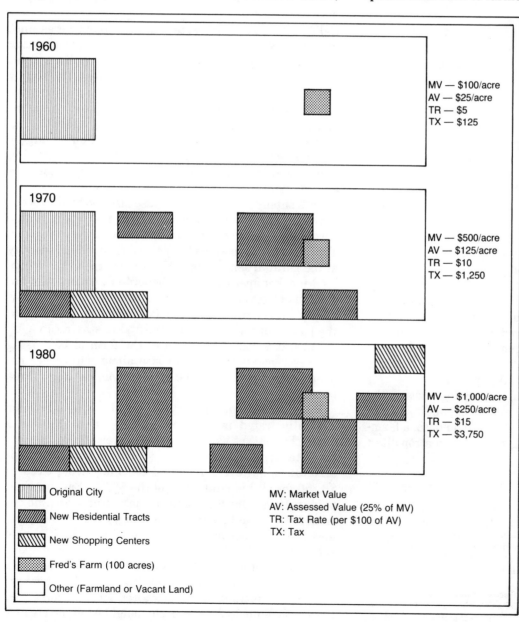

Figure 11.20 Rising property taxes on farmland: the hypothetical case of Farmer Fred from 1960 to 1980. (Marc Blodgett)

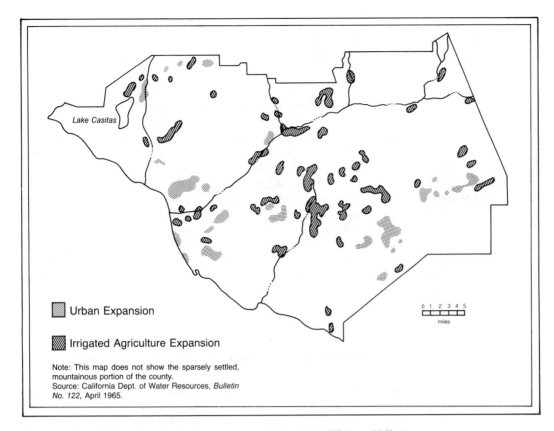

Figure 11.21 Ventura County, land use changes, 1950–1961. (Whitney Miller)

Figure 11.22 Sprawl in Ventura County takes its toll of productive farmland even before urban development begins. Note, for example, the decline of the citrus groves adjacent to the new housing tract in the upper left of the air photo, while more remote crop areas appear better irrigated and generally better maintained. In the ground photo, suburbia is poised on the horizon ready to invade nursery cropland and orchards. In both cases, the incompatibility of agricultural and suburban land uses bordering each other is not always apparent at first glance, but it's there. The Medfly crisis of 1981 served to bring the problem to the public eye. (Crane Miller)

the day of actual development is at hand, although such practices are usually limited to companies with significant financial resources and situations where highly remunerative crops can be grown.

A more insidious shadow cast by urbanization is its *irreversibility*. Prior to suburbanization in metropolitan California, when land use change usually meant that one agricultural use replaced another, the results were not necessarily irreversible. That is, an irrigated parcel of land could readily revert to being dry farmed or even to supporting its original natural plant cover. Not so with urban development of land, for residential subdivisions, shopping centers, industrial parks, freeways, and the like seemingly cover former agricultural land forever. It would be nothing short of miraculous if there were ever any reclamation of an agricultural land resource once urbanization has occurred. Instead, as seen in Figure 11.23, abandoned urban land all too often becomes dead land with a bombed-out look to it.

Where Will New Suburbanites Live?

There were years during the 1970s when it seemed California had attained zero population growth, but by the early 1980s immigration was up and a minor population boom in progress. Where will more Californians live, especially those eager for detached residences out in the countryside? In other words, how and where should urbanization be directed in the future?

Admittedly, the primeland, alluvial valleys will remain the most profitable land for the spread of suburbia. But what would the benefits and costs be if urbanization were diverted away from prime irrigable land to surrounding benchlands, foothills, and areas of lower-grade soils? There is ample land of this sort throughout metropolitan California, as exemplified in suburban developments like Mission Viejo (Fig. 11.24) and Westlake Village. It may be that higher grading and construction costs on hilly, marginal agricultural lands such as these may be partially or eventually even fully offset by savings in social overhead for flood control, drainage, and sewage disposal. Other benefits possibly accruing to hillside suburban residents are availability of view sites and living above the smog level. Best of all, there might still be some orchards and other useful greenery left to see in the valleys below instead of wall-to-wall rooftops and pavement with an occasional park thrown in for aesthetic embellishment.

CONSERVING AGRICULTURE IN SUBURBIA

Short of proposing the retention of farms in suburban areas as subsidized open space or greenbelt amenities, a practice that would openly interfere with operation of a free, competitive real estate market, several different methods of institutionally preserving agriculture have been tried. The expedients submitted thus far in various

Figure 11.23 Graffiti and weeds appear to be the only things developing in this abandoned shopping center in northern Pomona. Lack of recent residential development around the former shopping center helps explain this sad state of affairs. Development of the Montclair Plaza regional shopping center a few miles east may be a factor as well. A few miles south, downtown Pomona has also suffered from regional shopping center competition, although a refurbished mall area in the central business district may stave off further decline. In general, though, Pomona is growing (from 87,384 in 1970 to 92,636 in 1980), an increase due in part to the continued presence of General Dynamics (aerospace) and the residential development of Phillip's Ranch and Diamond Bar in the hills to the south. (Crane Miller)

Figure 11.24 Mission Viejo lake, which was excavated and filled late in the 1970s, is the centerpiece of this unincorporated southern Orange County community. Irvine Ranch, also in Orange County, and Westlake Village, at the Los Angeles–Ventura County line, are other examples of extensive and basically residential suburbs incrementally developed with long-term master plans by private firms. (Crane Miller)

metropolitan regions in California and the nation include incorporation of exclusively agricultural cities, establishment of conservation easements, rural or agricultural zoning, and preferential assessment of farmland. All these proposals are interrelated to varying degrees and in some cases have been employed as tools in compiling general plans containing an agricultural element.

Agricultural Cities

Incorporation of cities to function primarily as agricultural entities has been attempted in California, but with no real success. Probably the best known case is that of Dairy Valley, incorporated by dairy operators, mostly of Dutch ancestry, in 1956 on several parcels of land in southeastern Los Angeles County. The idea was to preserve an agrarian way of life and keep suburbia out. By barely a decade after incorporation, however, suburbs had surrounded Dairy Valley and driven property values up to between $15,000 and $30,000 an acre for residential development and to $35,000 an acre for the 135-acre Cerritos regional shopping center site. At these prices, it is hardly surprising that dairy farmers began selling more land and less milk, with some moving their operations 40 miles east to Chino. By the end of the 1960s, Dairy Valley was renamed Cerritos and the city began acting more suburban than agricultural. Faced with operational obsolescence, incompatibility with neighboring urban land uses, and no doubt temptingly high bids for their land, the four dairies that remained as of 1980 will probably be gone well before the end of the decade.

Conservation Easements

Assuming it is in the public interest to preserve agricultural land, cities or counties in California are empowered to obtain easements through voluntary sale or by eminent domain (the right of government to take private property from a landowner for the "public good"

by paying fair market value). Many urban planners, however, feel that acquiring the *fee simple* or total rights to real property is less complicated and accomplishes the same ends as easement acquisition. Probably the major methodological drawback to introducing a program of agricultural easement procurement in California would be that of simultaneous acquisition of large, contiguous blocks of prime developable land and the negative influence such acquisition would have on the value of development rights sacrificed. In any event, acquisition of easements or fee-simple rights solely for purposes of preserving agriculture seems an unacceptable tactic in a free land market economy.

Agricultural Zoning

Zoning ordinances constitute the oldest and most widely used method of control over land use that can be exercised by a local government. They can also act as the most effective tool in the hands of a planner for promoting orderly development of a community. But critics of rural zoning argue that it is a stop-gap measure at best. They contend that if the market value of land soars high enough, a variance, or new urban zoning ordinances, can be obtained and the land in question will convert to highest and best use.

No more classic case of implementation of agricultural zoning to thwart urban sprawl exists than in Santa Clara County in Northern California. Near the city of San Jose in the 1950s, subdivisions became scattered over 200 sq mi of fruit land while actually occupying only 12 sq mi. This left 188 sq mi of land beyond financial reach because of its overinflated speculative value, thus serving as a classic example of urban sprawl.

In 1954, before too much of the prune and pear land became vacant, a group of growers banded together and acquired from the Board of Supervisors the first exclusively agricultural zone in Santa Clara County. A general pattern of rural zoning soon followed to protect farmland from subdivision, but this did not preclude strip annexing by San Jose and other municipalities. As a result, the farmers went to Sacramento and persuaded the legislature to pass an interim law to forbid poaching by cities.

But zoning in this case only proved to be a stop-gap. In 1958, William H. Whyte observed that: "While the farmer continues to pay relatively low taxes, the surrounding land keeps soaring in value, and so, potentially does his own. What will happen when the land goes to $15,000 to $20,000 an acre? Farmers got the zoning approved; they can get it disapproved. The local Farm Bureau is quick to admit it, and now feels additional means must be sought to preserve farmland."[12]

Twenty years later, San Jose (population 573,805 in 1978) by itself had become the state's fastest-growing major city during the 1970s and Whyte's misgivings about rural zoning had largely come true. Now San Jose's corporate boundaries extend dozens of miles from the northern to the southern end of the Santa Clara Valley and most of the original agricultural zones are long gone. But there are signs that city administrators and residents increasingly favor putting the brakes on urban sprawl and returning to compact growth. Will this happen in time to save what is left of the Santa Clara Valley's reputation as the prune capital of the nation?

Preferential Assessment and the CLCA

Laws aimed at preventing assessment of farmland at subdivision values have been on the books of several states since the 1950s, and in some cases these and related laws have been declared unconstitutional. In the 1966 California election, voters approved an amendment (Proposition 3) to the state constitution allowing for preferential assessment of land used solely for the production of food or fiber and other so-called open space uses.

William H. Whyte looked with disfavor on this means of preserving agricultural land as well, noting that: "When the price is right the farmer will sell out, low taxes or no. And, why not? He is not going to foreswear a large capital gain so suburbanites will have pretty scenery. Unless there is some compelling incentive, he is going to relocate."[13] Whyte goes on to cite the example of a Maryland county that lost $2,343,000 in tax assessments because of preferential assessment. With this money the county could simply have bought 1,500 acres of farmland and thus done a more permanent job of preserving the land for agriculture.

Despite its shortcomings, the state government in essence supported preferential assessment as the best tool for controlling conversion of farmland to nonagricultural uses with passage of the California Land Conservation Act of 1965 (AB 2117, sponsored by Assemblyman John Williamson). The basic goals of CLCA are (1) to preserve a maximum amount of farmland in order to maintain the state's agricultural economy and ensure adequate food supplies for the nation, (2) to discourage premature and unnecessary conversion of farmland to urban uses,

and (3) to maintain farmland in developing areas as valuable open space.

The key feature of CLCA has landowners sign annually renewable contracts with their respective counties to keep their land in agriculture for a minimum of 10 years. In return, the county agrees to assess the land on the basis of agricultural use rather than on a typically higher valuation based on what it would bring for subdivision use. In other words, *use value* assessments instead of *market value* assessments are made on the land if the owner restricts its use to agricultural production for 10 or more years. Rarely, if ever, in metropolitan California will the agricultural use value of land come anywhere close to its subdivision market value.

A parcel of land receiving a property tax break under CLCA is referred to as an *agricultural preserve* and, depending on the county party to the contract, such a preserve will be of a specified minimum size. A farmer can get out of an agricultural preserve simply by filing notice of nonrenewal at the end of the first year of a contract, but he or she will have to keep the preserve in agricultural production for the remaining nine years of the contract. A farm owner who wants to cancel a contract altogether must pay a penalty equal to 50 percent of the reassessed value of the preserve unless waived by the State Director of Agriculture as being in the public interest.

The California Land Conservation Act (CLCA) has been in force now for nearly two decades, yet there remain serious doubts about its appeal in primeland metropolitan areas. As Table 11.4 indicates, the act was slow to catch on in its early years and even by fiscal year 1975–1976 only about one third of California's 12.5 million acres of primeland (Fig. 11.25) was in agricultural preserves.

Making CLCA's performance even more questionable was a case study of land under contract in 11 central California counties that found that farmland near incorporated areas was much less likely to be under contract than was more remote land. Another study determined that initial preserve signups were concentrated in nonprime areas located some distance from cities. Referring to these studies, University of California agricultural economists Hoy F. Carman and Cris Heaton noted that: "Much of the land under contract was in little or no danger of being converted to nonagricultural use, whereas much land not under contract is viewed by its owners as having development potential."[14]

Because property tax revenues are either lost or shifted to other taxpayers, perhaps the most glaring defect of the CLCA is the negative fiscal impact it has on local governments and school districts. Compounding the problem in 1978 was overwhelming approval by the voters of the property tax slashing initiative, Proposition 13. Not only have local government's revenue-producing capabilities been further reduced, but in looking to state government for fiscal bailouts, local governments may

[12]William H. Whyte, Jr., "Urban Sprawl," *Fortune* 52, 1 (January 1958): 106.

[13]William H. Whyte, Jr., *The Last Landscape* (Garden City, N.Y.: Doubleday, 1968), pp. 116–117.

[14]Hoy F. Carman and Cris Heaton, "Use-Value Assessment and Land Conservation," *California Agriculture* (March 1977): 12–14.

Table 11.4
Impact of the California Land Conservation Act

Ending Year	Total Acres Under Contract	Primeland Acres Under Contract	Counties Participating
1968	200,000	N.A.	6
1969	2,061,968	131,273	23
1970	4,249,374	572,611	37
1971	6,234,052	1,653,716	39
1972	9,562,658	2,622,648	42
1973	11,476,416	3,428,437	44
1974	12,719,389	3,914,988	45
1975	13,742,978	4,179,752	47
1976	14,427,087	4,371,027	47

Figure 11.25 Sonoma Valley primeland. Will it still look like this in 100 years or will it become just one more California city? (Crane Miller)

be witnessing their own political clout being weakened beyond recourse. The concept of *home rule,* whereby local communities plan their own destinies, has indeed suffered a severe blow in the implementation of Proposition 13.

Proposition 13 is a mixed blessing insofar as the California Land Conservation Act and agriculture in general are concerned. Farmers for the most part favored it, for they realized a rollback of their land taxes from about 3 percent to 1 percent of 1975 market values. It is noteworthy that agricultural landowners are in the dubious position of being the highest per-capita property taxpayers in the state. Obviously, where tax savings are greater under Proposition 13 than under CLCA, there will be a sharp drop in CLCA participation. Furthermore, the farmers enjoying bigger tax savings under Proposition 13 will no longer have to worry about tying their land up in 10-year contracts; they can now sell

their land to a developer whenever they please. Whether or not all this will encourage landowners to stay in agriculture or get out is difficult to predict. But one thing seems fairly certain: Proposition 13's attenuation of home rule will open the door for state government's playing a tougher role in planning conservation of agricultural resources. Whether or not state government ever assumes such a role, however, is purely speculative at this time.

Perhaps even more significant than the impact of Proposition 13 on the California Land Conservation Act was the February 1981 California Supreme Court ruling that agricultural preserve contracts may be canceled only in extraordinary and unforeseen circumstances. Conservationists agree that the decision strengthens the CLCA by making a contract much more difficult to cancel. More than 15 million acres of California farmland are now protected under the Land Conservation Act.

12

CALIFORNIA ON THE THRESHOLD

With the year 2000 fast approaching, we find ourselves on the threshold of a new century. No country has more reason to feel thankful for past blessings than the United States, and no state has a better position within this realm of affluence than California. Advances in medicine, technology, and government have made our lives longer, healthier, and generally more enjoyable. It is becoming increasingly evident, however, that current rates of consumption must be reversed, and that current ideas about progress must be reexamined. What we do to resolve and meet the needs of today will have a vital bearing on whether we will be able to fulfill the needs of tomorrow.

THE PROSPECTS

A few years ago, author Curt Gentry wrote a book entitled *The Last Days of the Late, Great State of California*[1] in which he envisioned a catastrophic end to the state brought about by a devastating earthquake. More important, he used this natural disaster as a starting point to reflect on the problems the state had created for itself. Gentry questioned whether California would have destroyed itself even without a natural disaster. His conclusions were troubling.

Of course, California has not yet been destroyed by any natural disaster. The question of self-destruction, however, remains an unsettling idea. Little progress has been made toward creating an efficient mass transit system in California. In a state where mobility and effective transportation are critical needs, the dominant mode is still the economically inefficient and energy-wasteful automobile. Although some control has been imposed in the area of pollution, standards of air quality, noise levels, water quality, and chemical waste disposal are still far from satisfactory. Indeed, recent revelations concerning hazardous chemical dumps in residential areas

have exposed a whole new category of physical maladies suffered by unfortunate and unwary Californians.

Violence has become an accepted fact of life in large urban areas, and the increase in the numbers of guns being purchased reflects the level of confidence many residents have in current standards of police protection. Extremism of various types continues to threaten the social fabric of the state. The persistence of groups like the Ku Klux Klan, the John Birch Society, numerous religious cults, terrorist groups, racial hatred groups, and the American Nazi Party raise doubts concerning the overall stability of California culture and society. The philosophy of greatest impact and largest following, however, remains apathy. The majority of Californians persist in ignoring the pressing problems of the present and the future. In their frantic pursuit of pleasure, citizens of the Golden State tend to gloss over the cracks in the social, political, and environmental structures.

Certainly, many of the difficulties are a function of size. California has a yearly budget, a resource base, and a population greater than those of many countries. The complexity of maintaining an orderly society in a population that numbers 10 percent of the total population of the United States is often overwhelming. The problems in coordinating interests in a geographical and political entity that contains approximately 158,693 sq mi of area are enormous. This sort of diversity has frequently led to discussions about dividing the state. To date, these discussions have never moved past the proposal stage, although the legislative branch has debated and acted at counterpurposes more than once, and it is still a remote possibility in the future.

In short, the prospects for California are quite mixed. Problems exist. Solutions are possible. Actions are often confused. As with most of the development of the state, the future depends upon the interaction between people and the natural environment. The major concerns in these two areas provide a two-part approach to the question of California's future. Each of these areas of concern acts upon the other. Whether they are in conflict or in harmony will decide the destiny of the state.

[1]New York: G. P. Putnam's Sons, 1968.

THE PEOPLE

The people of California face many changes. Increase in population is both a growing problem and an exciting challenge, the solution to which can dramatically affect both the prosperity and the lifestyle of the state. The changing ethnic character of California also will impact upon cultural styles, social stability, and political power. As with other states, the development of California will be influenced by the overall strains on the social fabric of the nation as a whole. The people, however, are the first resource of the state, and it is up to them to find the solutions (Fig. 12.1).

Growth and Population

The first reality about people involves the number of them who call the state their home. Well over 21 million persons resided in the state as of the beginning of the 1980s. Census Bureau statistics show no indication of a decline in the constant growth rate, and the upward trend suggests an area of concern.

Although California's population density is not yet at a critical juncture, distribution of the people is a problem. Concentration of population in the south is a con-tinuing phenomenon that severely stretches existing resources. The south already has a water shortage potential. The south already has too many cars on the roads. The south is already straining to provide full employment for its population. The south is already experiencing a housing problem. Unfortunately, there appears to be little relief in sight. The north is in no better position to absorb excess population and at times expresses open reluctance to do so. This is an issue of major proportion and, so far, too little thought has been directed toward its solution.

Ethnic Balance

Another difficulty involving people in the state concerns the shifting ethnic balance. Californians are struggling to resolve their ambivalent attitudes about race relations. Although the state has had a long history of mixed races, it also has had a rather poor record of promoting social equality and tranquility. The continuing existence of tension between racial groups cannot be denied. White flight to the suburbs accelerates.

Certainly other factors are also involved, but distrust between races is one major component. It is not a white-only phenomenon. Tensions among black, Asian, and

Figure 12.1 California is a state of vast ethnic and social diversity, as the mix of buildings on an urban San Francisco street shows. (Roger M. Rhiner)

Latino populations are just as real. Although this question is nationwide in scope, California holds a unique position. If current trends persist, by 1990 California will become the first Third World state in the United States. The large influx of Asian and Mexican immigrants, both legal and illegal, has only speeded up the process.

Californians of every ethnic background need to face the challenge of an integrated society. With the wealth, diversity, and potential already present in the state, the ethnocentric tensions should be easy to control. How well Californians are able to accomplish this will be a lesson for the nation.

The Social Fabric

An additional, broad, people-oriented difficulty involves strains on the general social fabric of the state. Various stresses of modern life are taking their toll on the citizens of California. Sociologists have expressed deep concern over the fallout of "future shock" in America. As society moves faster and faster, people become more confused, alienated, and maladjusted. Unfortunately, California leads the nation in symptoms of this social instability. Currently, the state has the highest divorce rate, the highest crime rate, the largest alcoholic population, the greatest level of mental health disorders, the highest venereal disease rate, and the greatest number of deaths by automobile.

These statistics are depressing and raise important questions about the overall quality of life in the state. Certainly California can ill afford to ignore the social, economic, and political imbalances that feed these problems. The actions taken to create a more healthy and stable society will determine how many people will wish to continue to live in the state.

THE NATURAL ENVIRONMENT

The treatment of the natural environment is as critical to the state as its people. A fine balance must be struck to maintain maximum utility from the air, land, and water without creating irreparable damage. Nature has proved to be relatively tolerant of abuses perpetrated by human beings, but the mistreatment must cease. Fortunately, recent developments in environmental control appear to be working. Several acts are of particular interest.

The *National Environmental Policy Act of 1969* is the basis for most modern environmental protection laws. It states that U.S. national policy is to foster "harmony between man and his environment." The act mandated the establishment of a Council on Environmental Quality, directed the President to present an annual state-of-the-environment message, and led to the use of environmental impact reports on federal plans that would affect the quality of the environment.

The *California Environmental Quality Act of 1970* was patterned closely after the federal act. It commits the state to maintaining a quality environment for the people of California, "now and in the future." Following this act, the state legislature passed an overwhelming number of laws that addressed specific problems. Over half

of the state codes soon contained sections on environmental problems and controls. Laws were passed that dealt with general pollution, water quality, air quality, particulate pollutants, open space, parks and recreation areas, wildlife and wilderness areas, and nuclear power. These laws have attempted to set reasonable standards to protect the environment from excessive polluting or encroachment on natural areas.

The *California Coastal Zone Conservation Act of 1972* and the *Coastal Act of 1976* have established control over development of the state's coastline. These measures set up a Coastal Commission responsible for all development within the coastal zone. These acts have been relatively effective in preserving natural coastal environment from further erosion and have placed severe limitations on high-density development and modifications of the natural landscape (Fig. 12.2).

Various specific regional planning programs have also been added to state law. The Tahoe Regional Planning Compact saw five California counties and the state of Nevada join together to create a regional development plan which would transcend state jurisdictions. The Regional Planning Agency has met with mixed success in its efforts to provide a comprehensive approach to the area. Similarly, the San Francisco Bay Plan was set up to protect the delicate balance of the Bay and coordinate all development bordering its waters. As a result of its efforts, overall water quality has steadily improved, and the Bay is gradually becoming an attractive recreation and wildlife environment again.

The trend for the future in the area of environmental legislation is encouraging. Further refinements of both federal and state laws have occurred on a regular basis. California has recently dealt with tobacco smoke, noise, engine emissions, hazardous wastes, and flip-top containers. Federal legislation has likewise updated and refined the procedures established to protect the environment. In the area of legislation, the people have shown a willingness to pay the price for improvement.

WATER, WATER EVERYWHERE, BUT NOT A DROP TO DRINK

The persistent problem of water allocation in the state has not been resolved. Few other issues can raise emotional and political hackles as effectively as this one, and Californians recognize that water is power in this state. California has been able to achieve its enviable position because of the riches made possible by extensive irrigation. Agricultural and residential properties appreciate in value precisely because water can be brought to otherwise barren regions.

In spite of a comprehensive water management system, however, a crisis is present. As the drought of 1976–1977 illustrated, even one dry year has far-reaching consequences throughout the state. In vast portions of California, failure of water supplies not only impinges upon normal agricultural and household uses, but also exacerbates a perennially explosive fire danger. The brush fire season is one of growing concern as more people build in former brush areas. Many Californians have learned, to their dismay, that disaster can strike at home.

Figure 12.2 Although large sections of the Santa Monica Mountains have been protected from development, the population continues to encroach on the hillsides (A) and coast (B). (National Park Service, photos by Richard Frear)

The water future is truly a question mark due to several factors. As water from the Colorado River is reduced drastically in the mid-1980s as a result of the Central Arizona Project, new sources will have to be found. Yet long-term solutions have not been determined or implemented as Californians continue to argue about the Peripheral Canal and other issues. While drought threatens one year and floods the next, citizens of the state seem unable to agree on viable alternatives. Unless the state can find a satisfactory approach soon, the water crisis will haunt Californians well into the new century.

THE PROBLEM OF MOVEMENT

The enduring difficulty of handling movement of persons and things around this huge state will only intensify in the future. Californians have made some efforts toward resolving this problem, but a coordinated and committed approach is still needed. Population pressures, air pollution concerns, energy scarcity, and other similar problems mandate serious development of viable alternatives and expansion of experimental techniques that will provide greater transportation efficiency in the state.

Most discussions categorize California's transportation question into the three areas of land, sea, and air. Because of the varied topography of the state, different problems have arisen and different usages have developed for these forms.

In terms of transportation by water, California has become a leading international trade focus, particularly for the nations of the Pacific Rim. An extensive shoreline with many excellent ports has encouraged ocean transportation, and the ports of Los Angeles, San Francisco,

Oakland, Long Beach, San Diego, Richmond, Sacramento, Stockton, and others serve the varied needs of this trade. The rise of container ships has also acted as a spur to this area of transportation in California. Although travel by water does not account for a major portion of people movement, it does constitute a significant mode of industrial mobility.

The revolution in air travel has certainly affected California in a major way. Access to the state is immediate and easy for travelers from throughout the country and world. Major airlines serve most large cities in the state, with San Francisco and Los Angeles connected by air with almost any place on the globe. As far as intrastate transportation is concerned, the extreme size of California is no longer as formidable for the casual traveler or business executive who needs or desires to move from one end of the state to the other in a short time span. Air California and Pacific Southwest Airlines can provide connections almost anywhere in the state. To a lesser degree, the airlines now also provide rapid cargo movement for the state. Although volume may be lower than land or ocean transport, air cargo does serve as an immediate and efficient means of prompt delivery.

Surface or land transportation is, by far, the dominant form in California. Here the choice is movement by rail or road. In recent years, road has been the primary choice. As noted previously (see Chapter 8) the railroad played a key role in the growth and development of California. In addition, the expansion of San Francisco and Los Angeles was facilitated by the San Francisco Key Route Electric Railway and Henry Huntington's Pacific Electric line in Southern California.

Railroads as such, however, have largely surrendered their role as passenger carriers and now concentrate heavily upon the transport of goods. The freight-hauling function of railroads has been augmented by piggybacking, container cargo, and other techniques for maximizing the efficiency of rail shipping. Passenger carriage is not viewed as a profitable venture, and most railroads prefer to leave this aspect of rail transport to Amtrak. The once popular passenger train is now largely a romantic tale from the past.

California's road system is another story. This is *the* heart of transportation in the Golden State. As energy inefficient and costly as it may be, the private automobile is the icon of the state. From the early beginnings of El Camino Real connecting the 21 missions, the road system in California has grown into a phenomenal series of arteries, freeways, expressways, and roads. Financed by a state gasoline tax, the highway system has become a thing of wonder, reflecting the fact that California is the heaviest user of automobiles of any state in the country.

To provide some organization and structure, the California Master Highway Plan was adopted in 1959. This plan envisioned an eventual pattern whereby approximately 60 percent of the state's total road travel would move on the freeways and expressways. This system of rapid thoroughfares was targeted for completion in the early 1980s as a coordinated means of dealing with the heavy transportation needs of the state. Unfortunately, the system was already overused and inadequate long before the 1980s arrived. California's heavy urban commuter traffic placed a severe strain on the system. The additional fact of California's position as the leading trucking state placed an impossible burden on the highway system and demonstrated that alternatives were sorely needed.

Some experiments have been undertaken in an attempt to solve some of the commuter pressure. One of the most notable efforts is the Bay Area Rapid Transit system (BART) (Fig. 12.3). Recognizing the peculiar and unique topographical problems of the area, with its pen-

Figure 12.3 BART train glides past the Oakland skyline. The BART system is one of California's few attempts to provide mass rapid transit to its citizens. (BART)

insulas, growing population, and limited space, planners sought a system whereby commuters could be moved more rapidly in and out of the urban work centers of the region. Traffic snarls on the various bridges emphasized the need to get individual drivers out of their cars and into a mass transit system. What eventually emerged was an automated electric diorail train/subway system that connected downtown Oakland and San Francisco with outlying areas such as Concord, Berkeley, Hayward, Richmond, Fremont, and Daly City. The system was built to provide rapid service and dealt with some geographic problems by constructing a subway tunnel under the floor of the Bay and through the Berkeley hills. Although BART has been plagued with some difficulties and was almost inadequate from date of completion, nonetheless it did demonstrate that such a system could operate and would be patronized by the public.

Los Angeles has had a less successful story in the realm of mass transit. The Southern California Rapid Transit District has relied upon a bus system to serve the public transportation needs. It has been exceptionally difficult, however, to entice the Southern California driver out of the private automobile. Indeed, private automobiles still account for the overwhelming bulk of commuter traffic, as rush hour freeway traffic shows. Some experiments have proven partially successful, such as Commuter-Computer, Park-n-Ride, bus and car pool lanes, special lanes on metered ramps, and similar devices.

Political pressure has resulted in commuter train runs (Amtrak) between Los Angeles and San Diego, Los Angeles and Orange County, and Los Angeles and Riverside/San Bernardino. Other efforts have proven less successful, as the now-defunct downtown "people-mover" proposal attests. Public mass transit bond issues have proven to be a disaster at the polls. In all, the severe problems of transportation in California are well exemplified by the problems of the Los Angeles–Southern California region.

What does the future hold in the area of transportation for Californians? Indications are that some Californians are beginning to recognize the need for alternatives. San Diego's "Tijuana Trolley" is an interesting recent effort. These bright red electric trolley cars cover a 16-mile route between downtown San Diego and the Mexican border, carrying in excess of 10,000 people daily. This light rail system was conceived and funded by local and state effort and has met a real need in the area. Depending upon its continuing success, extension of the system is contemplated for the future.

The state highway system has now appeared to reach a critical mass. Few additional projects are planned, and maintenance of existing freeways and expressways has proved a substantial chore. Some modifications are in process, including a proposed system of rail and bus corridors along center medians of existing freeways. Other modifications have included video camera monitoring of heavily traveled routes, computerized signboards for traffic information, metered ramps, and other electronically controlled devices.

Basically, however, these are attempts to keep a transit system of private automobiles in operation, and are short-term answers only. It remains for long-range planners to develop more comprehensive solutions. With the continuing air pollution problem, the increasingly limited energy sources, and the population pressures in the state, alternatives to the internal combustion engine and private auto are needed.

Some discussion has revolved around electric or solar powered vehicles. Other planners have envisioned totally automated freeways. More interest has been generated in modified residential-work patterns. "Old"

abandoned systems of mass transit are being reexamined with an eye to learning and profiting from lessons of the past, such as the Los Angeles Pacific Electric Red Cars (trolley) or Angel's Flight cable system of downtown L.A.'s Bunker Hill area. The one certainty is that creativity and dedication are needed in this vital area of California life.

THE FUTURE

What can California expect from the future? So far, the interplay between people and environment has been quite uneven. On the positive side, Californians are generally healthier, younger, better educated, more affluent, and more advanced scientifically and technologically than anywhere else in the nation. On the negative side, however, they often seem confused about how to use and control the technology that has made their lives better. Further, they often are myopic when it comes to recognizing the impact of their actions on the environment.

One obvious area of interaction between people and environment is population size. With demographers projecting a population of 50 million by the year 2000, Californians still cannot fully deal with the impact that their current population is having on the environment. Given a doubling of the current problems, how will California respond? How will land use policies be set? How will the already critical water problem be resolved? How will strained energy sources serve the future needs? How will the economy of the state absorb additional workers? Most importantly, how will quality of life in the Golden State be affected? These are open-ended questions. The solutions will depend on how thoughtful and concerned Californians react to the challenges now.

Roger M. Rhiner

BIBLIOGRAPHY

American Automobile Association. *California/Nevada Tourbooks.* Annual editions. Falls Church, Va.: American Automobile Association, 1978–1982.

Amerine, M. A., and Singleton, V. L. *Wine: An Introduction.* 2d ed. Berkeley and Los Angeles: University of California Press, 1977.

Association of Bay Area Governments. *Bay Area Regional Planning Program—Agricultural Resources Study.* San Francisco, Aug. 1969.

Atherton, Gertrude. *California: An Intimate History.* New York: Harper and Bros., 1914.

Bailey, Harry P. *The Climate of Southern California.* Berkeley and Los Angeles: University of California Press, 1966.

Bakker, Elna. *An Island Called California: An Ecological Introduction to Its Natural Communities.* Berkeley and Los Angeles: University of California Press, 1971.

Bancroft, Hubert Howe. *History of California.* San Francisco: The History Co., 1886–1890.

Baur, John E. *The Health-Seekers of Southern California, 1870–1900.* San Marino, Calif.: Huntington Library, 1959.

Bean, Walton. *California: An Interpretive History.* 3d ed. New York: McGraw-Hill, 1978.

Beck, Warren A., and Haase, Ynez. *Historical Atlas of California.* Norman: University of Oklahoma Press, 1974.

Boesch, Donald F. *Oil Spills and the Marine Environment.* Cambridge, Mass.: Ballinger, 1974.

Brodine, Virginia, ed. *Air Pollution.* New York: Harcourt Brace Jovanovich, 1971.

California (magazine; formerly *New West*). Various issues.

California Coastal Zone Conservation Commission. *The California Coastal Plan.* Sacramento, 1975.

California Department of Agriculture. *California Agriculture—A Report of California Principal Crop and Livestock Commodities.* Annual editions, 1969–1981. Sacramento: California Crop and Livestock Reporting Service.

California Department of Education. *The Central Valley Project.* Sacramento, 1942.

California Department of Parks and Recreation. Various publications, including *A Guide to the California State Park System, California Historical Landmarks,* and *Golden Days of San Simeon.* Sacramento.

California Department of Water Resources. *California's Ground Water—Bulletin No. 118.* Sacramento, Sept. 1975.

California Department of Water Resources; California Department of Fish and Game; U.S. Bureau of Land Management; U.S. Forest Service; Mono County; Los Angeles Department of Water and Power. *Report of Interagency Task Force on Mono Lake.* Sacramento: California Resources Agency, Dec. 1979.

California Division of Mines and Geology. *Earthquake Planning Scenario for a Magnitude 8.3 Earthquake on the San Andreas Fault in Southern California.* Special Publication 60. Sacramento, 1982.

————. *Fault-Rupture Hazard Zones in California.* Special Publication 42. Revised. Sacramento, March 1980.

————. *Geologic Atlas of California.* San Francisco, 1958–1966.

————. *Geology of California.* Compilation of various monthly issues from volumes 21–23 of *Mineral Information Service.* Sacramento, March 1968–Oct. 1970.

————. *Mammoth Lakes, California Earthquakes of May 1980.* Special Report 150. Sacramento, 1980.

————. "Mammoth Lakes/Long Valley Microearthquake Project." *California Geology* 36 (Sept. 1982): 187–191.

————. *San Fernando, California, Earthquake of 9 February 1971.* Bulletin 196. Sacramento, 1975.

————. *Studies of the San Andreas Fault Zone in Northern California.* Special Report 140. Sacramento, 1980.

————. *Urban Geology: Master Plan for California.* Sacramento, 1973.

California Energy: The Economic Factors. Invited Papers on California's Future Energy Sources. San Francisco: Federal Reserve Bank, 1976.

California Governor's Office of Planning and Research. *The California Water Atlas.* Ed. by William L. Kahrl. Los Altos, Calif.: William Kaufmann, 1979.

California Office of the Lieutenant Governor. Council on Intergroup Relations Intern Research Project. *Third World Population in California.* Sacramento, June 1977.

Carlson, Oliver. *A Mirror for Californians.* Indianapolis, Ind.: Bobbs-Merrill, 1941.

Casebier, Dennis G. *The Mojave Road.* Norco, Calif.: King Press, 1975.

Caughey, John Walton. *California.* 2d ed. Englewood Cliffs, N. J.: Prentice-Hall, 1953.

————. *Gold Is the Cornerstone.* 1948. Reprinted under the title *California Gold Rush.* Berkeley and Los Angeles: University of California Press, 1976.

Caughey, John, and Caughey, La Ree. *Los Angeles: Biography of a City*. Berkeley and Los Angeles: University of California Press, 1977.

Cleland, Robert Glass. *The Cattle on a Thousand Hills: Southern California, 1850–1880*. San Marino, Calif.: Huntington Library, 1951.

———. *From Wilderness to Empire: A History of California, 1542–1900*. New York: Alfred A. Knopf, 1944.

Continents Adrift. Readings from *Scientific American*. San Francisco: W. H. Freeman, 1971.

Crain, Jim. *Historic Country Inns of California*. San Francisco: Chronicle Books, 1977.

Dana, Richard Henry. *Two Years Before the Mast*. New York, 1840. Available in various editions.

Darley, Ellis F.; Nichols, Carl W.; and Middleton, John T. "Identification of Air Pollution Damage to Agricultural Crops." *The Bulletin*, California Department of Agriculture 55, no. 1 (1966): 11–19.

Delano Historical Society. "The Lakeside Story." *The Plow* 12, no. 1 (Sept. 1976).

De Voto, Bernard, *Year of Decision: 1846*. Boston: Houghton Mifflin, 1950.

Donley, Michael W.; Allan, Stuart; Caro, Patricia; and Patten, Clyde P. *Atlas of California*. Portland, Ore.: Academic Book Center, 1979.

Dumke, Glenn S. *The Boom of the Eighties in Southern California*. San Marino, Calif.: Huntington Library, 1944.

Durrenberger, Robert W., ed. *California: Its People, Its Problems, Its Prospects*. Palo Alto, Calif.: National Press Books, 1971.

Durrenberger, Robert W., and Johnson, Robert B., *California: Patterns on the Land*. 5th ed., rev. by California Council for Geographic Education. Palo Alto, Calif.: Mayfield Publishing Co., 1976.

Early Man in America. Readings from *Scientific American*. San Francisco: W. H. Freeman, 1973.

Englehardt, Zephyrin, O. F. M. *The Franciscans in California*. Harbor Springs, Mich.: Holy Childhood Indian School, 1897.

Federal Writers Project. *California: A Guide to the Golden State*. St. Clair Shores, Mich.: Somerset Publishing, 1939.

Finklestein, Charles, and Baxter, Laurence D. *Planning and Politics: A Staff Perception of the Tahoe Regional Planning Agency*. Davis: University of California Institute of Government Affairs, Nov. 1974.

Fradkin, Philip L. *California: The Golden Coast*. New York: Viking Press, 1974.

Gentry, Curt. *The Last Days of the Late Great State of California*. New York: G. P. Putnam's Sons, 1968.

Gilliam, Howard. *Weather of the San Francisco Bay Region*. Berkeley and Los Angeles: University of California Press, 1962.

Gillies, James, and Mittelbach, Frank. "Urban Pressures on California Land: A Comment." *Land Economics* 34, no. 1 (Feb. 1958): 80–83.

Gribbin, John R., and Plagemann, Stephen H. *The Jupiter Effect*. New York: Vintage Books, 1976.

Grossman, Harold J. *Grossman's Guide to Wines, Beers, and Spirits*. 6th ed., rev. New York: Charles Scribner's Sons, 1977.

Gudde, Erwin G. *California Place Names*. 3d ed. Berkeley and Los Angeles: University of California Press, 1969.

Guiness, P. "The Changing Location of Power Plants in California." *Geography* 65, no. 288, pt. 3 (July 1980).

Hart, James D. *A Companion to California*. New York: Oxford Press, 1978.

Hartman, David N. *California and Man*. 4th ed. Santa Ana, Calif.: Pierce Publishers, 1977.

Harvey, Robert O., and Clark, W. A. V. "The Nature and Economies of Urban Sprawl." *Land Economics* 41, no. 1 (Feb. 1965): 1–9.

Heizer, R. F., and Whipple, M. A., eds. *The California Indians: A Source Book*. 2d ed., rev. and enl. Berkeley and Los Angeles: University of California Press, 1971.

Helen, Alfred, ed. *The California Tomorrow Plan*. Los Altos, Calif.: William Kaufmann, 1972.

Hill, Mary. *Geology of the Sierra Nevada*. Berkeley and Los Angeles; University of California Press, 1975.

Holtgrieve, Donald. *The California Wine Atlas*. Hayward, Calif.: Ecumene Associates, Environmental Research, 1978.

Howard, Robert B., and Shiroma, Debra. "Windmill Sites in Mountainous Areas of the United States." In *The California Geographer*, Vol. 18, 85–93. Rohnert Park: California Council for Geographic Education, 1978.

Huber, Walter Roy. *California Real Estate Principles*. 2d ed. Glendale: California Real Estate Publications, 1977.

Hunt, Charles B. *Death Valley: Geology, Ecology, Archaeology*. Berkeley and Los Angeles: University of California Press, 1975.

Hutchinson, W. H. *Oil, Land, and Politics: The California Career of Thomas Robert Bard*. Vols. 1 and 2. Norman: University of Oklahoma Press, 1965.

Jackson, David D.; Lee, Wook B.; and Liv, Chi-Ching. "Aseismic Uplift in Southern California: An Alternative Interpretation." *Science* 210 (Oct. 31, 1980): 534–536.

Jackson, Helen Hunt. *Ramona*. Boston, 1884. Reprint. Boston: Little, Brown, 1939.

Jackson, W. Turrentine. *Early Planning Efforts at Lake Tahoe: The Role of Joseph F. MacDonald*. Davis: University of California Institute of Government Affairs, Jan. 1974.

Jaeger, Edmond C. *The California Desert*. Stanford, Calif.: Stanford University Press, 1965.

———. *North American Deserts*. 1957. Reprint. Stanford, Calif.: Stanford University Press, 1967.

Johnson, Hugh. *The World Atlas of Wine*. London: Mitchell Beazley, 1971.

Kerr, William S. "Impact of Urbanization on Agriculture in Orange County, California." In *Yearbook of Association of Pacific Coast Geographers*, Vol. 34, ed. by John F. Gaines, 161–170. Corvallis: Oregon State University Press, 1972.

Kroeber, Theodora. *Ishi in Two Worlds*. Berkeley and Los Angeles: University of California Press, 1961.

Lake Tahoe Area Council and Engineering-Science, Inc. *Comprehensive Study on Protection of Water Resources of Lake Tahoe Basin Through Controlled Waste Disposal*. Al Tahoe, Calif., June 1963.

Lantis, David W.; Steiner, Rodney; and Karinen, Arthur E. *California: Land of Contrast*. 3d ed., rev. Dubuque, Iowa: Kendall/Hunt, 1981.

Lee, W. Storrs. *California: A Literary Chronicle*. New York: Funk and Wagnalls, 1968.

Lewis, Oscar. *The Big Four*. New York: Alfred A. Knopf, 1938.

Los Angeles Department of Water and Power. *Draft Environmental Impact Report on Increased Pumping of the Owens Valley Groundwater Basin*. Los Angeles, Aug. 1978.

———. *Eastern Sierra Cloud Seeding Program: Draft Environmental Impact Report*. Los Angeles, Oct. 1981.

———. *Final Environmental Impact Report on Increased Pumping of the Owens Valley Groundwater Basin.* Vols. 1 and 2. Los Angeles, June 1979.

———. *Los Angeles' Mono Basin Water Supply.* Briefing Document. Los Angeles, May 1982.

———. *Water Rights and Operations in the Mono Basin.* Los Angeles, 1973.

Los Angeles Times. Various daily issues, 1962–1982.

McWilliams, Carey. *Southern California: An Island on the Land.* Santa Barbara, Calif.: Peregrine Smith, 1973.

Metropolitan Water District. *Aqueduct* (magazine). Various quarterly editions, 1977–1981. Los Angeles.

Miller, Crane S. *Agriculture in an Urbanizing Environment; A Study in the Impact of Metropolitan Growth on Specialized Agriculture in Ventura County, California.* Ann Arbor, Mich.: University Microfilms, 1971.

———. "The Changing Agricultural Landscape of Simi Valley from 1795 to 1960." *Quarterly of the Ventura County Historical Society* 13, no. 4 (Aug. 1968).

———. "The Southern Great Basin." In *Association of American Geographers Field Trip Guide, 1981,* 24–34. Washington, D.C.: Association of American Geographers, 1981.

———. "Spectral and Spatial Signature Recognition in Urbanizing Areas of Southern California from U-2 Color Infra-Red Imagery." In *Proceedings of the International Symposium on Image Processing,* ed. by Franz W. Leberl, 141–147. Graz, Austria: Graz Technical University, Oct. 1977.

Monkhouse, F. J., and Small, John. *A Dictionary of the Natural Environment.* New York: Halsted Press, 1978.

Montgomery, Richard H., and Budnick, Jim. *The Solar Decision Book.* New York: Wiley, 1978.

Muir, John. *The Mountains of California.* Berkeley: Ten Speed Press, 1977.

Munz, Philip A., and Keck, David D. *A California Flora.* Reprint. Berkeley and Los Angeles: University of California Press, 1973.

Murphy, Raymond E. *The American City: An Urban Geography.* New York: McGraw-Hill, 1966.

Nadeau, Remi, A. *The Water Seekers.* Garden City, N.Y.: Doubleday, 1950.

National Academy of Sciences and National Academy of Engineering. *Urban Growth and Land Development: The Land Conversion Process.* Washington, D.C., 1972.

Nelson, Howard J. "The Spread of an Artificial Landscape over Southern California." *Annals of the Association of American Geographers* 49, no. 3, pt. 2 (Sept. 1958): 80–99.

Norris, Frank. *The Otopus.* Available in various editions.

Norris, Robert M., and Webb, Robert W. *Geology of California.* New York: Wiley, 1976.

Oakeshott, Gordon B. *California's Changing Landscapes: A Guide to the Geology of the State.* New York: McGraw-Hill, 1971.

Oliver, John E. *Perspectives on Applied Physical Geography.* North Scituate, Mass.: Duxbury Press, 1977.

Ponte, Lowell. *The Cooling.* Englewood Cliffs, N.J.: Prentice-Hall, 1976.

Pryde, Philip R., ed. *San Diego: An Introduction to the Region.* Dubuque, Iowa: Kendall/Hunt, 1976.

Robinson, W. W. *Land in California.* Berkeley and Los Angeles: University of California Press, 1948.

Rolle, Andrew F. *California: A History.* New York: Thomas Y. Crowell, 1969.

Ross, Michael J. *California: Its Government and Politics.* North Scituate, Mass.: Duxbury Press, 1979.

Salvador, Martinha, and Salvador, Jose. "Portugese Pioneers of Southern California." Senior project for California State Polytechnic University, Pomona, 1978.

Schaffer, Jeffrey P.; Schifrin, Ben; Winnett, Thomas; and Jenkins, J. C. *The Pacific Coast Trail.* Vol. 3, *California.* Berkeley: Wilderness Press, 1977.

Schoenman, Theodore, ed. *The Father of California Wine: Agoston Haraszthy.* Santa Barbara, Calif.: Capra Press, 1979.

Security Pacific National Bank. Research Department. *Monthly Summary of Business Conditions for Southern California and Northern Coastal California.* Various issues, 1972–1982. Los Angeles.

———. *Northern California: Economic Issues of the Eighties.* March 1982.

———. *San Francisco Bay Area Report: A Study of Growth and Economic Stature of the Nine Bay Area Counties.* April 1971.

———. *Southern California: Economic Issues in the Eighties.* Sept. 1981.

———. *Southern California: Economic Trends in the 1970s.* May 1977.

Sedway/Cooke (firm). *Land and the Environment.* Los Altos, Calif.: William Kaufmann, 1975.

Sierra Club. Angelas Chapter. *Southern Sierran.* Various monthly issues, 1974–1981. Los Angeles.

Sinclair, Upton. *Oil.* 1972. Reprint. Cambridge, Mass.: Robert Bentley, 1981.

Smith, Genny Schumacher, ed. *Mammoth Lakes Sierra: A Handbook for Roadside and Trail.* 4th ed. Palo Alto, Calif.: Genny Smith Books, 1976.

———, ed. *Deepest Valley.* rev. ed. Los Altos, Calif.: William Kaufmann, 1978.

Southern California Association of Governments. *SCAG-76: Growth Forecast Policy.* Los Angeles, Jan. 1976.

Southern California Edison Company. Education Service Division. *E² Report: Energy Education* (newsletter). Various editions, 1978–1982.

Spencer, J. E., ed. *Day Tours In and Around Los Angeles.* Los Angeles Geographical Society Publication, no. 3. Palo Alto, Calif.: Pacific Books, 1979.

Starkey, Otis P.; Robinson, J. Lewis; and Miller, Crane S. *The Anglo-American Realm.* 2d ed. New York: McGraw-Hill, 1975.

Steinbeck, Elaine, and Wallsten, Robert, eds. *Steinbeck: A Life in Letters.* New York: Viking Press, 1975.

Steinbeck, John. *The Grapes of Wrath.* New York: Viking Press, 1967.

Steinhart, Carol E., and Steinhart, John S. *Blowout: A Case Study of the Santa Barbara Oil Spill.* North Scituate, Mass.: Duxbury Press, 1972.

Steiner, Rodney. *Los Angeles: The Centrifugal City.* Dubuque, Iowa: Kendall/Hunt, 1981.

Stobaugh, Robert, et al. *Energy Futures.* New York: Random House, 1979.

Storer, Tracy I., and Usinger, Robert L. *Sierra Nevada Natural History.* Berkeley and Los Angeles: University of California Press, 1963.

Strahler, Arthur N., and Strahler, Alan H. *Elements of Physical Geography.* 2d ed. New York: Wiley, 1979.

Taylor O. C., principal investigator. *Oxidant Air Pollutant Effects on a Western Coniferous Forest Ecosystem. Task B*

Report: Historical Background and Proposed Systems Study of the San Bernardino Mountain Area. Riverside: Statewide Air Pollution Research Center, University of California, Jan. 1973.

Thomas, William L., Jr., ed. "Man, Time, and Space in Southern California." *Annals of the Association of American Geographers* 49, no. 3 (Sept. 1959), supplement.

Thrower, Norman J. W. "California Population: Distribution in 1960." *Annals of the Association of American Geographers* 56, no. 2 (1966). See also map supplements for 1960 and 1970.

Twain, Mark. *Roughing It.* Available in various editions.

University of California, Agricultural Experiment Station and Cooperative Extension. *California Agriculture.* Various issues, 1969–1982. Berkeley.

U.S. Department of Agriculture. Soil Conservation Service. *Soil Survey, Ventura Area California.* Washington, D.C., April 1970.

U.S. Department of Commerce, Bureau of the Census. "California: Final Population Counts," PC(VI)-6, and "California: General Population Characteristics," PC(V)-6. In *1970 Census of Population.* Washington, D.C., Feb. 1971.

———. *1980 Census of Population and Housing: California.* Preliminary Reports, Feb. 1981.

———. *1978 Census of Agriculture.*

———. *1977 Census of Manufactures for California.*

———. *1977 Census of Service Industries.*

U.S. Department of Commerce and Environmental Protection Agency. Council on Environmental Quality. *The Eco-*

nomic Impact of Pollution Control: A Summary of Recent Studies. Washington, D.C., March 1972.

U.S. Department of the Interior. Bureau of Land Management. *The California Desert Conservation Area: Plan Alternatives and Environment Impact Statement.* Washington, D.C., Feb. 1980.

Vance, James E., Jr. "California and the Search for the Ideal." *Annals of the Association of American Geographers* 62 (1972).

Ventura County Agricultural Commissioner. *Agricultural Crop Report, Ventura County.* Annual issues, 1968–1981.

Ventura County Planning Department. *The Economics of Conserving Agriculture in Ventura County.* Ventura, Calif., Dec. 1970.

Watkins, T. H. *On the Shore of the Sundown Sea.* San Francisco: Sierra Club, 1972.

West, Nathanael. *The Day of the Locust.* 1939. Reprint. Cutchogue, N.Y.: Buccaneer Books, 1981.

Western Water Education Foundation. *Western Water.* Various 1982 editions.

Winkler, A. J.; Cook, J. A.; Kliewer, W. A.; and Lider, L. A. *General Viticulture.* Berkeley and Los Angeles: University of California Press, 1974.

Yeadon, Anne, and Yeadon, David. *Wine Tasting in California.* Los Angeles: Camaro, 1977.

Zedler, Joy B. *The Ecology of Southern California Coastal Salt Marshes: A Community Profile.* Washington, D.C.: U.S. Fish and Wildlife Service, Biological Services Program, 1982.

INDEX

Italicized numbers refer to material in figures and figure captions.
Numbers followed by "n" refer to material in footnotes.